*If you don't know what you've been
missing—find out now!*

Sex and the Single Man has all the direct answers, tips and techniques you've been looking for. Now you can be a man and enjoy it in more ways than you ever dreamed possible.

Read the chapter entitled "The Art of Seduction" and you'll find material so frank, so revealing, it will open up a whole new world for you. And this is just the beginning . . . just a sampling of the solid advice Dr. Ellis offers.

Twenty extraordinary fact-filled chapters, including:
- Where and How To Meet Females
- How To Pet and Like It
- What Every Young Man Should Know about Bedmanship
- How To Be Happy Though Married
- Plus, the latest birth-control techniques and venereal-disease preventions

Books and Monographs by Albert Ellis

AN INTRODUCTION TO THE PRINCIPLES OF SCIENTIFIC PSYCHOANALYSIS (*Journal Press*, 1950)

THE FOLKLORE OF SEX (*Charles Boni*, 1951; rev. ed., *Grove Press*, 1961)

SEX, SOCIETY AND THE INDIVIDUAL (with A. P. Pillay) (*International Journal of Sexology Press*, 1953)

SEX LIFE OF THE AMERICAN WOMAN AND THE KINSEY REPORT (*Greenberg*, 1954)

THE AMERICAN SEXUAL TRAGEDY (*Twayne*, 1954; rev. ed., *Lyle Stuart*, 1962; *Grove Press*, 1963)

NEW APPROACHES TO PSYCHOTHERAPY TECHNIQUES (*Journal of Clinical Psychology Press*, 1955)

THE PSYCHOLOGY OF SEX OFFENDERS (with Ralph Brancale) (*Charles C Thomas*, 1956)

HOW TO LIVE WITH A NEUROTIC (*Crown*, 1957)

SEX WITHOUT GUILT (*Lyle Stuart*, 1958; *Hillman*, 1959)

WHAT IS PSYCHOTHERAPY? (*American Academy of Psychotherapists*, 1959)

THE PLACE OF VALUES IN THE PRACTICE OF PSYCHOTHERAPY (*American Academy of Psychotherapists*, 1959)

THE ART AND SCIENCE OF LOVE (*Lyle Stuart*, 1960)

THE ENCYCLOPEDIA OF SEXUAL BEHAVIOR (with Albert Abarbanel) (*Hawthorn*, 1961)

CREATIVE MARRIAGE (with Robert A. Harper) (*Lyle Stuart*, 1961)

A GUIDE TO RATIONAL LIVING (with Robert A. Harper) (*Prentice-Hall*, 1961)

REASON AND EMOTION IN PSYCHOTHERAPY (*Lyle Stuart*, 1962)

THE INTELLIGENT WOMAN'S GUIDE TO MAN-HUNTING (*Lyle Stuart*, 1963)

IF THIS BE SEXUAL HERESY . . . (*Lyle Stuart*, 1963)

SEX AND THE SINGLE MAN (*Lyle Stuart*, 1963)

THE CASE FOR SEXUAL LIBERTY (*Seymour Press*, 1964)

NYMPHOMANIA: A STUDY OF THE OVER-SEXED WOMAN (with Edward Sagarin) (*Julian Messner*, 1964)

THE THEORY AND PRACTICE OF RATIONAL-EMOTIVE PSYCHOTHERAPY (*Lyle Stuart*, 1964)

SEX

and

the

Single

Man

LYLE STUART, Inc.
New York

by

Albert Ellis, Ph. D.

Table of Contents

To
Brooking Tatum
best damned editor I ever had

Introduction

For a man there are three certainties in life: death, taxes, and women. It is often difficult to say which is the worst. The man who thinks he can handle women well is either an optimist or a super-optimist.

This book is about sex and the single man. Which means that it is largely about the single man—and *women*. It will also consider some of the non-heterosexual aspects of bachelorhood: such as the problem of masturbation and the dangers of homosexuality; and the all-important relationship of the man *to himself*.

Largely, however, this book tells you, the presumably male reader, how to meet, get involved with, have satisfactory sex relations with, and perhaps marry a suitably selected person of the other sex. Not, of course, that you *have* to do so. As a respectable, independent member of the human race, you do have other choices.

You could, for example, consort only with other men. Or become a Trappist monk. Or live happily (though probably not too sexually) with a bird dog.

If any of these choices be your particular cup of tea, take it—with my blessing. But if you *do* want to get along successfully with women, that's what this book is designed for: to tell you how. And it *will* tell you—it will give you the *knowledge*, at least, that will enable you to get along much better with the fair sex than you probably ever have before.

Is knowledge enough though? Will *knowing* how to make it with the members of the other sex automatically enable you to do so?

No; decidedly not. In addition to know-how, you will need several other requisites if you are to have good sex-love relationships with females. Specifically (to name only the minimal other requirements) these are:

Intelligence
Emotional stability
Experience and practice
Sympathy *for* and interest *in* women, and
Good luck

Without a fair degree of intelligence and emotional stability, all the knowledge in the world will not appreciably help you to understand and deal adequately with females. Without experience and practice at heterosexual relations, there is a very low probability that you will succeed very well at them. Without some genuine sympathy for and interest in women, you will almost certainly soon antagonize them and defeat your own best ends. And without some measure of good luck —without your possessing, for example, the right age, or body-build, or esthetic sensitivity, or talent, or something else that just happens to appeal to a particular girl in whom you are interested—you are not likely to get exactly what you want in love or marriage, even though you are otherwise amply blessed.

This book will not appreciably increase your Intelligence Quotient; nor, most assuredly, is it any kind of good-luck charm. But, assuming you have a reasonably good mind and are prepared to use it assiduously to improve your heterosexual affairs, *Sex and the Single Man* is designed to give you pertinent knowledge about women, show you how you can become more emotionally stable, encourage and aid you to get sex practice, and help you to understand and become more sympathetic toward females.

Is this a hell of a lot for one volume to attempt? It doubtless is; but you can't kill a book for trying. And although the material presented here may seem to be easily stated and cavalierly arrived at, this is far from true. Almost twenty-five years of intense preparation have gone into compiling it, in the course of which time I have—

read and digested thousands of books and articles on sex-love relations;

done primary research in the psychology of human love;

intensively worked with hundreds of psychotherapy patients and marriage counseling clients;

written scores of articles and published sixteen books on sex, love, marriage, and family relations and allied fields of living; and

personally (and without editorial assistance!) been involved in about a dozen major and almost countless minor sex-love relationships with women.

On this last count, I enjoy telling a story of what happened to me, some twenty-three years ago, when I was doing research at the library of the Academy of Medicine in New York City. After I had finished my work for the day, I stopped to view a medical exhibit the library was holding at the time, and ran into my physician. Although this man had known me for a good many years, and intimately knew all about my physical condition, he had never bothered to ask what kind of work I did, whether or not I was married, or similar personal questions. I think he thought I was an accountant or some other type of conventional business man.

Surprised, therefore, to see me in such medical surroundings, he asked: "What the devil are *you* doing here?"

"Research," I retorted. "I'm here at the library, almost every day, doing research."

"Research in *what?*" he half snorted.

"Sex," I said.

"Oh?" he ejaculated, almost unbelievingly. Then he smiled and made a beautiful comeback: "Well," he said, "I certainly hope you get in some laboratory work!"

Ever since then—doctor's orders, you know—I have been doing my best to fulfill this physician's hopes. And the results of my first-hand (not to mention -lips, -tongue, and -genitalia) sex research have been included in this and several of my other books.

Sex and the Single Man, then, is the product of a quarter-century of clinical, experimental, and personal investigation of (what I am still prejudiced enough to believe is) a highly fascinating field of human endeavor. It attempts to answer the most important questions that almost any unmarried male in our society is likely to have in regard to his intersexual and intrasexual affairs. With the use of the information in this book, you may well go far in the sex-love field. With this book *and* some intelligence and a little luck, you almost certainly will.

ELLIS, PH.D.
ork City

Acknowledgments

The manuscript of this book was read by Fiddle Viracola, Edrice Reynolds, and N. D. Mallary, Jr., all of whom made valuable suggestions, but none of whom are responsible for the views herein expressed.

Chapter 1

What Price Sexual Abstinence?

Millions of words have been written and declaimed during the past several centuries to prove sexual abstinence is not only perfectly harmless to the young male (and female) but it is actually a good and beneficial form of (non-) behavior. And what do these words really prove? That their authors were asses.

To begin with, as modern sex research has shown, there is practically no such thing as true sexual abstinence in the human male. Although the theory of sex sublimation, stoutly propounded by no less an authority than Sigmund Freud (1938), is still widely held among professionals and laymen, there seems to be not an iota of fact behind it as far as normal males are concerned. W. S. Taylor (1933) showed in a classic monograph that not even highly ethical, clerical-minded college boys are able to refrain completely from sex activities. All that happens, when these youngsters stop engaging in one form of sex (such as, say, premarital intercourse), is that they immediately augment their other sex outlets (such as masturbation, petting to orgasm, or homosexual copulation).

Alfred C. Kinsey and his associates (1948, 1953) went far beyond Taylor's original investigation of sex sublimation and studied the sexual outlets of over six thousand males from all walks of life and at all ages. They conclusively discovered that the average male's number of sex outlets, at any given period in his life, is surprisingly constant, so that he merely substitutes one form of sexual behavior for another and practically never remains truly abstinent.

When a young man does, for any considerable period of time, remain even moderately (not to mention completely) abstinent, there is every reason to believe that he may do himself considerable harm and that he is practically never likely to do himself any good. Not that he will probably die of sexual abstention. But, more often than not, he will wish after a while, that he would!

What are some of the results of prolonged avoidance of sexual orgasm in the male? These:

Impairment of physical health. Although some peculiarly low-sexed individuals can remain abstinent for long periods of time without any physical consequences, these individuals seem to be rare. The normal male often develops numerous physical complaints, including headaches, gastric upsets, congestion of the pelvic region, and high blood pressure (Robinson, 1930). When his sexual desires are aroused but frustrated, he may easily be stricken with urticaria or other psychosomatic symptoms (Saul and Bernstein, 1941). The war between his regular sexual desires and his belief that it is wrong to give in to these desires may "throw his visceral responses into a sort of confusion as well as create within him the most dramatic and dramatized conflict" (Myerson, 1936).

Impairment of psychological health. The main dangers of abstinence are not physical but psychological. All kinds and degrees of emotional tenseness and disturbance have been reported on the part of many highly sexed individuals who forced themselves to refrain completely from sex activities (Arlington, 1958; Guyon, 1934, 1950, 1951; Kirkendall, 1963; Lanval, 1963; Russell, 1929; Schroeder, 1929; Stokes and Mace, 1953). Beigel (1961) notes that "in young people, abstinence is apt to increase sexual desire and to evoke an abundance of sexual imagery. This may result in inability to concentrate, irritability, insomnia, extreme nervousness, or more serious complications, the extent of the disturbance depending on the individual's drive intensity, temperament, and environment. These conditions may become so distracting to some people that they cannot work." The Abbé Monchanin (1939) indicates that "there are others in whom sexual instinct is so strong that continued chastity induces excessive repression and lays them open to the danger of psychasthenia, sexual obsession and then perversion."

Stekel (1923) notes the case of "a young man of medium strength who could practice masturbation with ejaculation, five to ten times in an hour, without showing any neurotic symptoms. As soon as he ceased the practice of onanism, he developed severe neurotic symptoms."

Freud and many of his leading followers—such as Farrow (1942), Reik (1961), and Hendrick (1934)—believed firmly that unrelieved sexual tensions lead to a physical build-up, and to eventual anxiety neurosis; and that to ward off this kind of disturbance "nothing but the adequate activity (orgasm) would be effective; for, once it has reached the required level, the somatic sexual excitation is continuously transmuted into psychical excitation; the activity which will free the nerve-endings from burdensome pressure and so abolish the whole of the somatic excitation present, thus allowing the subcortical tracts to reestablish their resistance, must absolutely be carried into operation" (Freud, 1924-50). Modern psychoanalysts do not posit the specific mechanisms of excitatory buildup and consequent neuroticizing of the whole personality which the early analysts believed in; but they generally are opposed to sexual abstinence and continually encourage their patients to engage in premarital sex relations (Ellis, 1963a). Magnus Hirschfeld, who was not a Freudian but nonetheless an outstanding sexologist, pointed out that "as a result of the constraints of a hypocritical social morality, all men have become to some extent neurotic where sex is concerned" (1935).

Impairment of sexual adequacy. There is considerable evidence that in many (though not necessarily all) humans complete abstinence seriously interferes with sexual performance, and may render an individual temporarily or permanently impotent or frigid (Rubin, 1962; Walker, 1963). Hirschfeld (1934), after studying the results of sexual abstinence during World War I, concluded: "We have every reason to assume that the abstinence enforced by the war resulted in all forms of sexual neurosis. This is particularly true of the most important of these neuroses, ejaculatio praecox. The war, with all the hardships and dislocations it imposed upon sex life, seems to have increased tremendously the number of these cases. . . . Scarcely a week passed in which female patients did not come to the Institute for Sexual Research with the complaint that their husbands, who had formerly been healthy, had returned from the war suffering from this complaint."

Wilhelm Reich (1948), studying the effect of continence on marriage, concluded that although the demand for abstinence might possibly make the adolescent male submissive and therefore capable of being monogamous once he married, "in doing so it creates the very sexual impotence which in turn destroys marriage and accentuates the problem of marriage." Henri-Fréderic Amiel (1930), drawing from his own sex experience, wrote: "I seem to have lost my sex. My general softening comes perhaps from my complete abstinence." And St. Augustine (1962), after trying sexual abstinence for some time, reported: "I now neither seek nor desire anything whatever of this sort [sexual intercourse]. It is with horror and loathing that I even remember it."

After doing a comprehensive review of the effects of abstinence, Taylor (1936) concluded that "physically, also, despite many misleading arguments to the contrary, it seems reasonable to conclude with modern authorities that prolonged sexual abstinence often produces, in men, weak erections and premature ejaculations, impotence, prostatic and testicular disorders; in women, chlorosis, dysmenorrhea, shrinking of the breasts, and congestion of the ovaries; and, in both sexes, insomnia and metabolic and nervous disorders. Abstinence after habituation to intercourse is especially conducive to these disorders. In short, sexual abstinence (like probably any continually unsatisfied urge), considered solely in its direct individual effects, is usually if not always an evil."

Impairment of social values. Not only is sexual continence physically, mentally, and sexually injurious to numerous individuals who attempt (usually unsuccessfully) to practice it, but it also has grave social disadvantages. This is recognized by J. D. Unwin (1933), one of the greatest prudes of this century, who in spite of his espousal of sexual inhibition has written: "In the fourth century the Christian fathers began to compel the acceptance of the doctrine that marriage was a compromise with sin and that those who married fell from an immaculate ideal. As Jerome put it, 'Nuptiae terram replent, virginitas Paradisum.' It then became the fashion for new converts to found religious houses which were soon filled by male and female votaries of celibacy. This is what happened among the Anglo-Saxons at the end of the seventh century and again in the tenth century, and among the Normans in the twelfth century. By their voluntary acceptance of compulsory continence the women who first entered these houses proved themselves to have been the very ones who, being fruitful, would have bred a generation of energetic sons. If you examine the records of the events which took place in Western Europe between the seventh and thirteenth centuries, you will find that after the acceptance of this type of Christianity a society soon ceased to manifest the same energy as before. It does not matter whether the people were Anglo-Saxons, Danes, Normans, Franks, or Venetians; their social energy varied according as they permitted or did not permit the custom of voluntary sterility."

From quite a different standpoint, Freud (1924-50) also noted the dysgenic influence of abstinence: "Let us add that together with the restrictions on sexual activity in any nation there always goes an increase of anxiety concerning life and of fear of death, which interfere with each individual's capacity for enjoyment, and do away with his willingness to incur risk of death in whatever cause—showing itself in a diminished inclination to beget offspring, thus excluding any people or group of such a type from participation in the future."

Anthony Ludovici (1923), writing from the standpoint of a social reformer, agrees that "psychoanalysis has at last shown what all decent and clean-minded people knew about prolonged sexual abstinence—that it is both wrongful and harmful." Walter Heaton (1919) concurs: "Not only are all forms of asceticism directly contrary to nature's law, but they are decidedly immoral and work in direct opposition to the prowess of the individual or nation." Agreeing with these views, Edward Carpenter (1923) insists that "in the social life of the future . . . the state of enforced celibacy in which vast numbers of women live today will be looked upon as a national wrong, almost as grievous as that of prostitution—of which latter evil indeed it is in some degree the counterpart or necessary accompaniment."

We can perhaps best sum up this short survey of the harmful effects of sexual abstinence by quoting from two authorities who made intensive studies of the subject thirty-seven years apart. Writing in 1924, the great sexologist, Dr. William J. Robinson, noted: "In the vast majority of men and women continence produces unpleasant and undesirable effects. . . . In some people however continence after maturity produces distinctly unfavorable results; sometimes they are purely physical, sometimes purely psychic, but usually they are a combination of both. In some cases the symptoms are very grave, and in a certain percentage the condition brought about is incurable. . . . To say it in one sentence.

Sexual abstinence in the majority of both men and women is abnormal and undesirable."

Over three and a half decades later, writing in 1961, the well-known sexologist and psychologist, Dr. Hugo G. Beigel, concluded his own intensive survey of the results of sexual abstinence with this statement: "Varied though the consequences of abstinence may be, the gratification of the sexual drive is a necessity for the normally developed human, and the disregard of this necessity over a long period of time is likely to break the life impulses and thus to affect not only happiness and well-being but also physical and mental health."

To the question, then, What price sexual abstinence?, we can unhesitatingly answer: The price is too damned high. Naturally, complete sexual abstention has *some* advantages. It is, for example, time-saving (assuming that the abstainer does not become continually *pre*occupied about the acts with which he is not occupied!). It eliminates certain dangers, such as incurring venereal disease or getting a girl pregnant. It avoids entangling alliances (such as marriage) which may have their own inconveniences. But almost all its advantages could be just as well—nay, sometimes better—achieved if the abstainer avoided heterosexual relations, but at least regularly resorted to masturbation (Hefner, 1962-63; Johnson, 1963).

Its disadvantages, moreover, are enormous. For only the unusually low-sexed individual, or he who is fanatically devoted to some nonsexual cause and consumes practically all his time and energy in its pursuit, can *easily* remain abstinent. The normal human being, and particularly the normal male, must (sometimes literally) work his guts off to remain totally inactive sexually. He must continually brush aside incipient and full-blown sex thoughts and fantasies; convince himself over and over that he *should* remain sexually inviolate; rigorously keep himself away from all kinds of easily available temptations; and almost obsessively-compulsively endeavor to keep his mind and his body from automatically returning to sexual enticements.

Almost all the time, as indicated above, he will more or less fail in his abstinence endeavors. Most of the time, in fact, he will not merely fail occasionally, but will find that he is frequently lapsing into overt sex activity of one kind or another. And when he does lapse, he will tend to go off on a series of sexual binges, rather than minor occasional interludes. Even when he succeeds in remaining abstemious, he will almost always be *anxious* about his continued success. And when he fails, he will tend to be self-recriminating and self-punishing about his slips.

Finally, as we have also just seen, if the abstinence-minded individual somehow manages consistently to succeed in his puritan-minded aim, his very success will involve its own failure; since he will in the great majority of cases injure himself physically, emotionally, sexually, and/or socially. He won't I again concede, die of his self-imposed sexual constraint; at least, it doesn't happen very often. But neither will he, in any true sense of the word, *live* with it.

The price of sexual abstinence, then, is almost always exorbitant. When, in very rare cases (as when you happen to be seriously afflicted with some illness and your physician proscribes any kind of sex activity), total abstinence is necessary, it can be stoically accepted—or, as I teach my patients, gracefully lumped—just as any necessary evil can be. But *voluntary* abstinence is an *un*necessary evil; and to accept *that* kind of misery is to be off your rocker. Better you should see a psychologist, fast, then keep afflicting yourself with that kind of nonsense.

"But how about remaining abstinent for religious reasons?" you may ask. "After all, didn't Paul say that it is better to marry than to burn, but it is far better not to marry at all, and to be virginal and sexually unpolluted all one's life?"

Yes, Paul did say that; and so did various other, non-Christian, religious fanatics say similar things, and espouse varying kinds of temporary or permanent abstinence. And if you wish to be religiously fanatic, and to assume that some superhuman deity will welcome you to his (abysmally boring) Heaven if you forego all earthly sex pleasures, you have a perfect right to do so. You also have a perfect right to think that you are Jesus Christ (or Napoleon); to sleep on nails; and to eat dirt instead of roast beef. But in all these instances you will be a nut: which, of course, you have a perfect right to be. Far be it from me to deprive you of your psychotic "pleasures."

"All right," you say, "but suppose I merely want to forego one kind of pleasure—namely, sex activity—for another, and to me higher, kind of nonpsychotic enjoyment, such as an intense devotion to athletics, or chess, or politics. Would that be so crazy?"

No, it usually would not be—assuming that you wanted to be *moderately* or *mainly* nonsexual in your hedonic outlets. But if you wanted to be *totally* unsexed, then I would suspect that something was rotten in your thinking and emoting processes.

A patient of mine, whom I shall call Malcolm B., maintained that he found it better to refrain completely from sex participation because he wanted to devote all his spare time to studying the stock market, and that sex thoughts and acts would only interfere with this great interest.

"But wouldn't your not having any sex relations lead you to become somewhat obsessed with sex thoughts and fantasies?" I asked. "And would not this kind of obsession detract even *more* from your interest in the stock market than a moderate amount of sex activity would?"

"Oh, no. I'm ready to put up with that kind of thing," Malcolm replied. "I can easily handle my fantasies."

"No doubt," I said. "But won't they *still* be rather time-consuming? And won't the effort that you have to take to squelch them—if that's what you intend to do about them—won't *that* detract from your absorption in the stock market?"

"No, the sex itself would take still more time and energy," he insisted.

By this time, I was getting quite suspicious. "How so?" I asked. "Let's suppose you did engage in some kind of sexual pleasure. How often would you do so every week, on the average? And how much time would you take each time you engaged in this sex activity?"

"Oh," Malcolm answered rather vaguely, "a good deal of time, I guess."

"You mean," I said, "that if you dated girls, and finally were able to pet to orgasm with them, or get them to go to bed with you, that it would take at least five or ten hours a week?"

"Well, wouldn't it?" asked Malcolm, somewhat belligerently and defensively.

"Yes, it very well might," I replied. "But there are, you know, various methods of achieving some form of sex satisfaction, *other* than petting or having intercourse with girls."

"What do you mean?"

"Well, there's always masturbation, for example. You don't mean to tell me, now, that *that* would take you five or ten hours a week, even if you did it almost every day."

"Oh, I would never do a thing like *that!*" Malcolm exclaimed.

"You wouldn't? Why?"

"Well—uh—I just wouldn't."

I soon saw that my suspicions were well founded. Malcolm's ostensible objection to the time- and energy-consuming aspects of sex relations were pure rationalizations. Actually, as I soon induced him to admit, he thought that *any* kind of sex act was wicked, and that he would be a most worthwhile, holier-than-thou individual only if he refrained from every form of sex satisfaction. Malcolm, like so many other males who attempt to remain completely abstinent, was a severely disturbed person who demanded perfect performance of himself in all significant areas of his life, who loathed himself when he fell a few degrees below this expected level of perfection, and who tried to compensate for his assumed worthlessness by being "better" than other males in the presumably all-important sexual areas. Where many other people like Malcolm will try to be the most potent Don Juans (or even the most frequent masturbators) and thereby "prove" their superiority over others, he took the overcompensatory road of sexual "purity," and tried to excel in that respect. After we had worked several months at intensive psychotherapy, and he no longer needed to excel over all other males but could accept himself as a worthwhile person in his *own* right, he realized that his obsession with continence and "purity" was a symptom of his former emotional sickness, and began to have quite enjoyable masturbatory and heterosexual outlets.

This is not to say, now, that *all* totally abstinent males are mentally ill. A few, because they are physically low-sexed, are normally and harmlessly continent. If you are one of these few, you may have nothing to worry about. Sex—and, for that matter, marriage—may just not be your cup of bouillon. But if you are quite, or even moderately, highly sexed; if, that is to say, you are continually aware of sexual arousal and excitement; and if you *still* feel that you must remain completely abstinent; then you'd better get you, pronto, to the nearest psychologist or psychiatrist and find out the reason why. To refrain from over-eating may be very sensible behavior; but to refrain from *any* eating is sheer lunacy. Abstaining from all sexuality, at least when you are young and physically healthy, is a form of abstaining from happy living. He who puts his sex urges behind him, viewing them as aspects of satanism, would better put aside enough funds for prolonged psychological treatment.

Chapter 2

To Masturbate or Not:
That Is the Question

Although American attitudes toward masturbation have been remarkably liberalized during the last fifty years, it is still rare for writers on the subject of sex to take a completely objective, nonmoralistic attitude on this touchy subject. Complete public endorsement of sexual self-stimulation is prevalent only among some widely scattered primitive peoples; and it is almost shocking for someone born and raised in any civilized nation to read about the unusual freedom in this connection afforded by such peoples.

Thus, Linton (1939) tells us that, among the Marquesan Islanders, "The child found early in life that it got nowhere by yelling, for if the adults were busy, they just let it cry. However, if the child became too troublesome, an adult might quiet it by masturbating it. The masturbation of female children began very early; in fact, from the moment of birth there was systematic manipulation of the labia to elongate them, as elongation was considered a mark of beauty."

According to Elkin (1940), among the Northern Arapaho Indians of Wyoming, "much of the Arapaho humor, told only among the men and often for the purpose of genital rubbing, revolved about the unusual and unexpected in the love quest. It frequently related to sodomy, in nonhuman form, and masturbation, in which the young men seemed to have engaged rather often, in a spirit of good-natured sport."

Laubscher (1938) tells us that among the Tembu people of Africa, "Masturbatory manipulations of the penis are quite common and may receive a playful rebuke, but are not viewed at all seriously. They are merely considered as the playful activities of children." Devereux (1937) notes that among the young Mohave Indian males "masturbating and urinating competitions were frequent. In masturbating competitions both the shortness of the time required to cause ejaculation and the distance to which the sperm was projected were taken into consideration. Urinating competitions consisted of urinating figures and letters on the ground."

So much for some of the "uncivilized" primitives. In our own "higher" civilization, attitudes toward masturbation tend to be infinitely primmer. Menninger (1961) notes that "even today there are few authors brave enough and honest enough to make the flat statements that masturbation never harms a child and that the child whose sexual life evolves without a period of masturbation is an exceptional and, one may say, an abnormal child." He also points out (1959) that even psychoanalysts tend to view masturbation as self-destructive because it represents a preoccupation with the self, based on aggressive feelings toward others. What he fails to note is that this psychoanalytic concept is largely a biased view that is not based on any factual evidence, and that it is most unlikely that more than a small minority of individuals masturbate because of their hatred of others.

Some of the most recent Boy Scout Handbooks (1945) have, albeit more subtly than earlier editions of this same manual, inveighed against masturbation: "It is a bad habit. It should be fought against. . . . It is something to keep from. Keep control of yourself in sex matters. It is manly to do so. It is important for your life, your happiness, your efficiency, and the whole human race as well." And Kinsey, Pomeroy, and Martin (1948) tell us: "The United States Naval Academy at Annapolis rules that a candidate 'shall be rejected by the examining surgeon for . . . evidence of . . . masturbation.'"

As Dearborn (1961) notes, "No other form of sexual activity has been more frequently discussed, more roundly condemned, and more universally practiced than masturbation. . . . It is also noteworthy that the superstitions regarding masturbation have not been entirely annihilated, for we find in a few of our modern writings an insistence upon classifying it under the heading of perversion. Whenever modern religious leaders feel under the obligation to discourage masturbation, they are not now likely to refer to any horrible consequences but rather to consider it a religious offense. The Catholic Church, for example, deals with it dogmatically as a sin. This attitude is also held by some Orthodox groups and by certain fundamentalist Protestant bodies." Spitz (1949,

1952) and Wettley (1959) have also indicated that many negative attitudes toward autoerotism still exist on the part of our laymen and professionals.

Objections to Masturbation

I have examined, in my books *Sex Without Guilt* (1958) and *The Art and Science of Love* (1960), the various objections that are raised against masturbation and shown how invalid they are. Let me again briefly consider these objections, particularly as they apply to the adult single male, to see if they hold any water.

1. It is held that although masturbation may be perfectly normal for adolescents, it is immature for older males, and should be completely foregone for other, presumably heterosexual, types of sex activity. This is nonsense. As every study of masturbatory activity has shown—including studies by Finger (1947), Kinsey and his associates (1948, 1953), Hamilton (1952), and Peck and Wells (1923)—autoerotism is not merely practiced by youngsters but is the main (yes, the *main*) sex outlet of the great majority of unmarried adults in our society. Because masturbation is so prevalent among our adults, it is quite possible to say that our *society*, which forces them to engage in this kind of outlet rather than heterosexual affairs, is immature. But it is senseless to call masturbatory activities immature when they are so harmlessly engaged in by most unmarried adults—and by a surprisingly large proportion of married adults as well.

There is no doubt that autoerotism *may* be childish or deviant when a male who has the choice of several other modes of sex activity finds that he can enjoy *only* masturbation or when he employs masturbation fantasies and activities to reduce his feelings of anxiety (Abramson, 1955; Faust, 1957). But such pathological masturbators are rare; and the great majority of adults males (and females) who masturbate regularly or irregularly are not, by mere virtue of this activity, in any pathological state.

2. It is often contended that autoerotism is an asocial or antisocial habit, and that those who are addicted to it tend to withdraw from social life. There is no evidence whatever to back this hypothesis; and the facts actually show that some of the most extroverted and highly socialized individuals are steady masturbators. Certainly, *some* males may masturbate rather than face their anxieties involved with trying to en-

gage in heterosexual relations, but this hardly proves that *most* or *all* masturbators are socially anxious. The vast majority of people who masturbate seem to do so because they find it much easier, in this antisexual world we live in, than to court successfully a member of the other sex and have mutually satisfying affairs with this other person. It is not the difficulty of getting along *socially*, but of making it *sexually*, with other-sex individuals that leads them to masturbate. Our antisexual customs, moreover, actually *create* social difficulties, since they make it so difficult for males and females to get together sexually and to succeed in their relationships with each other that many of them tend to *become* socially inhibited because of the difficulties that develop around social-sexual relations. So our rules against sex, including those against masturbating, make these individuals much more asocial or antisocial than any amount of masturbation, in itself, could possibly do.

3. It is sometimes held that masturbation does not produce full emotional or sexual gratification. Havelock Ellis (1960), for instance, noted that "in the absence of the desired partner the orgasm, whatever relief it may give, must be followed by a sense of dissatisfaction, perhaps of depression, even of exhaustion, often of shame and remorse." With all due apologies to the great sage of sex, this is clap-trap.

Certainly masturbation leads to dissatisfaction, depression, and remorse—*when* one does not wholeheartedly accept it as a good and beneficial act, and when one erroneously *believes* that it is not satisfying. Or when, again, one is so childish that he absolutely refuses to accept a lesser, and available, sex satisfaction instead of an ideal, and presently unavailable, one.

No sex act, in fact, including heterosexual coitus, can give ideal or full emotional or physical gratification at all times to all persons, simply because all human beings are unique individuals and because they continually differ *from themselves* (as well as from each other) from day to day, and often even from hour to hour. Objective observation quickly shows that there are literally millions of people who at least *at times* obtain *more* emotional and physical gratification from masturbation than from any other kind of sex participation. It is only (as noted above) when these individuals *always* enjoy autoerotism more than intersexual relations that they begin to fall into the pathological range.

Even more millions of people practically never enjoy masturbation *as much* as they enjoy heterosexual activities; but they do enjoy it, when it is the only kind of sex practicably available, with full emotional and physical impact. Still other individuals derive no emotional feelings, in the sense of love for another person, from masturbation; but since when is love *necessary* for full sex enjoyment? Desirable, yes; preferable, in most instances. But sex that is engaged in without love (or even friendship) can certainly be, and in innumerable cases is, one of the most satisfying of human pursuits. Let us not sell it short because it is not ideal.

4. It is often alleged that masturbation leads to impotence in the male or frigidity in the female. This allegation is not supported by factual evidence. On the contrary, I have found in my clinical practice that males who are impotent tend to engage in considerably less autoerotism than those who are potent. And the Kinsey research group (1953) has discovered that while approximately 33 per cent of females who do not masturbate before marriage are unresponsive in intercourse during the early years of their marriage, only about fifteen per cent of females who do masturbate are equally coitally unresponsive. In treating both males and females who come to see me because of sexual inadequacy, I often find that inducing them to masturbate to orgasm helps them to overcome their sexual inadequacy.

5. It has been held by many so-called authorities that masturbation is dangerous because it more easily leads to sexual excess on the part of the masturbator. This allegation is directly contradicted by the findings of Kirkendall (1958, 1961a), who studied the masturbatory activities of young males and showed that they usually have considerably more sexual potential than they actually use. Moreover, as I have pointed out in previous writings on this subject (Ellis, 1958, 1960; Ellis and Harper, 1961a), it is almost impossible for anyone to masturbate to excess, unless he is absolutely psychotic, because erotic response depends upon a remarkably foolproof mechanism. When a person, particularly a male, reaches the limits of his physiological endurance, he no longer responds sexually. There is much more likelihood, in fact, that a person is in danger of neurotically going beyond his limits heterosexually, when he feels obliged to satisfy his sex partner even though his desire has faded, than he is in danger of exceeding his capacities in masturbatory activities.

Advantages of Masturbation

As can be seen from the foregoing discussion, the main reasons raised against masturbation turn out, upon closer examination, to be specious and nonsensical. On the contrary, the indubitable advantages of autoerotism are almost invariably ignored in our contemporary literature. Thus, it is obvious that masturbation is most easily available; interferes not a whit with the sex rights or desires of others; is free from the dangers of venereal infection, pregnancy, and abortion; serves as a fine apprenticeship in erotic fantasy, which is often so necessary for later heterosexual relations; has a most calming effect on the sex urges and emotional excitation of millions of people who require relief quickly, and who are not likely to get it in non-masturbatory ways; involves a minimum of expense; requires much less expenditure of time and energy than do most forms of sexual activity; can be practiced in many circumstances where heterosexual activity is impractical; can easily be interspersed with various nonsexual occupations that the individual is required to perform; ordinarily requires no preliminary steps; involves no apparatus or hygienic precautions; can be engaged in when one is sick, lying in bed, or living under other conditions which normally preclude other forms of sex relations; and has various other advantages.

This not to say, now, that autoerotism is *better* or *more desirable* than intersexual relations. For the most part, it isn't. And there is little likelihood that, as long as heterosexuality is as intrinsically enjoyable as it seems to be for most people, it will ever be totally replaced by masturbation. Most people would much rather copulate with members of the other sex once a week than masturbate daily; and there is every reason to believe that they will continue to feel this way.

The choice, however, is not normally forced. It is not usually a matter of whether you should masturbate *or* have heterosexual relations, but whether or not you should do, at various times, *both*. And the answer should be obvious to any sane and thinking person. Of course, when heterosexual affairs are truly not available, or when they would require your going far out of your way to obtain them, there is no reason why you should not *then* masturbate. Indeed, if you don't do so in such circumstances you should be suspected of being sexually perverse or neurotic.

As I say in the concluding paragraph of my chapter on masturbation in *Sex Without Guilt*: "It is difficult to conceive of a more beneficial, harmless, tension-releasing human act than masturbation that is spontaneously performed without (puritanically inculcated and groundlessly held) fears and anxieties. Let us, please, now that Kinsey and his associates have stoutly reaffirmed this fact, see that our sex manuals and sex education texts unequivocally say it in plain English."

Chapter 3

How to Avoid Guilt Without Sex

In our own country there seems to be much more guilt without sex than vice versa, in spite of my own and others' efforts over the past several decades to help make it otherwise. Our females are obviously exceptionally guilty about many of their sex activities—and even many of their sex thoughts—and our males are not too far behind them in self-blame.

"Is any of this sex guilt justifiable?" you may ask.

No, not an iota, say I.

"But are not *some* of the sex things people do today wrong? And shouldn't they at least be guilty about *those* things?"

Yes to the first; and No, absolutely no, to the second of these questions.

"That seems confusing. If some of the sex deeds people perform are bad or wrong, why shouldn't they be guilty about performing them?"

For the very good reason, I contend, that *no one should ever be guilty about anything he does.*

"No one should ever be guilty about anything! Why, aren't you asking for a state of total anarchism—or even satanism —when you say that?"

Not in the least. I am asking for a state of true self-discipline and sanity when I say that.

"I don't get it. Explain!"

All right, I shall be glad to. Let us take, by way of illustration, the case of one of my psychotherapy patients, Norman S., who came to see me because he was having terrible nightmares almost every night, was in a near-panic state during most of each day, and was almost totally impotent with his girlfriend. We quickly determined, during my first session with Norman, that he was very guilty and upset because he had no intention of marrying his girlfriend and he felt he was unfairly leading her on in continuing to have sex relations with her. He believed, moreover, that he was a bastard for devirginizing her.

"Apparently," I said to Norman S., "you are mightily blaming yourself because you have done two terrible wrongs to this girl: (a) taken her virginity and (b) kept seeing her when you knew you were not going to marry her. Is that correct?"

"Yes, I'm terribly guilty about both these things," he replied. "If she only had had other men before me, it wouldn't matter that much. But even then I'd hate myself for continuing to lead her on, as I am now doing."

"O.K.," I said. "First let's look at your acts to see whether there's any real wrongdoing in them. Take your devirginizing this girl. What do you think was wrong about that?"

"Well—uh—I don't know. I just think it was wrong. After all, I was the *first* to have her, you know. And—well, it just seems wrong."

"But you said, before, that if you were *not* the first man to have this girl, you then would have had her without qualms. Is that right?"

"Yes; that wouldn't have bothered me at all."

"Then what's the magic which devirginization adds to— or perhaps subtracts from—her? If you had had her *second,* you'd think that she (and intercourse with her) was fine. This means, presumably, that if *anyone else* has her, now that you have taken her virginity, he should also think she (and intercourse with her) is fine. Isn't that so?"

"Uh—yes, I guess so."

"So neither *your* having her first nor anyone else having her first seems to change the girl, or change intercourse with her. Obviously, then, it's not the devirginization which has changed her or done her any harm. Why, then, should *you* be disturbed about taking her virginity?"

"Mmmm. I see what you mean. *I* wouldn't look down on her, or refuse to see her, if she were already a nonvirgin when I met her; so why should *anyone else* look down on her, or refuse to have sex or love with her, now that I've taken her virginity. She's not really changed by being with me sexually, or being with anyone else. Hmm."

"No, she's obviously not changed. And yet you seem to think that by devirginizing her she *has* changed—and for the worse—and that you're a bastard because you're responsible for this bad change in her."

"I guess I do."

"Would you prefer it, then, if you had *not* slept with her, that she go on being a virgin forever? Do you think that virginity *itself* is a fine state for her to be in?"

"Hell, no! I'm sure, as I said before, that I would have liked her better, from the start, if she had *not* been a virgin. And I certainly don't think that virginity *helps* any woman."

"Then why are you such a heel for devirginizing her? Looks to me like you've sort of, in your own view, done her a favor, and perhaps should be praising yourself, rather than blaming yourself, for performing it!"

"I never thought of that!"

"No, I'm sure you didn't. But shouldn't you? Or are you afraid that someone else—some other man—who comes along next in her life won't like her loss of virginity, and she will *then* regret its loss, and *that* will make you a bastard for taking it from her?"

"Well, that *could* happen, couldn't it? The next guy she goes with *could* be upset about her not being a virgin."

"Yes, he could. But he could also be upset, if you had *not* slept with her, about her *not* being a virgin. Or he could be upset about her not having red hair, her not being a millionairess, her not having had the right kind of sex relations with you, and a million other things. Are you going to worry about all *those* possibilities?"

"No, of course not. But *she* could be upset, now, about giving me her virginity, when I am not going to marry her."

"True; she certainly could be. But did you *promise to* marry her before she first slept with you? Did you induce her to surrender only *because* you would stay with her forever?"

"Oh, no. Not at all. I was very honest with her, right from the start, and didn't even tell her I loved her when we first went to bed. So she can't accuse me of *that* kind of thing."

"Very well, then. You were perfectly honest with her; and she went to bed with you because, for one reason or another, *she* wanted to do so. Maybe she just wanted to have the sex, or lose her virginity, or take the *chance* that she would marry you, or something else. But you hardly twisted her arm—or her leg. She *voluntarily* fornicated with you. Right?"

"Yes, quite right. Come to think of it, I'd say now, she

was even a little over-eager. Perhaps she thought it was high time that she *did* give up her virginity. Or perhaps she merely loved me and wanted to cement our relationship. Anyway, I hardly had trouble getting her into the sack."

"Which means that even if she should *now* regret very much having gone to bed with you and should *now* blame you taking her virginity, she actually has no one but herself on whom to place the responsibility for having sex with you. She did it with her eyes open—and because of what *she* thought *she* would gain thereby. And now, if you actually leave her, she has probably gambled and lost. But that's not *your* responsibility or wrongdoing, is it?"

"Mmm. No. I guess not. She knew perfectly well what she was doing, thought that she would gain by it, and would certainly have to assume responsibility for her act herself, if she should now regret it."

"So where is *your* wrongdoing in all this, even assuming that *she* made a serious mistake and now sees that she made it?"

"I guess there is none."

"No, there isn't any wrongdoing on your part; and obviously you have nothing to be guilty about. Now let's go on to your second element of self-blame. You are, you say, continuing to have sex with this girl, even though you know you won't marry her, and she apparently believes that you may. You are thereby, by an error of omission if not commission, misleading her—inducing her to believe that you will marry her when you know perfectly well that you won't. Is that the case?"

"Yes, that's it."

"Which means that you are deliberately keeping information from her which, if she knew about it, might well induce her to change her attitude toward you, and perhaps get rid of you as a sleeping partner."

"I'm sure she would. She only wants to be with me because she loves me, and wants me to marry her. And if she finds out there's no chance of my marrying her, she'll break off the relationship immediately."

"All right, so you are pretending that you love her more than you do; and thereby depriving her of the freedom to make up her mind about sleeping with you on the basis of full evidence. This kind of lying, where you are needlessly and deliberately depriving another person of her freedom of action and thereby potentially harming her, is distinctly unethical, is it not?"

"Yes, it is. I know it is. And that is why I'm guilty about doing it."

"Oh, no. *That's* not why you're guilty."

But it is! I know I'm doing the wrong thing, and I'm naturally guilty."

"What do you mean *naturally*? You really mean that you're quite *artificially* making yourself guilty. Because (a) you're doing the wrong thing, as you said; and more importantly, because (b) you've got an idiotic philosophy of life that induces you to *blame* yourself for doing the wrong thing."

"But shouldn't I blame myself, when I'm definitely wrong, and when I keep doing the thing I know is wrong? Shouldn't I be guilty?"

"No. Why should you be? You should have a sense of wrongdoing: a clearheaded admission that you *are* wrong, and that you're going to do your best to change, and to be *less* wrong in the future. But that would be far from having the sense of guilt, which you now have."

"I don't get it. What's the difference between what you call my having a sense of wrongdoing and what I call my guilt?"

"All the difference in the world. A sense of wrongdoing, or of responsibility to oneself and others, consists of two sane internalized philosophies: (a) 'I am wrong, or mistaken, or erroneous in performing (or, as the case may sometimes be, *not* performing) this act,' and (b) 'Therefore, let me see how I can work at performing better in the future.' "

"But isn't that exactly what I'm saying to myself?"

"No, not at all. You're saying *one* of these sane sentences, but then you're ending up with a completely different, and quite insane, sentence. More concretely, you're saying to yourself: (a) 'I am wrong in not telling my girlfriend that I'm not going to marry her,' and (b) 'Therefore I'm a louse for being wrong, and leading her on like this.' "

"But *am* I not a louse for acting this way? Wouldn't *anyone* in my place be?"

"No, not at all. You are certainly a wrong (as we already said), fallible human being. And we're not in the least exonerating your deed, or saying that it is a right or good one. We're assuming that it's still wrong. But a fallible human who does a wrong deed is *not* a louse—except by arbitrary, theological definition. He is just what we said he was: a fallible human who does a wrong deed. Period. And if and when he corrects himself, and no longer acts badly, he will still be a fallible human who is no longer doing *this* wrong deed—but who, you can bet your bottom dollar, will soon enough, just *because* he is fallible, be doing some *other* wrong deed."

"You mean that no matter how many times I correct myself, and keep trying to act well, I will still tend to become mistaken again and to act badly?"

"Well—*won't* you?"

"I—uh—. Yes, come to think of it, I guess I will. I'll always be more or less wrong—unless, of course, I get to be perfect."

"Right. And you'll never, at least as long as you're *human*, get to be perfect. Only angels are perfect. And there are no goddam angels. Not that I've met yet."

"Nor I, I have to admit."

"Then why are you striving, so idiotically, to be the first?"

"Am I *really* trying to do that?"

"Not consciously, perhaps. For consciously you know full well that you're no angel; nor will ever be. But unconsciously, as your behavior—your guilt—shows, you are demanding that you be perfect, be angelic, never make mistakes. And then when you do make them, you measure yourself against your impossible, perfectionistic demands, and conclude that you're utterly imperfect—in fact, no good whatever. So because you can't be a perfect angel, you consider yourself a perfect louse. And instead of seeing yourself, as you truly are, as an individual who is *now* making mistakes with your girlfriend, but who could quite probably correct them if he really tried to do so, you unwittingly view yourself as a man who has *always* made similar mistakes, who is *still* making them, and who always *must* continue to make them—not because, as we just said, he is a fallible human, but because he is an absolute skunk, a no-good rotter; and skunks and rotters, of course, *must* keep failing, failing, failing."

"What you seem to be telling me is that I observe the fact that it is impossible for me to make *no* mistakes, and difficult for me to stop making *this* present mistake; and I overgeneralize about these facts, so that I wrongly conclude that it is impossible for me not to make *every* mistake, and that it is particularly impossible, rather than difficult, for me to stop making this one. Is that right?"

"Yes, that's exactly right. Over-generalization is the core

of virtually all human disturbance. And you're taking a valid point, that it is *hard* for a fallible human like you to correct his mistakes, and falsely generalizing this into the 'fact' that it is impossible for you to correct it. Or, as I said before, you are taking the observable point that you are a wrongdoer, and making it into the metaphysical point that you are a sinner, a louse, a no-goodnik."

"Why is this a metaphysical point?"

"Because it is purely definitional; and there can be no proof or disproof of it. There actually *is* no such thing as a human who is a sinner, a louse, or a no-goodnik, any more than there is such a thing as a devil, hobgoblins, or gremlins. Because a sinner really means someone who is *hopelessly* wrong; a louse, someone who was born bad and must therefore *always* be bad; a no-goodnik, someone who makes mistakes and cannot possibly *ever* correct his mistakes. But there is no way, of course, of ever proving that a man, however many times he has been mistaken in the past or present, *cannot* possibly make fewer mistakes in the future; and there is no way of demonstrating that an individual whose *deeds* are wrong is *himself* wrong and worthless, and that he cannot possibly ever be good to himself or others."

"Lousehood, then, is another over-generalization, isn't it?"

"Yes, and a generalization that is carried to such ridiculous extremes that it becomes impossible to actualize. For it would be just about impossible, even if we wanted to do so, for us to construct a human being who absolutely, positively *could* not ever do well just because he has, so far, been doing badly. All present knowledge about human beings, in fact, proves just the opposite: that they frequently *can* remarkably change themselves, and do much better in the future than they have ever done in the past. Some of them, indeed, have managed to make such drastic changes in their modes of behavior that a virtual miracle has occurred in this connection."

"You mean people like Nathan Leopold, for example?"

"Yes. Leopold was a man who perpetrated one of the most horrible crimes in human history: for a thrill—not, mind you, for political motives, for philosophic ideals, or for anything but a thrill—with his partner in crime, Loeb, he helped kill an innocent young boy. Certainly this was a great crime; and there is no point in saying it wasn't. Yet, some thirty years after he had committed it, and during a life mostly spent in the penitentiary, he somehow managed to change himself drastically, so that today there is practically no likelihood of his committing any other crimes, nor in fact of being anything but a useful, helpful human being. So this man, whom almost everyone would be 'justified' in thinking of as a hopeless criminal in the 1920's, has become, in today's 1960's, a fine, upright citizen. This is just one of many cases that show that there are no hopeless, irreparable human 'lice'—but just billions of wrongdoers, virtually all of whom with proper care and treatment *could* theoretically become do-gooders instead."

"You seem to be trying to show, then, that even if I am dead wrong about not telling my girlfriend that I'm not going to marry her, I'm not a louse for *being* wrong."

"Yes. You're wrong. And if you want to live healthfully and sanely, you should try to correct your mistake, tell her the truth, and take the consequences. But being *guilty* about what you're now doing—that is, denigrating yourself as a human because you're wrong—will not help you to change. In fact, it will quite probably make you focus so much on what a louse you are that you won't have the time and energy to devote to changing."

"That's the real problem, then—*change* rather than *guilt*."

"Right! Moral codes are ridiculous unless they help us to *change* our behavior for the better. If they only 'help' us to be guilty, or to devalue ourselves as humans, they are senseless—and basically immoral."

I continued to talk in this vein to this patient; and he soon was able to see that he had nothing to be guilty about, even though he was wrong. Once he stopped blaming himself for being wrong, he was able to face the music with his girlfriend, tell her that he had no intention of marrying her, and break off his relationship with her on amicable terms. He later became involved with a girl who was more to his liking, and whom he finally married.

Similarly, I contend and have stated in several of my recent books (Ellis, 1962a, 1963a, 1963b; Ellis and Harper, 1961a, 1961b), *no one is ever to blame for anything*. We all, goodness knows, make plenty of mistakes and commit our fair share of misdeeds, including harm to other humans. And this is bad, and there is no excusing the fact that it is bad. Nor can we avoid taking any responsibility for our immoral acts—since, to some degree at least, we normally *could* control ourselves and *could* refrain from doing them. Nonetheless, we are still only good, intrinsically valuable *people* who do these bad *acts*. We are not, as our fiction and drama unfortunately keep telling us we are, villains, or bastards, or scoundrels.

Most of the so-called sex "wrongs," moreover, are nothing of the sort. They are only definitional misdeeds. Thus, millions of Americans and Europeans *think* that masturbation, premarital sex relations, adultery, and sexual deviations are wicked or perverse. But as long as these acts are committed between adults who voluntarily and straightforwardly engage in them, it is almost impossible to imagine what is *truly* wrong about them.

Certainly, your Aunt Matilda may become upset if she discovers that you have masturbated or have copulated with the nineteen-year-old girl next door. But that is generally Aunt Matilda's problem; and if the girl next door gets upset about your fornicative relationship, it is always her prerogative to stop it. Aunt Matilda or the girl next door (or the abstraction of these individuals that we call "society") will get hurt in these instances only because they insist on *hurting themselves*, by maintaining nonsensical puritan attitudes. *You*, whatever they may say, are not truly hurting them— although you may, if you masturbate or fornicate obsessively-compulsively and thereby keep yourself away from potentially more rewarding pursuits, possibly hurt yourself.

Actually, because most of the people in this culture take their Aunt Matildas too seriously, we tend to have much more guilt without sex than vice versa—particularly among the unmarried part of the populace. As I have shown in the two studies I have done of American sex attitudes and behavior (Ellis, 1961a, 1962b), and as several other recent sex studies have also shown (Chesser, 1956; Ehrmann, 1960; French Institute of Public Opinion, 1961; Kirkendall, 1961a; Kinsey, Pomeroy, Martin, and Gebhard, 1953; Reiss, 1960), arbitrarily condemning various harmless sex acts as wrong or immoral results in two kinds of human disturbance: (a) people guiltily refrain from the banned sexual behavior; or (b) they guiltily engage in this behavior.

For the most part, males tend to be guiltily sexual rather than nonsexual; and they consequently "enjoy" a considerable amount of masturbation, fornication, adultery, and other banned sex acts in a decidedly unenjoyable, self-blaming way

(Brown, 1961). But as Arlington (1958) has incisively noted, millions of American males are forced to stay away from sex activities that they otherwise would engage in either because they are too guilty to do so or because such activities are made exceptionally difficult for them to find in many of our communities.

In other words, what we actually have in Western civilization at the present time is a considerable amount of guilt without sex. Instead of having sex and enjoying it, or even having it and not enjoying it, lots of people are not having sex—and *still* being guilty about it! For these people can, of course, *think* about sex; and with their mere thoughts and feelings they create a focal point for self-depreciation and they end up by being woefully guilty.

I take, on the other hand, the somewhat heretical viewpoint that sex, per se, is good; and that sex without guilt is even better. Also: that sex with guilt is pretty bad; and that guilt without sex is much worse. Consequently, I spend a good deal of my time, with my psychotherapy patients and marriage counseling clients, showing them how they can get rid of their guilt—and have much more, and much more enjoyable, sex as a result. What are some of the rules I teach them in this respect? These:

1. Sex, on the whole, is an unusually beneficial and remarkable harmless kind of human participation—unless one deliberately makes it otherwise. It is almost impossible to imagine any truly injurious sex activities among sensible, consenting adults.

2. Sex acts which are physically or emotionally harmful do exist, but they are rare and are easily avoided. Forcing another human being to have sex relations with you, for example; or taking advantage of a minor who cannot very well give true consent; or being dishonest, and thereby unfairly taking advantage of an adult sex partner—these are examples of antisocial acts, which may be adjudged immoral or wrong. But as long as you do not obsessively blame yourself if you should commit such misdeeds, but quietly and determinedly work at eliminating them, you can normally stop this kind of antisocial sex behavior in a short period of time.

3. Many so-called sexual perversions—such as oral-genital, anal-genital, or occasional homosexual relations—are not truly perversions at all, but are a regular part of human sex

behavior. There is nothing immoral or abnormal about them, except by arbitrary (usually Biblical-inspired) fiat. Enjoy them, if you will, and do not permit anyone to propagandize you into believing that they are in any way wrong. If laws against such acts exist in your community, then you may have to obey these silly laws, or make sure that you most discreetly disobey them. But do not be deluded into thinking that various forms of extravaginal sex acts are intrinsically perverted—rather, it is the people who think they are who are sexually disturbed (Clough, 1962).

4. Some obsessive-compulsive, fetishistic, or exclusively performed sex participations—such as fixed homosexuality, or compulsive voyeurism, or obsessive preoccupation with sex thoughts—are true perversions or deviations. But the individuals who engage in such deviated sex behavior are not wicked or immoral just because of their deviations; instead, they are invariably emotionally disturbed, and should be treated rather than condemned or punished for their deviance.

5. The general rule to follow is that a sex act is truly wrong by exactly the same token as a nonsexual act would be wrong: namely, if it needlessly harms or takes unfair advantage of another human being. If it is only self-harming, then it is wrong in the sense of its being self-defeating or neurotic; but it is not immoral (antisocial) in the usual sense in which this term is employed.

6. When you do find that you have committed a distinctly wrong (antisocial) sex act, you should say to yourself: (a) "I have done this deed, and must assume full responsibility for having committed it." (b) "It was wrong (mistaken, erroneous) for me to have done this." (c) "Anything that I can do, I can also *not* do. Therefore, it is quite possible for me *not* to perform this wrong act again." (d) "Now let me figure out exactly what I must do (or not do) in order not to make this same sex mistake in the future." (e) "And once I have figured out a better mode of future activity in this connection, let me work and practice, and work and practice some more, until I become so proficient at not doing this misdeed that there will be little chance of my ever committing it again."

7. What you should *never* do after you have done a wrong sex act is (a) confuse the *act* with your*self*; (b) blame (or

devalue) yourself for having done the act; (c) keep repetitively blaming yourself for some time to come; (d) deliberately punish yourself for having committed the misdeed.

8. You have to keep in mind, pretty constantly, that your main goal in life, in the seventy-five or so years that you have to exist on this earth, is enjoyment. Yes, peculiarly enough: *enjoyment*. This enjoyment can preferably be long-range rather than short-range; it can be largely nonsexual rather than sexual; it can be enjoying of involved, serious, complex things rather than of the playboy aspects of life. But what you must frankly acknowledge is that you are not here primarily to achieve something wonderful during your lifetime, to be of great service to others, to change the course of the world, or to do anything else but (in one way or another that you find particularly appealing) to enjoy yourself.

In the course of enjoying yourself, and trying to protect yourself against being harmed by others, you will often find it useful to make sacrifices, to be nice to other people, to put off present pleasures for future gains, and otherwise *temporarily* to place other interests before your own. You will also often find that you do enjoy, and in a nonmasochistic way, being kind or loving or useful to certain other people—such as to your girlfriend, your wife, your parents, or your children. But, in the main, these should tend to be *secondary* aims.

Your main goal should still be to find what is most pleasing most satisfying to *you*; and then doing those things, if they are feasible, no matter what others may tend to think of you for doing them. Naturally, you must be somewhat sensible about how others take to your goals and aims, and must not unduly antagonize them—especially when they have some power over you. But don't, by any means, largely live for what others *think* of you; for that is the way of over-conformity and guilt.

In sum: if you can *think* about the things that are bothering you, discover your own philosophic assumptions with which you are *making* them bother you, and forcefully and consistently challenge and question these assumptions, you will stop being guilty about anything you do—particularly about sex acts. For it is never what happens to you at point A (say, your unfairly inducing a girl to have sex relations with you) that upsets you at point C (say, your becoming very guilty about what you are doing). Rather, it is the non-sense, the philosophic hogwash, that you tell yourself at point B *about* what you are doing at point A.

Thus, your (quite idiotically!) convincing yourself that you are a louse for seducing the girl at point A (when you really mean that you are a wrongdoer who should forthrightly go about correcting his mistakes); or that you *shouldn't* have seduced her (when you really mean that it was unwise and unfair for you to have done so, but that's the way it was, and what are you going to do about a similar situation *next* time?); or that the bitch, by her flirtatious manner, made you seduce her, even against your will, and that she is now unfairly blaming you for her own mistakes (when you really mean that the poor, insecure girl did actually lead you on, but that's what disturbed people do, and it's no crime for her to be disturbed)—*these* are the belief-systems with which you are upsetting yourself; and *these* are the self-indoctrinations that you will have to fight, and fight, and fight if you are to become unguilty and unangry.

Admit it, then: you are no goddam angel. You have very human sex desires, and they often lead you to stupid, even antisocial acts. That is too bad; but that's *all* it is, too bad. It is not terrible, horrible or awful. The world won't come to an end because of it. And you, being unangelic, are not a louse or a rat or any other low-down animal. You are still an essentially worthwhile—indeed, to yourself, completely worthwhile—human. Fallible, yes; wrongheaded, of course; imperfect, you can bet your life! But that's what *all* humans are: fallible, wrongheaded, and imperfect.

If this is your basic sexual (and nonsexual) philosophy, and if you can use this philosophy to work at—yes, w-o-r-k at—being a little less fallible, a trifle less wrongheaded during the course of your life, you will be doing the best a human can possibly do. If this is not your fundamental, deeply held viewpoint, you will guiltily (and angrily) suffer. So think about it; work on it; if necessary, get psychological help in connection with it. O.K.: on your mark . . . get set . . . *think!*

Chapter 4

Where and How to Meet Females

In the companion book to this one, which is entitled *The Intelligent Woman's Guide to Man-Hunting* (Ellis, 1963b), I have a chapter on where and how a female can look for a man. It is, if I may say so, quite a good (if highly unorthodox) chapter; and has much to offer the woman-hunting male as well. Let me quote a bit from it:

"If there is a gentle art of man-hunting, of what does it consist?

"It consists, by and large, of the same kind of art as that involved in writing, swimming, painting, collecting stamps, or doing almost anything else that you might really want to do. I am fond, in this connection, of quoting Sinclair Lewis's famous definition of the art of writing. 'What,' he was asked one day by an aspiring young writer, 'have you found, in all your experience as a novelist, the art of writing to be?' 'The art of writing,' Lewis is reputed to have said, 'is very simple. It consists of putting the seat of the pants to the seat of the chair—and writing!'

"So with the art of looking for a man. It largely consists of putting the balls of your eyes to the front of your head—and looking! Where should you look? Anywhere, naturally, that you happen to be: in the office, on the street, at a party, on a bus, at a museum or art gallery, in a classroom, on the beach, at a dance, around your own neighborhood, on a trip, at a picnic, at a meeting, etc., etc. As long as you keep actively, assertively looking, you are almost certain to find several good prospects within a reasonably short period of time. But you must, honest and truly, *keep looking.*"

What's sauce for the goose, as the old saying goes, can be even more flavorsome for the saucier gander. The art of love, the far from handsome Casanova and Cellini discovered, is largely the art of persistence; and the more you persist in seeking, searching, and scanning for a suitable girlfriend, the more likely you are to find, in a reasonable length of time, something approximating your ideal.

What you, as a young male, are likely to be looking for is probably not what the average reader of *The Intelligent Woman's Guide to Man-Hunting* will be seeking: since most females in our society are searching for a long-time mate or a husband; males are often only incidentally looking for the equivalent of this, while they are more directly hankering after a suitable bedmate. The rest of this chapter, therefore, is going to be appropriately different from much of the material in the equivalent chapter in its companion book.

Let us assume, to start with, that you are a reasonably intelligent and educated young man who desires, in terms of companionship, (a) a liberal-minded sex partner, (b) a girl who is fun to be with, (c) one to whom you can *talk* intelligently before and after (and perhaps even during) the sex play; and (d) one who likes you and who might just possibly be the ideal woman with whom you ultimately would want to be married and perhaps raise a family. This, I think you will agree, is a hell of a lot for you to ask for; but why shouldn't you honestly ask for it, with the full knowledge that it may be quite a while before you achieve what you would like?

Where to Look for Girls

Where, assuming that you want to find the kind of a girl who roughly fills in the above outline, should you go to look for one? As we noted at the beginning of this chapter: everywhere. For you never can tell where you will run into just the right girl for you, no matter how selective you are and how rare she is. And there's no point in overlooking any possible avenue (or street or country lane) of access, even though statistically the chances are against you on any given bypath.

So, to begin, you start out exactly where you are—at the office, at school, in your neighborhood, on the bus you take to work, etc. And you keep your eyes wide open, to see what's immediately (not to mention, more distantly) around you. And—as we shall indicate a few pages from now—you start making some suitable overture.

O.K.: but suppose this technique doesn't work very well, as is quite possible if you are truly selective in your tastes. Suppose the girls at the office just don't exist or are by no means up to your educational level; or that you've met all the eligible girls in your neighborhood, and none of them sends you; or that practically all the suitable girls you meet on the bus going to work just happen to be engaged or married. What then?

Then, naturally, you look for more logical places. You ask yourself a simple question: "Where are the kind of girls that I would be interested in *most* likely to congregate in sufficient numbers to offer me a reasonably good hunting ground?" And, depending on your particular tastes, you find the best possible answer to that question.

If, for example, you are a highly cultured, esthetically cultivated person, you obviously should look for a girlfriend in suitable culture centers: e.g., museums, libraries, concert halls, opera houses, theaters. If you are an enthusiastic sportsman, athletic gatherings or resorts are indicated—such as tennis courts, ski resorts, or ice-skating rinks. If you are a first-class intellectual, certain other places are patently better hunting grounds: such as, graduate courses in colleges, lectures, seminars, workshops, and professional meetings. If you are largely, and very frankly, interested in having sex affairs rather than love affairs with females, special places where liberal-minded young women are likely to congregate are likely to be your best bet. Such as churches and spiritualist movements? Hell, no! Then how about neighborhood bars, or certain dance halls, or the Bohemian section of your town? Ah, much better!

The wish, in other words, should be father to the search. Whatever you want in the way of young womanhood should be *somewhere* available in your immediate vicinity; and, if not, you may even have to travel a bit. But the more selective or esoteric you are in your tastes for female companionship, the more thought and action you may have to give to finding an appropriate aggregate of females from which to choose. If you just want to go according to the law of averages, you may talk to any girls anywhere you are. But you must expect, of course, a low percentage of favorable responses, as well as a low percentage of real "finds" even when the responses are all you can hope for. The better chosen your preserve, the better are your chances of finding someone you like who also will like you.

Should you use your friends, Romans, and countrymen to help you in your search for a desirable girlfriend? Why not? You generally have nothing to lose in this regard; and you may have a lot to gain. Remember, however, that the tastes of either your male or your female friends are most unlikely to be the same as your own; and no one, even one who knows you well, is likely to be a mind-reader. If, therefore, you let it be widely known—as you most certainly should in most instances—that you are in the market for a suitable girlfriend, also let it be known precisely what your tastes are—and are *not*. Nothing can be so gruesome as a blind date which, after you have spent two minutes with the girl you have met through a cooperative friend, turns out to be the type of thing you need like you need hay fever or tuberculosis.

Be specific, then. Tell your friends and relatives, as precisely as you can, what you would like in any girl with whom they date you. And no nonsense about it! Don't think, just because they are willing to help you meet a girl, that you must take *anything* they waft your way. And don't think their feelings will be terribly hurt if, after you have dated a girl that they feel is simply terrific, you calmly inform them that, no, she just isn't for you, for whatever reasons. You can be exceptionally nice, manage not to step on their toes, and *still* let them know that this girl may be fine, in her own way, or great for someone else, but that she is not your piece of pie.

Don't hesitate, moreover, to ask your friends for salient statistics on the girl they think would be just right for you. Her age, education, occupation, main interests, number of times she has previously been married, politico-economic persuasion—these are but some of the questions that it might be very relevant for you to have the answers to before you see her even for a single date. For the answers to such questions may enable you either to avoid wasting your time and hers by making the date; or to get along exceptionally well with her when first you do meet.

I say this, incidentally, from my own unfortunate past experiences. Several times I have cavalierly made blind dates with girls whom my friends *assumed* would be exactly the right age, occupation, or socio-economic adherence for me —only to find, when I had been with a girl about five minutes, that we both might just as well have stood in our own individual beds. Now, whenever I make blind dates, I ask the most "embarrassing" questions about the girl's age, looks, avocational pursuits, etc., and thereby frequently save myself a whale of a lot of disappointments.

Double dates, incidentally, may be a perfectly good way

of meeting a new potential girlfriend, but let's face it: they have distinct limitations. Unless you can make damned sure that you are not going to spend the *entire* evening with a blind date *and* the other couple who have arranged this date for you, you run the risk of having a pleasant gathering, all right, but never really getting to know the new girl. And, of course, your chances at making even preliminary passes at her that first evening are rather remote. If you *have* to make a double date in order to meet a girl, that may not be the worst way in the world to get acquainted with her; and it sometimes does help you over the rough hurdles that are likely to crop up on a blind single date. But by and large, if you really want to get to know something about your date in a minimum of time, you'd better try to arrange the blind date so that you call the girl and see her by herself, without any chaperonage, intended or not, by another couple.

How about parties and dances and such for meeting new female companions? Great—if they are the kind of affairs where you are likely to meet someone who is to your liking. If you are the intellectual type, dances may be the worst places to meet a good companion; but cocktail parties, on the other hand, may be some of your best bets. If you are nonintellectual, the reverse may be true.

The advantage of most kinds of parties and dances are: (a) They usually bring together a *number* of girls whom you haven't yet met, and consequently give you a wider choice. (b) The people who come to them, at least the unattached ones, often come especially to meet members of the other sex, and are therefore easily approachable. (c) The conventional ways of meeting others at such affairs are made exceptionally easy. Thus, at a dance you have merely to ask a girl to dance; and then at a cocktail party, it is most permissible merely to say to a girl you run into, "I'm Jim Jones; what's your name?" (d) If the affair is really a drag, and no one to your liking seems to be present, you can usually get away swiftly, and not waste too much of your time. (e) Even if you meet no girl to whom you take a particular shine at a party, you can often meet someone else there, either male or female, who can *later* lead you to some girl whom you do find suitable. Or you can learn about and be invited to better parties by attending one that, in itself, is not particularly enjoyable or valuable as a meeting ground. (f) Although a given affair may not work out well for you as far as meeting a girl you like is concerned, it will often give you much needed practice in socializing that will stand you in good stead at the next series of affairs you attend. Party-going is generally a learned response that needs some amount of habituation (just as dancing is a learned response that needs considerable practice if you are to attain competence at it). Even the most disappointing affairs, therefore, may provide you with experience that will serve you well when a more lively shindig comes along.

Are organized groups—such as classes, seminars, country clubs, and social groups—the best place to meet new female partners? Yes and no, depending on which groups you join. If you are devoted to a particular political party, and there are at least some females who are also devoted to that party, these girls may be the very best candidates for you to meet; since the chances are that you have something in common with each other at the start. If, however, you are a confirmed atheist, the chances of your making out well in a religious group—no matter how many pretty girls are members of the group—are not especially good.

Organized groups, moreover, have distinct limitations as meeting grounds for getting to know desirable members of the other sex. First of all, most such groups include small numbers of female participants. Consequently, you soon know all the members of the group who are eligible; and after you have eliminated them as possible sex-love partners, you still must keep meeting them, over and over. Secondly, you may have to spend too much time in a given group—perhaps three or four hours every week for an entire year as a member of a poetry reading circle—to meet only a few eligible members of the other sex. Thirdly, the kind of group you join, such as a Y, a church group, or a theatrical group, may have a large percentage of female ineligibles—may, for example, have a good many confirmed virgins or lesbians among its members.

For such reasons, it is well to select carefully any group that you may join if you intend, as a major result of your joining it, to meet suitable members of the other sex. Groups that you would normally participate in—such as professional, social, political, or other groups which you are intrinsically interested in for one reason or another—do not require so much caution anyway. As long as you are a member of such groups anyway, you might just as well use them to scout out choice members of the other sex who may appeal to you.

What about business contacts—can they be used for sex-love searching? They certainly can be—and very often are. As usual, such groups have their distinct disadvantages. Having an affair with your secretary can be rather complicated! During the affair you still have the problem of getting her to do her work well; and after it is over, it may be awkward for you to continue to be her employer. Moreover, if you have sex relations with someone who works in your office, you may bring into the situation other people who also work with you; and this may be undesirable.

At the same time, business contacts can sometimes be an excellent means of meeting suitable female companions. If you come into direct contact with the public in the course of your work—if, for example, you are a salesman, an insurance agent, or a hotel manager—you can often meet charming females in the course of your activities, and may be able to make dates with them. And while you are out working at almost any job—whether you're an accountant, lawyer, physician, or whatnot—you can take advantage of your mobility to speak to the eligible females you meet, and to try to make social-sexual contacts with them. At times, in fact, when you are finding difficulty in meeting many choice members of the other sex, you can consider taking certain jobs which are much more likely to result in such contacts than equivalent jobs which are likely to keep you away from eligible girls.

Are resorts and trips likely to be good places to meet members of the other sex? Yes: since most of the females who go on these kinds of vacations are exceptionally eager to meet males, and are often much more receptive to sex-love encounters at these times and places than they allow themselves to be in their own home towns.

As usual, however, various disadvantages exist in this connection. At resorts and on trips, you generally have a limited number of girls to choose from; and once you have gone through that limited number (several of whom may not find *you* a satisfactory partner), you may be stuck for the rest of the vacation. Secondly, if you tie up with a particular girl at a resort, it is not so easy, thereafter, to date the others, or even to get their phone numbers for the time when you come back to the city. Thirdly, many or most of the girls you may meet on a trip may live far away from your region and further contact may be difficult when the trip has ended. Fourthly, trips and vacation resorts are usually expensive, so that you cannot too well take the time and money to patronize them often during the year. Fifthly, a great deal of energy is often consumed going away for a trip, or even for a weekend to a resort, compared to the energy that would be *necessary if* you were able to meet girls in your home town.

Nonetheless, particularly if you like vacations and trips anyway, these may be a good means of contact for you. And if, in the course of such outings, you make it a point to look at the long-range as well as the short-range prospects, and to become at least superficially friendly with a number of girls whom you may later get in touch with when you are back home, you may find your out-of-town sojourns quite good girl-hunting fields.

We come, finally, to probably the most important and frequently most neglected source of contacts with members of the other sex. And that is, of course, the pickup. As I note in *The Intelligent Woman's Guide to Man-Hunting*, this is the quickest, easiest, and in most respects the best way for a girl to meet a man in whom she is interested—by picking him up right where she first sees him: on the street, in a restaurant, at the library, on a bus, or wherever else he happens to be. By the same token, and for similar reasons, it is just about the best way for you, as a male, to meet eligible females. Because:

1. The spontaneous pickup is the quickest and probably most efficient technique ever invented of meeting members of the other sex. As we have just observed, meeting girls through friends, or at organized groups, or at business, or on vacations—all these methods have their distinct disadvantages, particularly in regard to time, money, and energy that may be expended in employing them. But, whether you like it or not, you *do* have to walk on the street, wait for a bus, ride on trains, lunch at cafeterias, stand in line at the bank, etc. And whenever you do these normal acts, there is likely to be an attractive girl with whom you may open up a conversation. Nothing, if you come to think of it, is really more convenient than this kind of opportunity—if you have the guts to take advantage of it.

2. Picking up a girl in a public place is, oddly enough, one of the most discriminating methods of encounter that you can employ. For, as again we noted above, meeting females through friends, organized groups, or at resorts puts you, at best, in contact with a distinctly limited number of prospects in a given period of time; and consequently no

matter how active you are in these areas, your total number of possible good choices is apt to be distinctly restricted. Ordinarily, in fact, by using these methods, the chances are that, in an entire year, you will meet only a half dozen or so outstanding girls; and that, for one reason or another, you will get nowhere with any of these.

The pickup technique, on the other hand, gives you much broader leeway, in that it presents you, in any sizable community, with literally hundreds of girls to choose from each year; and out of these, you are much more likely to encounter and favorably be able to impress at least a few likely prospects.

3. In employing the pickup method, *you* do the active choosing, rather than allowing your friends or the situation to do the original sorting-out process for you. For, naturally, you will not try to talk to a girl you meet in a public place unless, to begin with, she particularly appeals to *your* first-blush tastes. If she seems ugly to you, or appears to be stupid, or is sloppily dressed, or has a disturbed look about her, you will simply ignore her, and go on to observe the next possible prospect. And since there are so many potential pickups available, you can easily confine your activities to those whom you are pretty sure that you are at least going to have *some* favorable feelings for at the start.

4. Although you are frequently stuck for an entire evening with girls whom you meet through friends or whom you date through regular organized channels, this is not true of those whom you may pick up. If you talk to a girl on a bus or in a luncheonette, and she proves to be a bore or exceptionally puritanical or to have other serious limitations, you can easily get rid of her fast by politely saying goodby, pleading another appointment, or even by taking her telephone number and then never calling her. You thereby can spend a minimum of time with those prospects who turn out to be duds.

5. In the long run, the law of averages is with you in regard to girls you meet in public places. For if you keep trying for the ones who seem to be desirable, even if you have a low average of acceptances, or find that those who do accept you later prove to be unsuitable, you have an almost unlimited source of supply, and eventually your efforts should be well rewarded. No matter how selective you may be, you should ultimately find *one* girl who is pretty much the way you would want her to be—*if* you keep looking and trying.

6. Using the technique of picking up seemingly desirable

girls whenever you chance to run across them does not, of course, preclude your also employing the other methods of girl-chasing that we have mentioned in the beginning of this chapter. There is no reason why only *one* single method has to be employed, when you can just as well try several simultaneously.

The Art of the Pickup

Assuming that you do try the pickup method, there are several pointers that you'd best take into account while you are using it. For one thing, although this approach requires a certain amount of boldness and brashness, the *form* with which you use it should not be particularly bold, but should instead be rather conservative and even noncommittal. That is to say, you do not, ordinarily, walk up to a strange girl and say to her: "My! you look pretty. Would you mind having a drink with me?" Maybe this direct attack on the problem works in movies and plays; unfortunately it is not very successful in everyday life, for the simple reason that, even if the girl in question thinks you are quite a guy and that she'd like very much to have that drink with you, she is usually herself so shy and hesitant that in most instances she will refuse to do so.

In this connection I often tell my patients the well-known joke about the fellow who was getting plenty of girls to go to bed with him, while his friend was getting absolutely nowhere with girls. "Look," this friend said to him one day, "how do you manage to do it? I just can't seem to get anywhere with girls myself. So please tell me your technique."

"Oh, it's really very easy," the successful fellow said. "I just go to Forty-second Street and Broadway, stop every pretty girl who comes along, and ask her: 'Will you lay me?'"

"My God!" exclaimed the other. "But don't you get many slaps in the face that way?"

"Sure I do," came the reply. "But you'd be surprised how many lay me!"

It's a good joke; and it does make the point I often want to make to my patients; namely, that in the game of girl-hunting, the main thing is to keep trying; for no matter how many times you lose, the chances are that you'll ultimately win what you want.

That is all very well; but trying to pick up a girl by asking her to lay you is still a very poor technique, since it scares off the great majority of the candidates. Considering what an essentially prissy society we live in, a quite different pickup approach is called for. Thus, you can ask an innocuous question—such as, "Do you happen to know where there is a good restaurant around here?" or "Do you know whether Lord and Taylor sells men's shirts?"—which requires some kind, and preferably a somewhat extended kind, of an answer. Or you can make a comment on a painting that you are both observing in a museum or art gallery. Or you can complain about how slow the bus on which you are both seated is moving. Or you can even use the old line: "Weren't you in my Spanish class last year at Columbia University?"

Notice that all these approaches are strictly *non*sexual, and even nonfriendly. They do not indicate that you want, above all else, to meet the girl to whom you are talking, or to get her promptly to bed. For you *could* really want to know where a good restaurant is or *could* just feel like giving your opinion of a painting or *could* be miffed with the bus driver. In responding to a question or a comment like these, therefore, the girl can feel free to think (if she chooses to do so) that you are *not* trying to pick her up; and just because she feels free to think this, she might just let you actually pick her up, instead of shying away from your overtures.

If, then, you take a casual, noncommittal approach to the conversation with a girl you are trying to meet in a public place, and if you follow this up with a series of similarly neutral statements and questions, the two of you will often, before she quite realizes what is happening, be engrossed in conversation. Once that occurs, you can ask her for coffee or a drink or some other still neutral affair (and *not* to your apartment or hotel room!), so that you will get more leeway to talk to her and *gradually* to draw her out about her marital status, sex attitudes, and other behavior in which you may be much more keenly interested than in the innocuous remarks with which you started conversation with her.

By the time you have talked to her an hour or two—if you can manage to keep things going that long—*then* you may consider yourself on somewhat friendly terms with her, and may (depending on how things have gone thus far between you and what kind of person you have discovered she is) ask her to your place, or arrange a future date with her, or something along those lines. The main point, however, is that the first part of the pickup should be casual and preferably should look as if it were not a pickup at all.

The same rules generally apply to other methods of meeting girls. First, you start off with fairly neutral questions or comments—with what is called small talk. Then, as quickly as is feasible, you graduate to more personal realms of discussion: to finding out as much as you can about the girl's work, interests, education, friends, family life; and to giving, in the process, similar information about yourself. Thirdly, you specifically try to discover her sex-love attitudes and behavior. Has she ever been in love? Would she like to get married? What does she think of using birth control in marriage? What are her views on premarital relations? Etc.

Finally, when you have led the conversation to this more interesting and crucial point, and have discovered a good many pertinent things about the girl and her sexuo-*amative* views and activities, you can judge whether it would be wise to proposition her, make sexual passes at her, or start moving into her apartment. To jump the gun and try to get to the sexual point too quickly, however, generally makes most girls feel that you are *only* interested in their bodies rather than in their personalities; and they tend to close the door on you.

Overcoming Inhibitions in Approaching Girls

In all that we have been saying thus far in regard to how and where to meet potential girlfriends, we have been assuming that you are emotionally *ready* to do so, and that all you have to know is where to seek and a few technical points as how to seek, and that you can easily take it from there. This, alas, is a cavalier assumption: since the fact remains that millions of single males—probably the majority of them— have distinct difficulties in approaching eligible females, even when they *know* where to look for them and what to do when they see them. These males suffer from what is all too lightly called "shyness"—or, actually, from acute anxiety stemming from the fancied fear that it would be terrible if they made overtures to members of the other sex and were rebuffed.

The shy, bashful, or over-anxious individual is saying to himself a perfectly sane and a perfectly insane sentence. The same sentence is: "If I approach this girl who looks appealing, and if she summarily rejects me, that will be unpleasant, and I won't like it." The insane sentence is: "Because I don't like being rejected by this girl, *it would be terrible* if she did reject me; I *couldn't stand* such a rejection; and I would have to feel utterly worthless if it occurred."

This second sentence is insane because it is completely definitional: it is true only because the individual thinks it is true, and not because it has any objective validity. But if he *does* think it true, it virtually becomes so, because he *then* actually feels that it *is* terrible if he is rejected, that he *can't* stand it, and that he *is* worthless because he has been rejected. His *feelings*, in other words, mirror his thoughts, or his internalized sentences; and he, in effect, *creates* these feelings by convincing himself of the thoughts or philosophies of living that lie behind them.

The shy, anxious individual, in other words, identifies *others'* evaluations of himself as being the same as his *own* evaluations of himself; and he thereby *makes* himself into what others may think he is. If, therefore, a girl rejects him, he assumes that she considers him worthless (which she may not, since she may only consider him an inappropriate *boyfriend* or *husband* rather than a worthless *person*), and he assumes that she must be correct in this low evaluation of him.

Because he fails, he thinks he is a Failure with a capital F —meaning that he can never thereafter succeed with virtually *any* girl whom he would like. Since he puts such tremendous store in a girl's evaluation of him, and feels worthless when he is rejected by her, he cannot afford to risk further rejections: because they "prove" to him, once again, that he *is* the slob he considers himself to be. He therefore tends to withdraw from all intimate contacts with girls, and thereby to not take the risk that they *will* reject him.

Ironically, in doing so the shy person *ensures* the continual failure that he is afraid will occur. For by not trying, he of course cannot possibly succeed with a girl; while if he did try, the worst that could happen would be that he would not *often* succeed, but he almost certainly *eventually* would. So he guarantees himself lack of success, by his withdrawal tactics; and then, even more ironically, he concludes from this lack of success that the original hypothesis of his being worthless *must* be valid—since look what a continual failure he is!

Stated differently, the shy person cannot conceive a failing or incompetent person being a worthwhile human being; he makes competence and worth utterly synonymous. By this senseless, unprovable definition he thus *makes* himself "worthless" whenever he fails; and he then inevitably fails all the more, since he cannot conceive a "worthless" individual succeeding at anything important. He thereby forges a vicious circle of incompetence = worthlessness = more incompetence = greater worthlessness. The only normal result of forging such a circle will be more and more withdrawal from trying to get what he wants—especially when what he wants is intimacy with a member of the other sex.

If, then, you *know* what you really have to do to meet potential girlfriends, and you are incessantly evading these requisites, the chances are probably ninety-nine out of a hundred that you are terribly afraid of failure and rejection, are thinking of yourself as a bum when you are rejected, and are thereby making it too risky to chance heterosexual encounters. Assuming that this is so, what can you do about your enormous fear of failure and self-created feelings of inadequacy? The following things:

1. Observe, as clearly and concretely as you can, the actual sentences that you are telling yourself to make yourself so afraid of failing. Are you telling yourself: "It is terrible to fail this time, because then I'll *always* keep failing!"? Or: "If this present girl rejects me, I can't stand it!"? Or: "Everyone else succeeds with girls and I don't; and therefore I am a total dud!"? Stop; observe your internal sentences until you see what they truly are; and don't, in any circumstances, stop noting what you are saying to yourself until you really find your own words, your own deeply held philosophies, that are creating your fears of failing.

2. Once you start seeing what your repeated, negativistic sentences are, *think* about them, question and challenge them, look for their internal inconsistencies and illogical conclusions. Ask yourself, for instance: "*Why* will I always keep failing with girls, just because I have failed this time?" . . . "*Who says* I can't stand it if this girl rejects me?" . . . "*Is it really true* that everyone else succeeds with girls except me, and therefore I am a total dud?"

3. Keep thinking about, challenging, and questioning your own self-defeating philosophies until you see that they *are* irrational, inconsistent, and illogical. Realize that if you have these views, and if they are making you desperately unhappy,

they *must* be idiotic: since there is just no reason why you *have to* be miserable if you are rejected or frustrated by a girl. Only sticks and stones can *really* hurt you; and names, no matter how many are hurled at you by how many girls, never can. See, therefore, that you *must* be hurting yourself by your own definitional nonsense.

4. While you are theoretically or verbally thinking about, challenging, and questioning your self-defeating philosophies of living, deliberately force yourself to *work* against them in actual practice. That is to say, while you are convincing yourself that being rejected by a girl cannot possibly be (except by your own metaphysical definition) indicative of your utter worthlessness, force yourself, at the same time, to practice what you are now beginning to preach to yourself: to *risk* picking up girls, asking them for dates, making passes at them, etc. Force yourself, if necessary, to be rejected many times, just to prove to yourself that you *won't* die of it (even though you may never like it).

5. Keep thinking and challenging, working and practicing, so that you continually reassess your present dysfunctional assumptions. Ceaselessly challenge, in every possible way, the validity of these assumptions. And show yourself, at the same time, the more positive and constructive philosophic positions which, if you come to believe in them, will almost automatically negate these self-sabotaging assumptions. Constructive views, for example, like believing that you are a worthwhile human being because you exist, and not because you are a great performer in any area; and that no one, including and especially you, is ever to *blame* for his errors, even though he indubitably is responsible for, or is the cause of, them.

If you will energetically and consistently follow this plan of counter-attack on your enormous fears of rejection and failure, it will be almost impossible for you to sustain these fears with any intensity, and quite impossible for you senselessly to maintain that you are a lout whenever you do fail. It will then also be relatively easy for you to approach, and to keep approaching, new prospective girlfriends, wherever you may chance to meet them, and however poor the chances may be of their fully accepting you.

Where you can meet eligible members of the other sex, then, is a question that is relatively easily answered. The general places you can go and the approaches you can make in this connection have been outlined in the first part of this chapter. More specific details can easily be filled in by you, in whatever region of the earth you happen to live, if you simply give the matter of encountering females even a little concentrated thought.

How to meet suitable girlfriends is a more difficult question to answer, since it frequently involves your changing some of your basic philosophies of life, and your consequent "personality" traits which stem from these philosophies. The general answer in this regard is clear: stop defining yourself as a no-goodnik whenever you fail, and keep trying, trying, trying. The specific answer, as we have noted above, involves looking at your self-defeating internalized sentences and contradicting and challenging them, in theory and in practice, until they are significantly changed. If you will do this, you will eventually, if not necessarily easily, lick your own "shyness" and standoffishness. If you will not do this, only accidental good fortune will get you what you really want in heterosexual companionship. The choice of these two paths is essentially yours. Choose!

Chapter 5

The Art of Seduction

Webster's New World Dictionary defines the word seduce in this wise: "to persuade to engage in unlawful sexual intercourse, especially for the first time; induce to give up chastity." The essence of the art of seduction consists of first convincing yourself that this dictionary definition is basically wrong: for it mistakenly states and implies that there is something unlawful or wicked about sexual intercourse and the surrender of chastity.

It is precisely this implication, in fact, which keeps millions of girls from having premarital sex relations. They erroneously believe—although there is no longer any evidence to support this belief—that if they engage in heavy petting or in copulation, they will be doing an immoral, socially and legally banned act; and even though they would often like nothing better than to give up their chastity, they steadfastly refuse to do so because of their sexual belief-system. Or—just as importantly—millions of potentially seducible females today do not personally believe there is anything wrong with premarital sex participation. But they think that their male companions believe there is; and their fear of what they think these males believe is what mainly keeps them chaste.

Not that these girls are entirely wrong. For there are, alas, many males who asininely believe that girls who surrender their virginity before marriage, or who pet to orgasm, are "bad" or are "tramps," and that in no circumstances should they marry such females. Even a minority of intelligent, college-level males believe this claptrap. And, noting or sensing that they believe it, the girls who go out with them naturally stay as far away from sex intimacy as they can, rather than risk the fascist-minded censure of this type of fellow.

All of which, peculiarly enough, makes it relatively easy for the truly liberal-minded male to seduce most intelligent and educated females in our society. For if such a free-thinking person is thoroughly convinced that chastity is *not* a good state, that he would *never* marry a virgin, and that a girl who remains sexually pure has something of a hole in her head, he is much more likely to be able to get his female companions to bed than if he has the opposite set of beliefs.

Psychological Techniques of Seduction

The art of seduction today, in other words, is largely the art of believing, as wholeheartedly as you can, that voluntarily entered sex relations are good, right, and proper in virtually all circumstances, and that there is nothing in the least admirable, sensible, or respectable about a girl's refraining from complete sex participation. You must not only feel, moreover, that sex is good at certain special times—such as when you are married, engaged, in love, or very friendly with your sex partner—but must sincerely feel that it is good in its own right, whether or not these other circumstances exist.

Let me emphasize, again, that your belief in the essential goodness of human sex relations must be real, and not faked, and must be held thoroughly and unconsciously, as well as on the top layer of your consciousness. For if you merely pretend to yourself and your female companion that you think sex is a great thing and that you have no negative feelings toward girls who participate honestly and actively in it, and if you actually feel that there *is* something dirty, or cheap, or devalued about a girl who has premarital sex relations, you will sooner or later communicate your feelings to your companion—and she will usually tend to feel guilty herself about what she is doing with you and to withdraw her sex favors.

How can you get a truly open-minded attitude about sex, if you don't really have such an attitude right now? By thinking—and thinking very hard and very long. For if you do think hard in this respect, instead of parroting the views and feelings of others around you, you will soon be able to see that there *is* not, nor can there possibly *ever* be, anything evil about mutually entered into and cooperatively carried out heterosexual relations. You or your girlfriend can certainly *make mistakes* sexually: can, for example, have intercourse with a person whom you don't even love, and thereby relatively waste your time; or can be careless, and have sex relations leading to unwanted pregnancy; or can enter into an adulterous relationship that has most inconvenient (and occasionally even illegal) complications. But such sexual mistakes are precisely and only that: mistakes. They are not horrors or acts of unalloyed wickedness.

Otherwise stated: it is never the sexual aspect, *itself*, of a given mode of behavior that makes it wrong or mistaken; it is, rather, the stupid or unthinking *way* in which you perform this behavior. Thus, it is not the act of copulation which is wrong when you have intercourse with girls for whom you do not care—for that act, in itself, is probably quite enjoyable and good. The promiscuous *way* in which you perform the act may be, however, self-defeating, since it may preclude your having *more* sex-love satisfaction with another girl, whom you *do* love. When promiscuity, moreover, is self-sabotaging, it is just as unwise nonsexually as sexually. Thus, your promiscuously accepting jobs that you do not really enjoy (but perhaps temporarily pay well) or your promiscuously remaining friendly with members of your own sex with whom you really have little in common is just as senseless as your promiscuously going with girls with whom you cannot possibly get emotionally involved.

By the same token, it is never *you*, as a person, who are bad, no matter how mistaken your sex acts may happen, for the nonce, to be. If you get three girls in a row pregnant, your *behavior* is certainly stupid and antisocial. But *you* are not intrinsically or hopelessly stupid or antisocial, since it is quite possible that, as a result of this experience, you will change tomorrow, and become most scrupulous about employing contraceptive technique. Similarly, if your girlfriend lies to you about some significant aspect of her life, her *behavior* is undoubtedly poor, but *she* is hardly proven to be a louse or a no-goodnik because of this behavior. Next month, particularly if you try to help her become less disturbed and more reliable, she may be able to be completely truthful with little difficulty.

To be sane and objective about sex, therefore, you must view sexual acts in exactly the same light as you would view nonsexual interpersonal affairs. You must not blame a girl for being sexually experienced or fickle any more than you would blame her for being experienced in business or being an unreliable employee. Preferably, you should never blame *her* at all, even though you may consider many of her *acts* to be unwise or mistaken. If *this* is the kind of an objective, unblaming attitude you take toward sex and toward a girl's sexual experience, you will be (in our society) one man out of a hundred, and the one who is almost certain to have a rare advantage when it comes to getting the average (or above-average) girl to bed.

The second attitude which is preferable if you are to be successful in your relations with women is that of respecting your girlfriends as *persons* rather than just as bodies. Not that there is anything wrong with frankly admiring the female form. As Hugh Hefner (1963) has noted, if there were a God, He would have created the beautiful female form, as well as everything else in the world, and it is silly to see feminine pulchritude and sexiness as instruments of the Devil. Female breasts and hips and thighs and genitalia are good; damned good! Let's have no nonsense about this.

But few women, and particularly few intelligent women, in our society like to be seen *only* or *mainly* as fleshpots. They also want to be accepted for what they consider to be themselves: for their interests, their attitudes, their conversation, their companionship, their lovingness, etc. And most of them resent deeply the male who *just* wants to get them to bed, and then quickly turns over and goes to sleep, or gets up and leaves.

The way to the female form, therefore, is generally through the heart and the mind. You have to please the *girl*, rather than merely arouse her physically. And, very often, you must get her to like *you*, and not merely to dote on your looks or appreciate your sex technique. This does not mean that every girl you meet has to be madly in love with you, and think that you are enamored of her, before she will let you undo her pantie girdle. Most of the time, you can quite honestly let a girl know that you are not about to sacrifice your life for her—and she will very willingly pet heavily with you or go still further. For she knows full well, in many instances, that *she* is not yet deeply moved by *you* either; and that perhaps if both of you *do* enjoy sex greatly, a more lasting and deeper involvement will spring up. Or perhaps she even knows that she will never love you, nor you her; but she *does* find you sufficiently attractive to give her a few hours of sex pleasure, and that is all she is interested in at this moment.

Nevertheless!—even the highly sexed, quickly bedded girl usually wants you to *like* her, *enjoy* her, *be friendly* to her. And the faster she discovers that you really *do* have some nonsexual as well as sexual interest in her, the faster she is likely to think of you as a potential sex partner. This, of course, is not *always* true: there are a few girls who actually seem to want to take lovers in whom they have no nonsexual interest and who are only interested in them in sexual ways. But these girls are very few—and far between!

In addition to your being interested in them, most females in our culture normally want to be nonsexually interested in *you*, to some extent, before they engage in sexual intimacies. I have often found, in my own case, that two or three hours of showing a girl what a good conversationalist I can be, confiding various things about myself to her, and generally being my unconstrained, easy-going *self*, will make her more sexually receptive than any amount of properly applied sexual technique will do. This, again, is not *always* the case: in some instances *no* amount of conversation will do the trick, and *only* making sexual overtures to a girl, and finally arousing her physically, will tip the scales in your direction. But more times than not, the bright, sophisticated female will have to be *talked* into being sexually receptive—and not necessarily by direct persuasion but by indirect conversation, which may have little or nothing to do with sex.

Not that direct persuasion itself is useless; for it frequently isn't. Literally millions of girls in Western civilized countries today seem to *want* to be persuaded to jump into bed with their male companions. They think, in their own minds, that it *probably* will be all right if they have intercourse with a male whom they only slightly know; but they are not quite *sure* of what he will think of them in case they do. Therefore, they require that he give them a good many intellectual reasons why they *should* go to bed with him, and why he *will* not despise them after they do so. They may have heard all these reasons before, and even largely believe them before he begins to state them. But they still want him to go through the ritual of stating them, just to make sure they are doing the right thing.

Even girls who *don't* want to be talked into having sex relations with a male can frequently be persuaded. For most girls have exceptionally poor reasons for not indulging, and these reasons can often be logically undermined. Females can be persuaded, for example, that you will not look down on them after intercourse; that you will use proper contraceptive methods; that you have nothing against marrying a nonvirgin; that the Biblical prophets and saints did not know what they were talking about sexually; that even though they won't admit it publicly, most girls today *do* have premarital sex relations; and so on and so forth.

Not only will this kind of persuasion help you to have sex relations with a girl at any given time, it is also likely to make it easier for you to have them with her on succeeding occasions. Physical methods of approach, on the other hand, may only work temporarily; since a highly aroused girl may copulate with you *now*, but may build up all kinds of ideological resistances to repeating this performance later.

Calm, consistent, forceful depropagandization, on the other hand, usually has a much deeper and longer-lasting effect. It has a more *generalized* result, as well. For the girl that you persuade to think well of sex relations today will usually be a more willing bed-mate for some other fellow tomorrow; and, likewise, the girl that he deindoctrinates or unbrainwashes when *he* sees her will tend to have the right sex attitudes and behavior when *you* see her. The more you propagate straightforward and sincere counterpropaganda against sexual puritanism, therefore, the more you are helping to make the general female culture more sexually liberal.

Will the line work that you mainly want to have sex relations with a girl for *her* good? Very rarely: for it is a damned lie. You may want to help a girl out sexually, particularly if she is senselessly hanging on to her virginity, to her own physical and emotional detriment. But let's face it: that is hardly the *only* reason why you want to roll her in the hay; and you might as well be honest about it. Admit to her that you expect to enjoy sex with her immensely, and that *you* want it for your own pleasure. But you can indicate that you want to see her enjoy herself, *too*. Then she is not likely to conclude that you are being hypocritical.

What is the best verbal "line" for seducing a girl? Generally, no "line" at all. Give her, if you will, all the sane and sober arguments you can muster; but give her arguments in which you truly believe, and that you have not merely dreamed up for this occasion, and for this "victory."

Don't tell the girl, for example, that you simply can't stand not having sex with her, and that it is going to make a mental and physical wreck of you if you don't. Tell her, more honestly, that you will *dislike* the discomfort of her not giving in to you sexually; but you are still going to be able to bear it and live. And don't tell her that every girl you know goes to bed very easily with guys, when this is untrue. Tell her instead that, of the girls you know who let down the sex barriers, almost all of them soon have a ball and lose their guilt feelings; while of the girls you know who continue to be sexually constrained, many or most of them have indefinitely prolonged conflicts and self-dissatisfactions. Don't try to convince her that she *must* suffer if she remains virginal; but merely that the chances are high that she *will*.

One of the best persuasive methods for getting a girl to go farther sexually than she originally intends is to convince her that you are not necessarily asking that she have actual intercourse with you, but you are largely trying to induce her to have some form of mutually satisfying relations that will result in orgasm for both of you. Most girls in our society are infinitely more afraid of intercourse than of any other form of sex—and with at least some reason—since there always is the possibility that they will become pregnant through intercourse. Moreover, they are often afraid that intercourse will be painful; that they will not be successful at it; that it will be messy; that it will mean technical loss of virginity; etc. So much has been made of this *special* act in our culture (and in most other cultures) that literally millions of girls will fairly willingly do everything *except* intercourse.

Many other girls, moreover, have actually tried penile-vaginal copulation and found it unsatisfying. This is not only because they are not used to it, but because it *is* essentially less satisfying for these particular females and less inducive to orgasm than various other methods of sex participation. As I have pointed out in several articles and books (Ellis, 1960, 1961b, 1962b, 1963a), and as Kelly (1960), Kinsey, Pomeroy, Martin, and Gebhard (1953), and Masters and Johnson (1961, 1962) have also shown, the so-called "vaginal orgasm" in a woman seems to be largely a myth, and many females find it is easier for them to attain full climax by extravaginal methods (particularly by manipulation of the clitoral area) than by vaginal intercourse.

If all these things are true, it can easily be seen why females who hesitate to have coitus will not hesitate half so much to pet to orgasm. And if you, as a girl's potential lover, will convince her that you do *not* necessarily require intercourse, and that you *do* want to satisfy her and yourself by non-coital methods, you have a much better chance to induce her to engage in sexual intimacies with you. Moreover, once you start petting heavily, there is a good chance that she will later change her mind and decide that she does want to copulate. But even if she does not, you and she can both be sexually satisfied if you get rid of your prejudices about the sanctity of intercourse and if you try everything in the book *except* penile-vaginal congress.

The rest of the art of seduction, from a verbal standpoint, is largely the art of conversation and friendship. Hundreds of books have been written in this connection—such as Dale Carnegie's *How to Win Friends and Influence People* (1954) —and it will do you no harm to look over some of these writings and give them serious thought. Some of the main points you can keep in mind in this connection are:

1. Don't be over-eager to impress a girl too quickly. She's generally not so stupid as you may think, and may easily see through you.

2. Learn to listen carefully to what she says and to use the information she gives you as leads to further conversation. Show her, by your manner and your talk, that you are particularly interested in *her*. Be prepared, tactfully but incisively, to ask her about her family, friends, work, schooling, hobbies, politico-economic views, and other aspects of her life. Few girls feel bored when you are getting them to talk about *themselves* and are sympathetically intent on *their* problems.

3. Find out as much as you can about the girl's previous love and sex life. You can, with freedom, generally ask her about her previous amative or marital involvements; and through asking about them can get some good hints as to her previous sex activities. You can also usually ask her about her sex *attitudes*: about how she *feels* about non-marital sex relations, birth control, adultery, and other aspects of sex behavior. The more information you can get in this connection, the better equipped you will usually be to time your sexual approaches to her.

4. Don't talk about things you don't know about. Gather as good a fund of knowledge as you can about various things —through reading, attending lectures, conversing with people, etc.—and tell her the more interesting items that you discover. But the more you can draw her out, the less you'll have to entertain or amuse her.

5. Don't hesitate to confide some of your own problems to her, as long as you do not go on too lengthily and boringly

about them. Confidence begets confidence; and if you are honest about some of the things that have bothered you, she will usually reciprocate. Don't falsely try to indicate that you have mastered everything in life and have no anxieties or difficulties.

6. Speak up! If you find that you are becoming tongue-tied, or hesitant, or glum, ask yourself what there *really* is to be afraid of. Show yourself that *it would be nice* if you impressed this girl favorably and perhaps got her to bed; but that this *isn't necessary*; and it does not mean that you're a bum if you fail. Always remember that the particular girl whose favors you are trying to gain is, no matter how desirable she may be, only *one* girl out of many many possibilities; and that it is most unlikely that you will never meet an equally desirable girl for the rest of your days. This means that although it may be regrettable or saddening to lose her, it will not be catastrophic. Try, therefore, to be yourself and to express yourself, as you talk to her and make approaches to her. If you fail, you fail. But at least you can speak up and give your whirl with her an honest try!

Physical Techniques of Seduction

Assuming that you are getting along fairly well verbally with a girl whom you are trying to make, how and when should you start to approach her physically? What are some rules of thumb that you can use in this important respect?

Well, first of all, try not to go too fast—or too slow! If, because you are afraid you will antagonize a girl if you quickly begin to make passes at her, you go to the other extreme and don't even try to give her a goodnight kiss during the first several times that you date her, she is likely to feel that you don't care for her at all, or that you are too shy, or that perhaps you're homosexual; and before you know it, there simply may not *be* future dates with this girl. Another possibility is that the girl whom you keep taking out but not making any physical overtures to will, because of her own feelings of inadequacy, soon conclude that *she* is not attractive to *you* physically, and she may find it so uncomfortable to be with you, on that account, that again she may disrupt your dating relationship.

On the other hand, of course, if you absolutely refuse to take no for an answer, and persist in kissing, embracing, or practically assaulting a girl who keeps indicating that she is just not as yet interested in that sort of thing, your stay with her is not likely to be unduly long, and you may possibly miss out on a sex partner who, if you had been more patient, might have turned out to be an excellent one for you. A girl's sexual *No*, especially at the beginning of a relationship, may well mean exactly that, and may not indicate that she is merely being flirtatious or making things somewhat difficult for you before she later gives in. Her *No* may be motivated by her not knowing you well enough yet; not feeling affectionate toward you; being temporarily in a state of low physical arousability; being terribly afraid of sex contacts; or it may be caused by a score of other quite legitimate reasons, none of which imply that she is not attracted to you nor that she will not ultimately go to bed with you.

If a girl's refusal to have sex relations persists and persists, and particularly if it includes a barring of even minor physical contact, such as hand-holding and goodnight kissing, then you should start to suspect that something is awry. Either she just does not care for you physically (and never may be able to do so, no matter how much she otherwise likes you); or she has some psychophysical problem which prevents her from becoming sexually intimate with almost any man, including you. In either of these cases, you may wisely conclude, unless the girl is extra special in several other respects, that the hassle of getting her to try sex with you just isn't worth it, and that you'd better peddle your amorousness elsewhere.

Assuming that the girl seems to be fairly normal sexually and that she has no known physical bias against you, you should usually begin, quite early in the dating relationship, to make *some* kind of physical advance. Hold her arm when walking on the street. Take her hand when you are in the movies. Put your arm around her when you are sitting together on a sofa. Try to kiss her goodnight when you leave. In any (or all) of these and other little ways, sound her out physically, to see how she responds.

Don't, incidentally, *ask* a girl whether you can make any light physical contact with her, since she will often, for the sake of propriety or for some other reason, feel forced to say no when, if not specifically asked, she would not have pushed you away. Never say, "May I kiss you goodnight?" Kiss her! Don't ask: "Is it all right if I take your arm?" Take it!

As soon as you start making physical contact with a girl,

carefully observe her response. Does she, when you hold her hand in the movies, let her own hand rest limply, lifelessly in yours, and perhaps pull hers away after a short while? Or does she warmly press your hand, and almost pull it off your arm? Does she snuggle up against you closely, when your arm is around her? Or does she lean forward in her seat, and somehow manage to slip away from your grip? If she is most cooperative with what you are doing, whether it be kissing, embracing, or hand-holding, you may assume that there is a good probability that you may go further with your physical approaches. If she is distinctly uncooperative, or at best neutral, then you may have to wait a while, keep doing just what you are doing, or even withdraw for a later attempt.

In any event, *watch* your girl's responses and responsiveness! Don't barge ahead blindly from one step to the next, assuming that she is going along with you, just because she is not kicking or biting you to make you stop. For even if she does not particularly resist, she may be giving in most grudgingly and unenjoyably; and you will then get your "way" while really getting nothing: for sex under such conditions is likely to be unenjoyable to you, too.

The goal you are aiming at, then, is a *warm* responsiveness. As females become physically aroused, you can often literally *feel* them warming up: a kind of heat radiates from their bodies, their skin becomes flushed, and their breathing quickens. These are the kinds of signs you should look for and be guided by. When they are entirely absent, it usually means that the girl is not yet ready for further approaches—though there are, of course, exceptions to every rule, and it is possible that she is one of these exceptions.

On the whole, even from the very first night you make any passes at your girlfriend—which may well be the first time you meet her—you should try to go as far as you can possibly go with her sexually: since, much to your surprise, you may even be able to go all the way right at the start; and usually the further you get with her this time, the further you are likely to get with her the next time. So you keep progressing if you can.

Starting with kissing, hand-holding, and light embracing, you go on, after a reasonable amount of time, to much firmer and deeper kissing and embracing. If she responds in kind, you go the full gamut in these respects—including French kissing, with your mouths wide open, and your tongue playing madly on her lips, jutting into her mouth, and tasting every part of her anatomy that is bared to you, and with your teeth and lips deeply enmeshed with her lips, tongue, and mouth, and nipping fiercely at various other parts of her body.

The same thing goes for your embraces. Starting lightly, these should soon become firmer and more impassioned; and, if she permits you to do so, you should in a while be pressing her as closely to you as possible, and vigorously kneading her face, neck, and body with your incessantly moving hands, or gently and sensuously kneading your fingertips to every possible square inch of her exposed surfaces. In the meantime, you should be using your caressing hands to loosen her clothing and to get as much of her body bare as quickly as you can. Deftness and speed often pay off in this regard: since, once you have fully bared a woman's breasts, or taken off her skirt, or removed her undergarments, it is unlikely that she is immediately going to get up and cover herself again. Feeling that she has been sort of unmasked, and that you are still continuing passionately to kiss and caress her, she frequently accepts the inevitable at this point, and may even volunteer to take off some more of her own clothes. But don't, normally, *ask* her to divest herself. Do it for her! And do it firmly, vigorously, in spite of some resistance on her part. Show her that you are determined to have her as nude as possible, even though you are not going literally to rip the clothes off her back and begin to rape her.

Mind you, now: in this undressing process, you are doing *two* things (at least!) at once: first, kissing and embracing her intently; and second, getting as close to her skin as possible while you do this. Don't just go about the second of these tasks while you are neglecting the first: since she then often becomes undistracted enough to resist your divesting her. Moreover, it is not necessary that you actually remove all the garments of the girl to whom you are making love. Very frequently, even while her clothes remain on technically, you can actually get to her skin with your lips, and especially with your hands.

Thus, you can slip your hands underneath her brassiere or down the top of it, without literally removing it. And you can get to a girl's genital region without necessarily removing her skirt, slip, or panties. In fact, if you insist on stopping your attempts to get at her breasts or genitals by fully undressing her, you frequently will defeat your amorous ends: for she will then forcibly stop you from going further, and that will be that. If, on the other hand, you get to her vital erotic zones while her clothes are still mainly on, and you massage and kiss these zones effectively until she becomes truly aroused, she *then* will often offer no resistance whatever to taking off her clothes completely, and may even voluntarily do so herself.

In all kissing, caressing, massaging, and other forms of heavy petting that are now going on between you and your girl, make sure that you constantly indicate to her that you are intent on pleasing *her*, not merely yourself. If she thinks that you are ripping off her garments mainly so that *you* can insert your penis into her vagina and have your *own* delicious orgasm, she will usually be most unenthusiastic, especially at the beginning of your relationship, about going along with your aims. But if she can plainly see that, whether or not you are sexually satisfied that evening, you are bent on pleasing her and bringing her to the most glorious kind of orgasms of which she is capable, she is much more likely to be cooperative. Arousing *her* is the main issue, whatever your own state of desire and wish for ultimate fulfillment may be.

Because you should show your girl how vitally absorbed in her pleasure you are, it is usually wise, especially during first encounters, to do relatively little about baring your own body until she is pretty well denuded herself and seems to be adjusted to remaining so. Don't think, with peculiarly masculine arrogance, that she is going to be notably thrilled by seeing your naked torso or the size and contours of your sacred genitalia. Most probably, she isn't: females rarely become as physically excited by the sight of the male body as males do by the sight of the female charms. So keep yourself out of the picture at first; and don't, for perhaps quite a while, invite or expect her to do anything special to get to *your* seats of pleasure and to satisfy *you*.

If she spontaneously does give you bodily tit for tat, and kisses and caresses you in virtually every region that you kiss and caress her, that is great; you have really hit the jackpot. But this kind of behavior on the part of a girl whom you are trying to get to bed for the first time is rather unusual. Much more commonly, she will do relatively little to you, in return for your exciting caresses and kisses, other than conventionally kiss you on the lips or hold you tightly to her. Very frequently, she will not seem to give a hoot for your satisfaction, and will let you do practically anything you want to satisfy her, with little or no reciprocation. No matter. At this stage of the game, you can well bear this lack of reciprocity; and should not in the least resent it. It is only much later, after you have really shown her what a great lover you can be, and have given her as much satisfaction as she is ever likely to get, that you can clearly indicate that you, *too*, would like to be satisfied.

Even in this respect, actions often speak louder and better than words. Don't make the mistake of saying to your girlfriend, once you have shown her how pleasurable sex with you can be, "Will you please hold me here or kiss me there?" Like as not, she will shyly or resentfully or lackadaisically refuse. Instead, firmly but not ungently *put* her hand or lips where you want them to be, and help them make the motions you want them to make. This kind of request she is much less likely to refuse; and with this kind of persuasive technique, she is likely to see that she is beginning to *enjoy* a particular sex act, such as oral-genital relations, that she would have previously believed she never could enjoy, and that she would have balked at it if she had been verbally asked to try it.

Don't also, if you can possibly help it, make the mistake of forcibly attempting intercourse with your girl too early in the game, just because it appears to you that she is quite aroused sexually—and because you know full well that *you* are sufficiently aroused at this point to copulate with an orang-utan! There is no reason why, the first time you really approach a girl physically, she *has* to have coitus with you; and it is frequently much better for future relations with her if you never *do* get around to actual penile-vaginal intercourse.

What we have just said about kissing, embracing, and petting a girl, and finally leading up to mutual climax, is a bare (no pun intended!) outline. It could easily take an entire book to fill in the relevant details. Later, we shall give some of these details in our chapters on petting and bedmanship. The main thing that we want to emphasize here is that discretion is generally *not* the better part of valor in making the first sexual overtures. While, as we noted above, it is usually not wise for you to try to go too fast or too far at the outset, it is also most unwise if you do not try at all.

You must, in other words, take some risks. You must try

and in some measure keep trying—if just to *see* how and where you are failing. As long as you keep trying, you can fill in a good many of the erroneous details yourself—since we only really learn by trial and error; and the more errors you make, the more you will be able to see what *not* to do next time.

The only detailed manual that I know of on the art of seduction is an unpublished manuscript by N. D. Mallary, Jr., of Atlanta, Georgia, who has written a long epistle to his son, "On Sex and Making Love," which has some excellent instructions, and which I think deserves to be published. Although Mr. Mallary's pointers would not be everyone's cup of tea, he has some ideas on preliminaries to petting which may well be personally, and idiosyncratically, developed by any male who wants to adapt them to his own use. In his section on kissing, for example, Mallary includes this information:

"Now, since most men wait till they park to try to kiss—you want to change that. There are many techniques. I'll illustrate a few.

"1. *The car exit approach.* No woman expects a man in his right mind to kiss on a public thoroughfare. Fine! Do just that! You are taking her to supper on the second night. You park. You go around to open the door. As she puts her feet on the ground her head is down. Judge the distance accurately and arrange to have your lips poised when she looks up. Then kiss her. Do it gracefully and be careful not to bump mouths. Do it gently and don't hold it. Don't hug her. Dart in and out but make it good while you are there. This gives you the opportunity to verbalize the 'goodness' of the kiss (at the right time and place) and simply proceed to kiss her again.

"2. *The standing approach.* a. Sudden. You walk her to the car (or anywhere else). You take her upper arms in each of your hands. Her head is down or level. You hold her with 'restrained intensity' (but really very gently) and mutter some sentimentality—only part of which she catches. You know she's going to look up. As she looks up you move down such that your lips meet. She'll never know what hit her. b. Gradual. (Same circumstances and position as above). With a sudden flood of 'controlled intensity' you start kissing her hairline—lightly with loose lips. Pluck gently at her skin and hair. Make the movements of the tickling kind that are apt to produce goose bumps. Sooner or later she will turn her face up. Kiss down her face until you reach her lips. If she never turns her face up—back off. You have lost nothing.

"3. *The stop-light approach*. a. You are stopped for a light. Start to reach in the glove compartment, stop midway, put your left hand on her jawbone and kiss her. b. Use the hairline approach at one light and take it to the lips at the next.

"4. *Drive-in or hamburger approach*. Note: Almost everyone has sensitive skin. Almost everyone can get goose bumps. Goose bumps constitute a mild shock and the instant they occur the girl's reflexes are slower. Learn to produce goose bumps and to judge the exact instant of shock. a. Tickle the back of her neck. Watch her face. At the instant of shock —kiss. b. Stroke the hair and face with your *outside* hand on the *outside* of her face. When she gets goose bumps or when she closes her eyes and sighs—pull her gently to you and kiss. c. Cradle her face with both your palms. This is frequently interpreted as a 'tender' gesture by women. Hold her eyes with your eyes, hold her face until you feel her body relax, throw in an intimate remark, then gently kiss her. d. The Happy Warrior. Here you share a joke and both laugh. Reach out and cradle her against your shoulder in a spirit of camaraderie. At the split second the laughter stops she will inhale a deep breath. Place your hand under her chin, make it coincide with the inhaling, and kiss her in one motion. e. Pick up her outside hand in your outside hand. Turn it palm up and kiss the palm, first with lips, then with tongue. Holding her hand from out, but in front of, her face, *start* down the wrist but go directly into her mouth.

"5. *The Louise Lift approach*. Pick her up (she will grab you around the neck and giggle), wait until she stops giggling —then kiss her."

As you can see, Mr. Mallary has given careful thought and imagination to the seemingly simple problem of preliminary kissing. Taking a leaf from his book, you too can think and experiment, and can devise methods of your own. As long as you remain *active* and *undiscouraged*, there is very little that can stop you. With any particular girl, perhaps no technique, no matter how beautifully devised or well executed, may succeed. But with girls in general, the more you try the more you are likely to achieve at least partial success.

Assuming that your seduction techniques have been well

thought out and adequately executed, what are the next steps you should take in regard to petting and intercourse? These are outlined in Chapters 9 and 10, which can be read at this point if you wish. For those of you, however, who can wait a little more patiently for sexual consummation, we shall now consider some important matters of sex ethics and love.

Chapter 6

Don't Kiss and Tell—and
Other Sexual Ethics

In your endeavors to win the sex-love favors of any girl there are various ethical rules which it is advisable for you to follow. Not because you will be a louse or a skunk, if you don't, but because the nonobservance of these rules is most likely to get you into difficulties and to interfere with instead of abetting your sexual satisfaction.

General Ethics and Sex Ethics

Don't forget, in this connection, that sane ethical principles are invariably based on self-interest (Branden, 1962a, 1962b; Rand, 1961, 1963). If you really want to be true to yourself, and get maximum enjoyment and minimum pain out of living, you *have* to be concerned to some extent with seeing that others also achieve painless satisfaction. For if you go after what you want antisocially and angrily, you will inevitably create numerous enemies who will do their best to block you from fulfillment of your desires. And if you help create a nasty, dog-eat-dog, completely inconsiderate kind of world around you, *you* will obviously have to suffer by living in that kind of world.

What are some of the ethical principles that it would be sensible for you to follow if you want to make out reasonably well in the area of heterosexual relations? First of all, you'd better practice being discreet. Although, as I frequently point out to my patients and to my lecture audiences, you can usually get away with almost any kind of sexual act in our society, even though there are statutory laws against many acts, you must often be discreet if you are to do what you like and stay out of jail.

It is against the law, for example, to have non-marital relations in a public hostel or carrier, such as in a hotel, train roomette, or steamship stateroom. But obviously, hotels, motels, and rooming houses would frequently go out of business if they did not overlook the fornication and adultery which goes on nightly under their roofs. Consequently, if you will copulate in such places quietly and unostentatiously, with the door shut and the shades drawn, no one is going to bother you, and you will hardly be known as a lawbreaker.

Similarly, in a city such as New York, you can easily have all kinds of technically illegal sex activities and go uncaught and unpunished—as long as you do not carry on your sex relations in Macy's window, Central Park, the Plaza Bar, or various other public places. You can even, in most of our large cities, literally live in "sin" with a woman, for a number of years, without paying any legal or social penalties, if you just take care to be moderately discreet and to refer, at certain times and places, to your mistress as your wife (even though everyone present may know perfectly well that this is not true).

Discretion is particularly called for if you are having coital relations with the average female. For even though *you* may have no inhibitions in this connection, and may be very proud to have everyone know that you are petting to orgasm with Susie Smith, or playing double-backed horsey every other night with Jane Jones, or crawling into the sack every once in a while with Mary Roe when her husband is away on a business trip. Misses Smith and Jones and Mrs. Roe may be totally unenthusiastic about having their affairs with you bruited around the neighborhood. They would normally be far more delighted to know that you kept your big mouth shut about your sex relations; and even that you denied having such relations, at times, when others assumed that you were.

Kissing and telling, therefore, has its distinct disadvantages in our society, and is self-defeating in many instances. You may feel mightily inflated after you have boasted to your male friends of your sex affairs. But woe is you if these boasts get back to the girls you are having the affairs with! This does not mean that you necessarily have to walk on eggs all the time, and pretend you are a goody-goody or a faggot. Your best and most confidential friends, both men and women, may well be told that you are having sex engagements, and may even at times be told who are your female partners. But— unless you are a frank propagandist for the cause of free love, and habitually go with girls who are equally liberal—often the less you say in this respect, the better.

A second valid point of sex-love ethics is that of remaining as honest as feasible. This does not mean that you should be a pathological truth-teller, and insist on letting every girl you meet know exactly what you think of her right from the start. If a girl, for example, looks badly on a given day or gets drunk and acts reprehensibly, you don't have to go out of your way and tell her that she looks like a fright or acts like a bitch. As long as her flaws are within tolerable limits, and especially when there is nothing much which (at least at the moment) may be done about bettering them, it is often wise for you to keep your own counsel, and to accept her pretty much as she is.

If, on the other hand, you definitely think that one of your female friends is the world's worst pain in the neck (albeit a delight in bed), and that you would never in a million years marry her, it is quite dishonest of you to say nothing about her failings to her, and let her assume that you are going to cart her off to the altar in a matter of weeks or months. Women are especially vulnerable in regard to affairs of the heart, and they are only too willing to believe that you love them madly when you show the slightest indication of seeing them steadily. Human decency requires, therefore, that you eventually, if not immediately, make your feelings about a girl known to her so that you can give her the freedom of action to decide for herself whether she wants to keep seeing you or not.

The general rule, in this as in other moral respects, is that you should try to refrain from needlessly and deliberately harming another human being. If, for instance, you think that you love a girl and that you may well marry her, but you later decide that you do not care for her enough to wed, and if she becomes terribly depressed because of your finally rejecting her, you have not gratuitously and definitely harmed her. In the first place, she has essentially harmed herself, by taking your rejection of her too seriously; and, in the second place, you have only *unintentionally* contributed to her harming herself, since you *did*, for a while, think you might marry her, and you were not dishonest with her about your feelings. She did get hurt, no doubt. But we would easily conclude, in such circumstances, that *someone* had to get hurt (since someone invariably to some extent does whenever one lover rejects another) and that it just happened to be her. It could just as well have been you who got hurt—since she might have ultimately rejected *you*, when you were ready to get married. But it was she who was hurt. And that is sad; that is regrettable; that is too bad. But that's all it is; too bad. It is not criminal; and you are not a blackguard for being involved in this sadly ended affair.

If, on the other hand, you know damned well that you don't love your girlfriend, or even that you love her but are determined not to marry her, and if you *then* deliberately lead her on to remain sexuo-amatively attached to you, and finally drop her, you would seem to be, under these conditions, definitely and gratuitously harming her, and you are acting immorally. You still are not a bastard for being immoral—for you, like every fallible human being, have a *right* to be wrong, and always have the power to change and be less wrong or immoral in the future—but let's face it: you are at least partly responsible for some of the sorrow that your girlfriend may undergo when you leave her, and it is unethical of you not to be more honest with her. Honesty, then, is the best sex-love policy in most—though not all—instances; and the closer you stick to the truth in your love affairs, normally the better it will be.

The Ethics of Sexual Seduction

"Isn't sexual seduction essentially dishonest?" you may ask. "After all, the girl often doesn't *want* to be seduced; and isn't it therefore wrong of the boy to attempt to get her to bed in spite of her antisexual beliefs?"

No, not necessarily. Sexual seduction *may*, of course, be dishonest and unethical—as when, for example, you attempt to seduce a girl who is still a minor, or a mental defective, and therefore cannot very well give her true consent to your seductive overtures. Or when you induce a girl to have intercourse with you because you lyingly tell her that you love her or intend to marry her. Certainly, seduction, under these conditions, may be immoral. But under other, aboveboard conditions, there is no reason why it need be in the least hypocritical or dishonest.

Suppose, for example, that you have a girlfriend who is most willing to have sex relations with you, but who has what you consider to be mistaken ideas on religion or politics. Isn't it perfectly ethical for you to try to disabuse her of these ideas by openly arguing with her against them, introducing her to other people who agree with you, taking her to meetings and lectures where she will hear her own ideas trounced, and otherwise using propagandistic methods of changing her viewpoints? Why should you not use various ideological, emotional, and other appeals to induce her to accept religious or political notions which are closer to your own?

By the same token, if your girlfriend disagrees with your sex outlook, why should you not try to openly argue and debate with her so that she comes to agree with it?

"But suppose," you say, "the girl can be induced, at least temporarily, to go along with your seductive proposals, and then she later becomes very guilty about having gone along with them. Have you not *then* contributed to her harm?"

No, not necessarily. First of all, you have no way of knowing that she *will* become guilty after you have seduced her—since in the majority of cases—as the Kinsey investigators (1948, 1953) discovered—girls do *not* regret having premarital sex relations, once they start having them. Secondly, if she does become guilty, she is of course *hurting herself*, by maintaining senseless, guilt-creating philosophies, and *you* are not really hurting her. Thirdly, even if she does become quite guilty, you then may well have the power to talk her out of her guilt-inciting views, and to help her tremendously to eliminate them. If you cannot talk her out of her guilt, and she insists on hurting herself greatly by it, then you are *still* not responsible for making her guilty—since you, obviously, did not rear her and unstill in her this guilt. Her idiotic parents, society, and the church did; and if anyone or any institution is truly at fault for her needlessly giving herself a hard time, obviously *they* are.

As long, then, as you attempt to induce a girl to have sex relations with you in an aboveboard, honest manner; and as long as you try to help her to eradicate any of her guilty feelings which may possibly arise as a result of her being seduced; you are then doing your best best to avoid needlessly and deliberately harming this girl and you are not, in any accurate sense of the term, immoral. Naturally, if you go about trying to seduce girls, you are not an angel. But since when are angels moral? Indeed, insofar as they encourage human beings to give up extremely real, earthly satisfactions of a harmless nature for the entirely hypothetical and improbable hope of a heavenly existence hereafter, angels are clearly immoral, and there ought to be a law against them. Fortunately, to the extent that any of them exist, they are their own worst enemies; and it is poetic justice that their virtue is its own "reward."

The Ethics of Sexual Deviation

Are you being immoral if you engage in various kinds of *so-called* perverse sex acts, such as oral-genital relations with a female or homosexual relations with another male? No, you aren't: at the very worst such acts are abnormal and deviated, but generally not antisocial.

Oral-genital relations or other forms of extravaginal heterosexual acts are not even abnormal or perverse, but are only *arbitrarily* defined as such by unscientific, Biblically inspired individuals, who frequently call all sex behavior which cannot lead to procreation deviated behavior. These acts, moreover, harm neither the individual performing them nor his willing sex partner; so they cannot possibly be immoral or unethical.

Real sex deviations, such as fixed homosexuality or obsessive-compulsive voyeurism, are abnormal in the sense of their being performed by *emotionally disturbed* individuals, who are driven to engage in such exclusive or near-exclusive, rigid forms of sex behavior usually because they are afraid of more labile, more variegated forms of sexual expression (Ellis, 1960, 1962b, 1963a, 1963c). But the mere fact that an individual is emotionally ill does not mean that he is immoral or unethical for being ill and for performing in a deviated manner. *Some* sex deviants—such as sex murderers or seducers of young boys—are antisocial, because they actually harm other humans or take advantage of minors in performing their deviations. But most perverts are, at most, harming only themselves by their activities, and therefore cannot be looked upon as being immoral or unethical in the usual sense of these terms.

There are, then, distinct sex crimes, ranging all the way from relatively mild offenses like lying to one's girlfriend to major offenses like forcible rape. And these crimes, of course, are wrong or immoral. But their perpetrators are *still* not rats or lice; they are fallible human beings who usually are driven by some emotional disturbance (or state of mental deficiency) to commit their wrong acts, and who should consequently be protectively institutionalized and treated instead of punitively incarcerated and berated for their immorality.

More Heterosexual Ethics

To return to boy-girl relationships: it is not only toward your girlfriend that you should have an ethical code; but also toward other individuals who may be involved with you in your sex-love affairs. Thus, you normally will find it inadvisable to date your best friend's girl; or a girl who is going with your roommate; and sometimes even your sister's close girlfriend. It is not that such relationships cannot ever work out; for occasionally, they can. But your best friend or your roommate or your sister is likely to be quite jealous of, or otherwise embarrassed or disturbed about, your getting sexually involved with his or her intimate friends; and therefore, usually, you do not do anything to jeopardize your relationship with the one who may be embarrassed.

After all, there *are* plenty of girls in the world; and it should consequently be fairly easy for you to forego sex activities with your best friend's wife or girl. Of course, if the girl in question really is outstanding, and if she is so keen on you that she is willing to risk the loss of her husband or her boyfriend, then it may sometimes be worth your while to gain a wonderful relationship with her. Even then, it is normally ethical for you to do so in an aboveboard manner: to let your friend know, for example, that you are interested in his wife or girl, and not merely make passes at her behind his back.

We must emphasize once again, in this connection, that there is nothing unusual about sensible sex ethics, and that they should be indistinguishable from nonsexual ethics. Under ordinary conditions, you would not steal your best friend's customers, if you were in a business similar to his; nor would you take your sister's best girlfriend as a partner, if your sister seriously objected. If this is so, then it should be easy to arrange your sexual affairs with friends and associates and relatives of your friends so that these affairs do not clash with your already established friendships. Simple common sense will help you figure out what to do in most of these instances; and if you are determined to be a reasonably ethical individual, you should have little difficulty in abiding by this kind of common sense.

All told, it is relatively easy to determine just what the ethics of sex-love relationships are and how you should go about applying them to a particular situation that arises. It is much more difficult, however, to adhere to the brand of long-range hedonism that gives you the philosophic push to carry such ethics into effect, and stick to them even when, for the moment, you are making some kind of sacrifice. But unless you do make some sacrifices along these lines, you will wind up with no ethics whatsoever. And that, as we said at the beginning of this chapter, is itself generally self-defeating. You don't *have* to be ethical, then; but to some degree, at least, you'd better! You puts down your principles, and you takes your choice!

Chapter 7

When Love Comes Along: How to Know It and What to Do About It

Women, and how to handle them, are difficult problems for the best of men; but compared to the problem of women *and love*, they are almost nothing. To be prepared for this more complicated aspect of managing the ladies, you must be just that: *prepared*.

What is love? What is its psychology? How does one go about obtaining affectional response from a woman?

The Kinds and Degrees of Love

When you are not in love, you have little interest in defining this phenomenon; when you are, you often have still less. Hence, perhaps, the usual inadequate definitions of what Vernon Grant (1957) calls the "sexual emotion."

Love—to attempt a relatively simple and comprehensive definition—is simply a reasonably strong emotional attachment between two individuals; and, heterosexually, it is an emotional attachment or attraction between a man and a woman, frequently of an intense and highly irrational nature.

Being an emotional feeling, and a peculiarly human one at that, love has many types and degrees, and is far from being monolithic. Thus: you may love mildly or insanely; for a long or a short period; sexually or nonsexually; deeply or lightly. You may also love neurotically, affectionately, blindly, motheringly, romantically, childishly, cautiously, and in numerous other ways, some of which overlap and some of which are mutually exclusive (Hunt, 1963; Katz, 1962). Indeed in the course of your normal existence, you usually love many persons in several different ways, some at the same time, some at different times.

As the famous woman novelist, George Sand, once remarked: "I have known several kinds of love: artist's love, woman's love, sisterly love, motherly love, a nun's love, and a poet's love. God knows what other loves! Some were born and died the same day, without their object ever knowing anything about them. Some of my loves have tortured my life and brought me to the brink of despair, nay, insanity. Others have held me in a purely spiritual bondage for years" (Seyd, 1940).

An essential point to be noted here is that, of all the different kinds and degrees of love that you may experience, none is uniquely "good' or "higher" and none intrinsically "bad" or lower." As long as you derive satisfaction from your special kind of amativeness, and do not harm yourself or anyone else in the process, it is meaningless to classify arbitrarily your feeling or to contend that it is good, bad, or indifferent. The main thing is that it must suit *you*—and not a half dozen or a half thousand others.

Short loves, therefore, and light loves; sensual loves and purely physical amours; blind infatuations and plural affections—all these, and many others which have been viciously maligned by puritan-minded bigots, are as good as you make them, as pleasant as you enjoy them. To think otherwise is not to think at all. As Alec Craig (1934) has noted: "To judge a love affair by its length is as absurd as to judge a picture by its size."

Individual Differences in Love

Each person, of both sexes, loves somewhat differently from all other individuals. In amativeness, as in so many other human respects, individual difference is the basic keynote. As Mantegazza (1936) has stated: "Every man loves in his fashion, and inasmuch as each one brings to it the greatest possible offering of psychic elements, human loves differ more among themselves than hatreds, than ways of eating, moving, wishing."

Love, theoretically, may be analyzed and classified into several categories; but lovers hardly can. They are unique animals. They are never found in identical pairs. To know and understand them is to watch and study them individually, in their novel environments, and to make all possible allowances for their inner thoughts and emotional processes which, indigenous to them alone, can never be precisely cognized by anyone but themselves—if, indeed, *by* themselves! So don't expect *this* girl's love to be exactly like *that* girl's.

Nor, for that matter, should you expect your *present* romantic feelings to be exactly like your *past* ones.

"Since no two races look alike," Henry T. Finck (1899) has observed, "and no two individuals in the same race, why should their loves be alike? Is not love the heart and soul and the face merely its mirror? Love is varied through a thousand climatic, racial, family, and cultural peculiarities. It is varied through individual tastes and proclivities."

Love's Tendency to Change

Intense heterosexual love—whether we like to admit it or not—in the vast majority of instances is subject to inevitable change; and most of the time its intensity eventually fades or dies. That passionate love fluctuates and ebbs, and that it usually does so within a few years of its inception, is as incontrovertible as the fact that it actually exists, and that it brings immense satisfaction to numerous persons. Yet, sadly enough, the *mores* of our society demand that the fiction of love's immortality be universally fostered, and that most of us be led to believe that, when love is "truly" experienced, it never changes, lasts for the lifetime of the lovers, and is even "immortal."

As some of the sages of love observe:

Johann Wolfgang von Goethe (1873): "Our passions are true phoenixes; as the old burn out, the new straight rise up out of the ashes."

Heinrich Heine (1937):

> "Don't send me off, now that your thirst
>   Is quenched, and all seems stale to you;
> Keep me a short three months or more,
>   Then I'll be sated, too."

Mary Borden (1933): "All passionate married lovers, like all unmarried lovers, cease to be passionate sooner or later."

C. G. Jung (1960): "He may suddenly fall mortally in love with a girl, and a fortnight later be no longer able to conceive how it could ever have happened to him."

Leo Tolstoy (1890): "It is only in stupid novels that it is written that 'they loved each other all their lives.' And none but children can believe it. To talk of loving a man or a woman for life is like saying that a candle can burn forever."

James Winfred Bridges (1935): "Whether it runs smoothly or roughly, love in human experience has a changing course, a natural history. Like a plant, it buds, blooms, and fades. . . ."

F. Scott Fitzgerald (1920):

> "For this is wisdom—to love and live,
> To take what fate or the gods may give,
> To ask no question, to make no prayer,
> To kiss the lips and caress the hair,
> Speed fashion's ebb as we greet its flow,
> To have and to hold, and, in time—let go."

Plural Love

Although romanticists and monogamists frequently deny it, many individuals are quite capable of loving, deeply and tenderly, two members of the other sex at one time. Fickle lovers, who become romantically involved with a series of girls in succession, are of course common. Those who fairly equally love two others simultaneously are much rarer; but they definitely do exist.

As Max Nordau wrote in *The Conventional Lies of Our Civilization* (1886): "It may sound very shocking, yet I must say it: we can even love several individuals at the same time, with nearly equal tenderness, and we need not lie when we assure each of our passion. No matter how deeply we may be in love with a certain individual, we do not cease to be susceptible to the influence of the entire sex."

Theodore Dreiser, in his autobiographical volume, *A Book About Myself* (1922), confessed: "One of the things which troubled and astonished me was that I could like two, three, and even more women at the same time, like them very much indeed. It seemed strange that I could yearn over them, now one and now another."

Passionate Love and Conjugal Affection

Most of what is called love in our fiction and drama is passionate, romantic love, which flames up to enormous heights for a period of time—rarely more than a few years—and then generally dies. Conjugal affection or marital love between males and females also exists, and is quite different from impassioned love, although it overlaps it at certain points. Conjugal tenderness is a calmer, usually more enduring kind of amativeness; closely resembles deep friendship and familial love; and sometimes, over a period of years, brings more enduring, and in a sense almost more real, satisfaction than you may experience with more intense, romantic affairs. Conjugal love frequently replaces romantic love; although the two can exist simultaneously.

As Henry T. Finck (1887) has realistically noted: "Unquestionably marriage is the best cure of love. For though cynics are wrong in claiming that wedlock changes love to indifference, it does change it to conjugal affection, which is an entirely different group of emotions."

In your own life, you may find that either passionate love or conjugal tenderness tends to predominate, and there is no need for you to feel upset or guilty in either event. Don't get snowed into thinking that you *must* be highly romantic in order to enjoy a love relationship; nor that you *have to be* tenderly affectionate with your inamorata before you "truly" love. Get as much actual experience in loving as you can, by taking the risks of throwing yourself into a series of likely involvements; and thereby determine for yourself what, exactly, is your own amatory preference. It is lovely if, somewhere along the line, you can intensely experience, either with one woman or another, impassioned romance *and* warm, conjugal affection. But you are not a monster nor a neurotic if you somehow tend to the one or to the other of these main amative feelings.

The Sex Element in Love

Many writers, especially Freud (1924-50) and his followers, have claimed that all love essentially stems from human sex drives, and that romantic love in particular is aim-inhibited sex. There is no evidence to confirm this view; and it would appear, rather, that love has important sexual and nonsexual components.

Nonetheless, impassioned romantic love usually tends to arise from frankly sexual attraction, to ascend on the shoulders of sex desire, and to reach its peaks in mutually satisfying coitus between lovers. While love enhances sex satisfaction, sex involvements also in many instances encourage the individual (and perhaps the female in particular) to fall in love (Ellis, 1963a).

"Can there," asked George Sand, "be purely spiritual love for one who is sincere with himself? Can there ever be love without a single kiss, and kisses without voluptuousness?" (Seyd, 1941). Obviously, she thought that there cannot be; and as far as heterosexual love is concerned, she may well have been right.

Impassioned love may be defined as bliss that's found between a woman's sighs and thighs. If you would best influence a girl amatively, you must realize that your chances of winning and retaining her will be immeasurably enhanced if you can manage to arouse her sexually and to be a satisfactory sex mate to her.

Romanticism and Love

Romantic love seems to exist among most peoples of the world, especially among adolescent lovers; but in its most generalized and idealized forms it is largely a product of Western civilization, and arose during the Middle Ages, as a by-product of adultery between the court ladies and their knightly or troubadour lovers. The essence of the romantic attitude is exaggeration, over-emotionalism, and fictionalization (Ellis, 1962b). As Oscar Wilde (1935b) wittily remarked: "When one is in love, one always begins by deceiving oneself, and always ends by deceiving others. That is what the world calls a romance."

Is romantic love, because of its lack of realism and its ephemeral nature, to be avoided? Not at all. It is one of the most charming, pleasurable experiences of life; and of this exciting, captivating form of love it especially may be said that 'tis better to have loved and lost than never to have loved at all. Moreover, if you want to win a girl, sexually or amatively, in this society, it is frequently required that you become romantically, and not merely practically or conjugally, in love with her. Anything less than flaming passion simply will not count in her book.

Moreover, the lack of durability of romantic love is not

necessarily a handicap: since many fine things in life, ranging from a picnic at the beach to a research project, hardly last; and yet they are beautiful and rewarding, and can be joyfully remembered long after they have passed. The main difficulty with romantic love is that it frequently becomes confused with enduring, more conjugal types of love; so that males and females who are passionately devoted to each other in a romantic way blindly believe that they will *always* be equally devoted, and consequently often make the mistake of marrying each other largely or purely on the basis of their romantic attachment.

As I explain to my patients and marriage counseling clients, you should not ordinarily, these days, marry anyone whom you are not somewhat romantically in love with; but neither should you marry *everyone* you love. If, therefore, you can manage fully to enjoy your romantic attachments, and even throw yourself wholeheartedly into them while they last, but refrain from fooling yourself into believing that they necessarily have much to do with marriage, you can gain the lovely delights of romance while avoiding many of its inherent difficulties.

How to Know When You're in Love

Many people find it difficult to tell when they are in love with a member of the other sex; and, proverbially, the lover is often the last one to admit that he is seriously emotionally involved with his inamorata, while his friends, by watching his behavior, may have noticed his attachment for some time previously. How, then, do you tell whether or not you are in love?

Very simply. Whenever you even lightly suspect, from your feelings or your overt behavior, that you are in love with a girl, immediately assume that you are. You may not, perchance, be completely or fully; or divinely and ecstatically; or deeply and movingly; or enduringly or permanently in love. But if you find yourself thinking a good deal about a girl, wanting to be with her a lot of the time, imagining nonsexual as well as sexual engagements with her, and even lightly considering the possibilities of a longtime relationship or marriage with her, the chances are that you do love her, at least in some manner or degree; and you might as well admit it and no nonsense about it!

The Art of Winning a Woman's Love

Let us assume that you want to win the love of a particular woman. How do you go about doing this? In many ways, some of which are general and some of which are unique for this particular female. Here are some pointers which may be helpful:

1. Try to avoid being desperately in need of the woman whose love you would like to win. You want her very much; and we'll assume that she is desirable. All right: but she is *not* the only possible woman in the world for you; you *won't* die if you lose her; and you *will* love again if she disappears from your life. You are, moreover, an entirely worthwhile individual, who is capable of leading a happy life *whether or not* this woman loves you (even though you may well lead a happier existence if she does care for you). Stick to your *preference* for your chosen one; and don't idiotically convince yourself that you have a *dire need* of her.

2. Carefully *observe* the traits and characteristics of your beloved. Watch her, listen to her with clearheaded attention. What does she like? How does she think? What are her main feelings, interests, attitudes, philosophies? What kind of a past amative history has she had? What are her sexual and marital goals? Find out, as concretely as you can, all salient data about her—and not about how you *think* she is, but how she *really* is.

3. Once you have discovered some of your beloved's main traits and characteristics, plan a campaign of satisfying many of her main desires and preferences. Does she adore good music? Learn to enjoy it with her. Does she dote on lively conversation? Supply it yourself or see that, with you, she is in an environment where it is found. Does she like to skate, swim, or row? Somehow arrange to do these things with her. Whatever she likes or *thinks* she likes, try to provide; or at least show her that you are willing to and ultimately will provide for her in these respects.

4. Watch for feedback! Don't merely assume that you are doing the right things with your girlfriend and that she is delighted with your performance. See if she really is happy with you: by asking her, checking with her friends and relatives, observing how she reacts when with you, and otherwise noting her responsiveness. Don't assume that because things

are going well for a while she can be taken for granted. Keep observing and checking your premises about her!

5. Take care of your appearance. While women, fortunately, do not emphasize beauty in males as much as contemporary men emphasize beauty in females, they do generally prefer a good-looking to an ugly partner, and favor one who is neat, clean, and reasonably well dressed. It may pain you that such superficialities are important to many females; but they are, and if your particular inamorata is among those attaching significance to looks, whatever you can do to accede to her "unreasonable" demands may be helpful. Of course, you can always say to hell with it all, and go out only with lady beatniks. But you will probably find your selection unduly restricted by this kind of choice.

6. There is usually no more important factor in winning love than showing love. Some freakish women have no interest whatever in being loved, and even masochistically prefer to be hated by the males in whom they are interested; but this rare species is rarely captured alive. My own studies of the love relations of young girls (Ellis, 1949a, 1949b, 1949c, 1950) show that the average college-level female does not *fall* violently in love with anyone who strikes her fancy, but instead tends to *let* herself more gradually become involved with the man who not only is pleasing to her but who *cares* for her. "To be loved," said the famous Roman epigrammatist, Martial (1877), "show love yourself." And the Greek philosopher, Epictetus (Hadas, 1961), "Let not him think he is loved by any who loves none."

7. Love begets love; but sex also begets love. Many a girl who thinks that she dotes on her boyfriend mainly because of his looks or his intelligence really cares for him deeply because he keeps satisfying her sexually. If you gratify your beloved's innermost sexuality, you will not *necessarily* win her affection; but it certainly helps! Know, therefore, all that you can scientifically know about sex (much of which is outlined in this book; and more in my manual, *The Art and Science of Love*). And really do your best to discover what pleases your mate, and precisely what you can do to give her maximum sex satisfaction.

8. A woman, particularly one who is thinking of marrying a man, normally wants to know that she can trust him. Consequently, you can help win or cement the love of a girl by showing her not only that you are kind and considerate of

her, but that you are a generally reliable, trustworthy, reasonably stable individual. If she thinks that you are a pathological liar, or an empty promiser, or a person who is so emotionally upset that you are not able to carry out the plans you make with her, she will tend to lose respect, and consequently love, for you.

9. Females, partly for cultural reasons and partly for what may well be biological reasons, tend to want a male who is in some significant respect strong. He need not be physically powerful (though that may help!) but he should normally have some goodly degree of strength of character, of determination to get what he wants out of life, and of pronounced socio-economic drive. Many intelligent and capable females will love and marry you if you are *currently* poor, or weak, or low in the social scale. But most of them want you at least to have some good *potentialities* in these respects; and if you show them that you are, and probably always will be, essentially unambitious and static, they will usually have no deep feelings for you, even though they like your superficial charm.

These, then, are some of the main pointers that you can keep in mind as you go about seeking the amative responsiveness of some special girl. Don't try to apply any of these rules mechanically; they are not likely to work if you do. But if you think about them carefully, let them get under your skin, practice carrying them out, and make them a real part of you, you are likely to have considerable success at the love game.

Not—we must warn—complete success. As we noted in the beginning of this book, the old element of luck is still there. No matter how much you want an individual girl, and how well you plan and scheme to win her, you never have anything like a hundred-percent probability of success. For many reasons, ranging from the color of your eyes to the family background you inherited, she may decide that she cannot care for you—or that she does care, but nonetheless is not going to be yours. That is too bad. You can't win 'em all. But you can, if you follow all or most of the rules outlined above, win a large percentage of the girls you go after. With a little talent—and a little luck!

Chapter 8

Surviving Disappointment in Love

Love, even when solidly won, can never be guaranteed. Your beloved may dote on you madly for a while—and then for one reason or another find you a bore. Or unkind fate—such as a move to a distant part of the country—may separate you from the woman you love. Or your inamorata may die, and be irrevocably taken from you.

For a number of reasons, then, you may fail to win a woman's love in the first place, or you may gain her affection and have it rudely torn away from you in the second place. In such an event, you will naturally tend to sorrow over your loss; and unless you do something to minimize or mitigate this sorrow, it may turn into depression, despair, or even suicidal tendencies.

Can anything effective be done about your falling *out* of love with a woman or your conquering sorrow over loss of a beloved person? Yes, if you want to work hard at thinking and acting in this respect, something very definitely can be done to lessen amative involvements and alleviate love's sorrows (Harper, 1963). Following are some of the most effective means you can employ in this connection.

Anti-catastrophizing

The sorrow that you may feel over failing to win, or over gaining and then losing, a beloved female is perfectly legitimate as long as it remains just that—sorrow. For it *is* a sorry, sad, regrettable thing to be frustrated in getting something you want very much, or in losing a treasured partner that you have had for a while but who is now no longer with you. But that's *all* it is—sad.

When love's sorrow (or, for that matter, any other kind of sadness or regret) turns into depression, despair, or rampant self-pity, something gratuitous and illegitimate has (unconsciously) been added to the original feeling of regret or frustration. And that unnecessary addition can be subtracted again.

Let us operationally define the terms *sadness* and *regret*, on the one hand, and *depression* and *self-pity*, on the other hand, by distinguishing the simple exclamatory sentences of which they consist. Sadness and regret essentially stem from the internalized sentence, which you keep saying over and over to yourself when a love loss or frustration occurs, "I certainly dislike the fact that I have not been able to win (or can no longer retain) Mary's love; now isn't that too bad!" And when you say this kind of sentence to yourself, and feel sorrowful or regretful as a result of your convincing yourself that it *is* a bad state of affairs, you also tend to follow through with the next sentence: "Now that I've lost Mary, and feel badly about this loss, let me mourn for a while—and then let me go out and look for another girl to replace Mary in my affections, and one with whom I hope I'll have much better luck."

When it is appropriate and unneurotic, in other words, sadness leads to action: (a) to a reasonable period of mourning and (b) to some kind of attempt to make up for the lost love, and to replace it with a happier, *present* relationship.

When sadness leads to depression or self-pity, the first part of the first sentence, the one that produces sadness, is retained; but a significant change is made in the last part of it. Thus, the sentence becomes: "I certainly dislike the fact that I have not been able to win (or can no longer retain) Mary's love; now isn't that terrible!" And this catastrophizing sentence soon leads to other, equally self-defeating thoughts: "What a fool I am for having lost out with Mary!" . . . "How could an idiot like me *ever* hope to win and keep a worthwhile girl again?" . . . "Oh, what a horrible, mean world this is, where things are so arranged that a poor slob like me has to keep losing out on girls like Mary!" . . . because of the lousy bastards, like Jack and Eddie, who exist in this town, I'll *never* be able to win a girl like Mary!"

These negative sentences, which are gratuitously added to the original sorrow-creating phrases that you tell yourself, are all blaming, moralizing sentences: since they state or imply that *you* are no damned good, because you lost Mary; or that *someone else* is a rat, because he kept you from winning and keeping Mary; or that *the world* is a horrible place, because it arranges conditions so that it is impossible for you ever to win girls like Mary. And by these blaming, moralizing sentences, you only make certain that you feel depressed, angry, or self-pitying; and that, in all probability, you *won't* do very much about making up for Mary's loss by keeping your eyes open for a suitable substitute. For if *you* are a no-goodnik for losing Mary; or *someone else* is a skunk for making you lose her; or *the world* is a dreadful place for preventing you from ever winning a girl like her; what, then, is the use of your doing anything *but* wailing and flailing about and refusing to seek a delightful Jane or Grace or Anna?

I stoutly maintain, in other words, that depression, despair, anger, self-pity, and similar self-destructive emotions are *not* an inevitable concomitant of your losing someone you love. Sadness, sorrow, regret, annoyance, and frustration may be inevitable, in such circumstances; but the more encompassing and debilitating emotions of anxiety and hostility that follow these inevitable feelings are gratuitous, quite unnecessary additions. They are statistically normal, these additions, in that the great majority of human beings, because of their biological tendencies and their social rearing, bring them on and suffer as a result of bringing them on. But they are abnormal in the sense that they are dysfunctional and *need* not necessarily exist in any intense and prolonged way.

If, therefore, you want to avoid depression and self-pity as a consequence of losing your beloved, you must look at the additional, gratuitous sentences that you are telling yourself *after* your appropriate sorrow-creating sentences. And you must vigorously, consistently *question* and *challenge* these unnecessary sentences, in theory and action, until they become significantly modified or disappear.

More concretely, you must ask yourself: "*Why* am I a worthless fool just because I have made human mistakes and have lost out with Mary?" . . . "*Why* is it impossible for me to ever hope to win and keep a worthwhile girl again?" . . . "Is the world *really* horrible and mean, just because I have lost Mary?" . . . "*Will* people like Jack and Eddie, who were partly instrumental in my losing Mary, actually be able to *keep* frustrating me in this way? And *are* they really bastards, just because they interfered with my relationship with Mary?"

While challenging your own catastrophizing, depression- and anger-creating philosophies in this way, you must also combat them in action. That is to say, you must force yourself to look for another girl like Mary; go out into the world and show yourself that there are other joys in life aside from sex and love; deliberately see people like Jack and Eddie, and show yourself that they are not blackguards, but do have good points in spite of their helping you lose Mary. If, verbally and actively, you fight your own despair-creating views, you will soon come to see and to *feel* how ridiculous they are, and will acquire a saner philosophy of life that will still leave you with normal sorrow and regret over the loss of Mary, but will prevent you from becoming intensely and prolongedly upset about this loss.

You can, then, observe your negative emotions; reassess and reevaluate the philosophic assumptions that lie behind and cause them; and change them so that you still remain an emoting, feeling human being, but one who experiences little or no deep despair or self-hatred, while still experiencing suitable levels of sadness, sorrow, and frustration. All this, naturally, is difficult for you to do, when you have been born and raised as you have been. But, as I keep telling my psychotherapy patients and marriage counseling clients, it is much more difficult for you *not* to do this.

Diversion Techniques of Overcoming Love Despair

While you are working on a basic means of doing away with love despair, in accordance with the principles just outlined, you can also employ a less involved and more temporary method of diversion; and, if properly used, diversion techniques will not only minimize, at least at times, your depression, hostility, or self-pity that you create in regard to your feelings of love loss, but will also even reduce your normal feelings of sorrow and frustration. Diversion may sometimes boomerang, since it does not actually do away with your underlying negative feelings, and allows them to rise to the surface again when the diverting people or things are no longer in force; but when properly applied, it can serve a very useful purpose, and has probably saved more people from love suicides than any other method.

Some of the main diversion techniques you can use are the following:

1. *Absence.* Absence does *not* generally make the heart grow fonder—except when it is temporary, and when there is an expectation that you will soon encounter and have good

relations with your beloved once again. Once the love relationship has actually ended, absence is one of the very best means of overcoming discomfort connected with your loss. For the emotions and sorrows of love, like other human thoughts and feelings, are experienced chiefly on the basis of memory association. They do not assail you unless you are actually thinking, directly or indirectly, of your beloved and of your failure to keep the affair with her going.

The more you see of your beloved, and the longer you remain in the environment in which you knew her, the more you will tend to think of her and mope over her loss. Streets that you once walked together, places that you visited, stores where you made purchases, theaters you attended—all these, if you continue to encounter them, will recall her to your mind, and encourage you to sorrow anew over her.

By all means, then: absent yourself from your beloved and the surroundings in which you knew her. Keep away from her neighborhood, or even city. Travel. Do not communicate with her; it may be best not to contact mutual friends for a while. Take yourself physically and mentally away from her —and stay away until you are convinced that you are no longer violently attached to her. As George Ramsay (1846) aptly noted: "Since love is born and fed by gazing on its object when present, and thinking on it when absent, the obvious cure is, not to gaze and not to think." And Guy de Maupassant (1926) observed: 'A lover at a distance is a lover cured."

2. *Other interests and occupations.* The main reason you may have the time and energy to sorrow over anything is because you are not occupying yourself sufficiently with other things requiring your full attention. No matter how sad or depressed you could be, if other occupations and interests become paramount and you have no time for idleness, your actual grief over a lost loved one will be appreciably reduced.

Wrote the Roman poet, Ovid (1930): "Love is born of idleness, and, once born, by idleness is fostered. . . . Love flees from toil; if, then, you would banish love from your heart, find some work for your idle hands to do and then you will be safe."

More specifically: if you are bewailing your unkind fate in fields of romance, try to vitally absorb yourself in something important to you, such as a political movement, a challenging new job, or writing a book. If you cannot find a main, overwhelming interest, at least see that your energies are involved in smaller affairs. Play games, attend functions, study some subject, meet new people, take up a hobby or two. At all events, do something that will occupy your time, thoughts, and energies; and your emotions, you will be surprised to find, will tend to be much more on the optimistic than the grief-stricken side.

3. *Acquiring new loves.* A French proverb says: "A new love drives out the old." And Heinrich Heine has semicynically remarked: "The most effective antidote to a woman is another woman. True, this implies an attempt to expel Satan with Beelzebub; and in such a case the medicine is often more noxious still than the malady. But it is at any rate a change, and in a disconsolate love affair a change of inamorata is unquestionably the best policy" (Reid, 1911).

You usually can, then—especially if you keep trying hard enough—down your amative sorrow by seeking a substitute beloved. This does not mean that you should take, on the rebound, the first girl you meet after your present affair has miserably ended; but you should sincerely try to discover one who will suit you as well as or better than your lost love. Even in *trying* to replace your past affair with a new one, you will divert yourself from your sorrow and become less grief-stricken. And if you succeed, you will certainly have no cause to continue surrowing. In fact, you may even become *glad* that the old affair has ended!

Emphasizing the defects of your lost beloved. The chances are that one of the reasons you violently loved your lost beloved was that you exaggerated her virtues and minimized her defects. Consequently, if you now want to fall out of love with her, or get over the grief caused by her loss, you can usually do so by emphasizing her defects and realistically pointing out to yourself what she *truly* was like. The famous Spanish playwright, Lope de Vega, clearly saw this several centuries ago, when he wrote:

"Desire pricks us daily, as the Spanish poet declares, or wrote, wherefore we must contrive to circumvent desire . . . Think up faults instead of graces, for the discreet, to forget, put faults in their places. Never picture love upon a balcony, perfectly proportioned and shod, for that is parade. A philosopher discovered once that beauty was what we owed the tailor. Think of a woman as a sinner condemned to torment, yes, and drape no glories about her. Defects are the best physic as has been proved time and again, just as bad food cures the appetite. Signor, recall her defects, and if your memory proves good enough love is done."

These are some of the diversionary methods you can employ to deemphasize the good qualities of the old love and to encourage the enjoyment of a new affair. And if you add, as you must as a mortal being, the passage of time to these techniques, you will almost certainly get over your love sorrows and depressions—and be able to go on to a new batch!

For time is still the greatest and best healer. Fortunately for unsuccessful lovers, amative emotions and griefs wear off or become dimmed as the weeks pass. Acute pangs of amorous sorrow rarely last a lifetime; and, indeed, endure for only a year or more in pathological instances. As the poet William Ellery Leonard (1927) noted: "Grief in its acuter pang with most people spends itself mercifully in six months." And Dorothy Parker (1936), after complaining that her friends were pitiful and mild who told her that her heart that broke in April would mend again in May, finally concluded:

> Who flings me silly talk of May
> Shall meet a bitter soul;
> For June was nearly spent away
> Before my heart was whole.

Mere lapse of time, then, will normally erase the memory of your unsuccessful love and diminish your grief about it. At first, you may be certain that your sorrow will last forever. But if you go about your regular business, and let Father Time do his usual healing job, you will be surprised how the grief lessens and vanishes. The one main trait that you need to survive even the greatest pangs of lost love is patience. Just have the fortitude to wait, and you will see!

Chapter 9

How to Pet and Like It

As I have heretically said in the past (Ellis, 1960, 1962b, 1963a) and shall probably keep shocking people by saying for many years to come, a man's main sex organ, as far as satisfying a female is concerned, is rarely his sacred penis; rather, it is his hand. And the primary source of his own sexual responsiveness is not always, as so many sex books misleadingly point out, the glans or head of his membrum virile; instead, it may be a large portion of his skin, ranging from the tip of his toes to his breasts, back, lips, and neck.

There is nothing sacrosanct about penile-vaginal intercourse—although it is usually great stuff and is never to be sneezed at—and if you think there is, and focus almost exclusively on getting a girl, as quickly as possible, to grant you her "final" favors, you are often missing the most of potential sex pleasure. Moreover, as we pointed out in a previous chapter, you are making yourself into a poor lover; since most females tend to get more excitement and satisfaction out of various forms of petting than they do from copulation itself, especially when the latter is not preceded by a goodly amount of preliminary play.

Assuming that you have already been able to get a girl to pet to orgasm or to have intercourse with you, and that there is relatively little trouble in continuing a sex relationship with her, what are some of the ways in which you can learn to pet and like it? This is the question we shall attempt to answer in the present chapter—before going on, in the next chapter, to techniques of penile-vaginal coitus.

Petting, as the Kinsey research group (1948, 1953) shows, consists of any form of sex play other than intercourse itself. It includes kissing, embracing, caressing, massaging, oral-genital relations, and various other forms of extravaginal activity. Petting may be engaged in as a form of preliminary sex play; or it may be, and often should be, done in its own right, either because it is intrinsically enjoyable or because it leads to sexual climax. Although much of the oldtime sex literature tends to indicate that petting can be harmful when it does not result in intercourse, there is no evidence to back this belief (Beigel, 1952; Harper, 1960).

What may actually be harmful or irritating, particularly to the male, is petting that is quite arousing but does not result in any kind of orgasm. Such prolonged, climaxless petting can lead to disorders of the male's prostate gland or seminal vesicles and to pelvic congestion in females (Secor, 1959; Clark, 1961). Even then, however, we must hasten to add: in *some* cases. For there are apparently millions of women, and some men, who can pet indefinitely without any harmful results. In the main, however, it is safer to pet to orgasm, whenever you engage in kissing and caressing, than to stop short of full climax.

The main techniques of petting may be briefly summarized as follows:

Lip Kissing

Many people seem to think that kissing consists largely of pressing one's lips, tenderly or tightly, against the partner's lips, and keeping them sort of locked in that position for a while before breaking apart. Well, that *is* kissing (I guess!); but of an exceptionally limited variety. The Hindu writer Vatsyayana, who wrote sometime between the tenth and thirteenth centuries, and has given us the famous treatise, *The Kama Sutra* (1962), described a great many kisses, including:

The nominal kiss—"when a girl only touches the mouth of her lover with her own, but does not herself do anything."

The throbbing kiss—"when a girl, setting aside her bashfulness a little, wishes to touch the lip that is pressed into her mouth, and with that object moves her lower lip, but not the upper one."

The touching kiss—"when a girl touches her lover's lip with her tongue, and having shut her eyes, places her hands on those of her lover."

The straight kiss—"when the lips of two lovers are brought into direct contact with each other."

The bent kiss—"when the heads of two lovers are bent towards each other, and when so bent, kissing takes place."

The turned kiss—"when one of them turns up the face of the other by holding the head and chin, and then kissing."

The pressed kiss—"when the lower lip is pressed with much force."

Vatsyayana also described a dozen other kinds of kisses; and he by no means exhausted the list. Van de Velde (1926), who has an extensive section on kissing in his sex manual, *Ideal Marriage*, particularly describes Maraichinage or Kataglossism, a form of "soul kissing" in which the lovers' kisses are deep and wet and where they insert their tongues into each other's mouths for long periods of mutual exploration.

There are, then, perhaps fifty or a hundred types of lip kissing, depending on how you divide and subdivide its various aspects. And you, with your girlfriend, can imaginatively experiment until you invent (or re-invent) a special type that is most pleasing to both of you. The main thing is that you learn to *use* your lips, tongue, and even teeth in kissing; and that you *actively* explore your partner's lip, tongue, and mouth surface, until you find mutually satisfying variations. Your kisses may be long or short, firm or gentle, deep or shallow, wild or mild—and all kinds of gradations and nuances in between.

Don't give up easily! And don't assume, just because a particular form of kissing is enjoyable, that you should stop right there, and always use that approach. Years ago, when I first started to have sex relations with girls, I learned a form of closed-lip kissing which I enjoyed immensely, and which I continued with subsequent girlfriends. But then I was rudely interrupted by one of my female partners, who showed me, in no uncertain terms, that my osculatory activities were distinctly limited, and that I'd better get wise and open my mouth and *really* kiss.

I learned quite a bit from this girl; and in turn used my skills successfully with a good many other girls. But over a decade later, I came across a few more females who could *truly* kiss. And was I surprised! What I thought had been the end, but *really* the end, in kissing, turned out to be somewhere around the middle. Now I kiss even better; but I realize I still may have much to learn!

So try everything in the books—and out of the books. Open your mouth and close your mouth. Kiss dry and kiss wet. Use your tongue and keep it quiet. Keep experimenting, experimenting, and experimenting. Forever!

Body Kissing

The parts of the human body that are kissable are equal to the parts of the human body that the lips and tongue can reach. "The following," said Vatsyayana, "are the places for kissing, viz., the forehead, the eyes, the cheeks, the throat, the bosom, the breasts, the lips, and the interior of the mouth." But N. D. Mallary, Jr., in his unpublished manual on love making, adds to these: the nape of the neck, the junction of neck and shoulder, the ear (lobes and/or inside), the shoulder, underneath side of the upper arm, the inside of the forearm, the shoulder blade muscle, the palms, the waist or small of the back, the hips, behind the knees, and the bottom of the feet.

And even these are not all! The fingers, the knees, the buttocks, the side, the anus, the stomach, and just about any other part of the body can be kissed, tongued, nipped, or bitten. Not that kissing all these various parts will bring equal pleasure to all girls; for it won't. Some women are quite insensitive in certain zones which theoretically should be, but in their cases aren't, erogenous. Thus, some women get just about nothing out of having their nipples kissed; and other women don't even particularly enjoy lip kissing, though they may go wild about some other kind of osculation.

Then, of course, there is genital kissing. According to conventional authorities, particularly those who are of a clerical bent, oral-genital relations are either abnormal, or else they are just not nice. As I note in *The Art and Science of Love* (1960): "The main reason for the existence of a negative attitude toward genital kissing is probably the concept of 'dirtiness' that for centuries has been attached to the genitals. Part of this concept, in turn, stems from the ancient confusions of genital and anal functions, which may have arisen because the anus and the genitals are in such close physical proximity (H. Ellis, 1936; Robie, 1925). The female vagina is also close to the urethra, while the male's sex organ, the penis, also serves as his urinary outlet.

"But where the anus is, at least to some extent, a 'dirty,' malodorous, and unhygienic organ, the genitals are hardly in the same class. Moreover, it is relatively easy to keep them scrupulously clean. Consequently, individuals who may have a legitimate objection to direct contacts with the anus of their partners may over-generalize their objections to include oral-genital relations as well. If they unprejudicedly tried passive and active genital kissing, they might well find it unobjectionable and enjoyable (Thornton and Thornton, 1939)."

As in lip-kissing, the art of body-kissing is the art of continual exploration and experimentation. You can never really know what parts of your girl's anatomy you truly enjoy kissing until you have attempted, perhaps on several occasions, and and with some persistence, to use your lips and tongue on virtually all its different regions. And she, likewise, can never know what she really enjoys with you, until she has permitted you to experiment widely in this regard.

Like lip-kissing, again, body-kissing can be quite variegated in terms of your mouth movements. For the mouth consists of the lips, the tongue, the teeth, and the inside of the mouth itself; and it is astonishing what a wide variety of movements and pacing you can achieve with these different parts of your oral equipment. Thus, you can nip, bite, suck, chew, nibble, tongue, lick, brush, rub, tickle, snap, crunch, etc. And you can do virtually all these oral activities slowly, rapidly, firmly, lightly, dryly, wetly, prolongedly, shortly, and in numerous other ways. So the number of permutations and combinations of body kissing that you may imagine and practice is surprisingly large. Try these permutations and combinations. See for yourself!

Caressing

Everything that has been previously said in this chapter about lip-kissing and body-kissing also goes for caressing. The primary male sex organ for satisfying the female, we again insist, is generally the hand: because the human hand, as any anthropologist will tell you, is uniquely adapted to a huge variety of tasks, and it can perform manipulations that no other appendage of any other animal can perform.

The hand, moreover, is far superior to the penis at most sexual occupations, since the fingers can do practically everything a penis can do while the reverse is hardly true. Even in the stimulating of the inside of a woman's vagina, for example, the fingers can remain stiff far longer than a penis normally can; they can reach certain parts of the vagina which the penis can never reach; they can bend and get to various sensitive spots which it is impossible for the penis to massage; and they can divine exactly what they are doing, while the penis cannot.

The hand is also quite superior to the lips in certain sexual performances, since it can reach parts of the body (such as a clitoris that is deeply imbedded in surrounding fleshy tissue) which the tongue and lips would have great difficulty in reaching; it can exert firmer and more consistent pressure on certain female areas than can the mouth; it can knead and massage various parts of the female anatomy for a period much longer than the easily tiring lips and tongue can do; it can make grasping and encompassing motions which are impossible for any normal mouth to make; and it can otherwise operate in a more efficient manner than can the lips. Moreover, the fingers and the hand can be gently caressive and can imitate most of the motions and actions of the teeth, lips, or tongue.

If, therefore, you learn uninhibitedly to use your fingers and your hands, you can move most women to the greatest heights of sexual arousal and satisfaction that they are capable of reaching; and, as I constantly shock people by saying, could thereby be a wonderful lover, even if you had no penis or were completely impotent. The key word here, of course, is *uninhibitedly*. For if you are really *free* to let yourself do whatever your hand is capable of doing sexually, you have (literally!) at your finger tips an almost infinite variety of sex "positions"; and, what is more, you can maintain most of these "positions," if you want to do so, for hours on end. Even a little imagination, plus the slightest amount of manual dexterity, will provide you with endless caressive possibilities in this connection.

Should you feel free to use your fingers and hand absolutely uninhibitedly in sex play? You damned well should! For there certainly is nothing in the least abnormal, perverted, or deviated about anything you may do in this respect, as long as you and your partner are mutually willing to do it, and as long as you do not become fetishistically fixated on or obsessively-compulsively attached to a special form of caressive behavior. Thus, if you enjoy giving a girl an orgasm *only* with your hand, and never get any fun out of kissing or copulating; or if you obsessively-compulsively feel driven to engage in manual forms of petting and just cannot stop yourself from doing so, no matter what circumstances exist or who your partner is; or if you are a great lover with your hands because you are terribly *afraid* to risk having intercourse or engaging in some other nonmanual form of sex participation—in *these* special kinds of circumstances, you would be a sex deviate, and could well use psychological treatment to help you overcome your fetishistic or obsessive-compulsive sex behavior.

If on the other hand, caressive forms of petting are enjoyable to you because they are a large *part* of your sexual behavior; or if they are *preferred*, without being absolutely *needed*, for your usual sexual fulfillment; then you are engaging in quite normal noncopulative forms of sexuality, and there is nothing unusual or abnormal about your activity. True, this mode of petting will never result in your impregnating a woman; but the notion that nonimpregnating forms of sex behavior are abnormal or perverted is a curious ancient superstition that has no reality basis.

"But," you may ask, "suppose you give a girl an orgasm with your hand and she similarly gives you an orgasm. Isn't that just a form of mutual masturbation? And isn't that perfectly disgusting?"

Yes, this is a form of mutual masturbation, all right—at least if you use this term broadly enough—since the term masturbation comes from the Latin, *manu stuprum*, which means to have forbidden sexual pleasure by means of the hand. As Theodore Schroeder (1936) points out, however, even in its original form masturbation implies genital friction by the use of the hand for the purpose of erotic self-gratification. And the latest edition of *Webster's New World Dictionary* defines masturbation as "genital self-excitation, usually by manipulation; auto-erotism."

Obviously, then, self-excitation or auto-erotism could hardly be the same thing as being brought to orgasm by the hand of a member of the other sex. The term mutual masturbation therefore, is really inaccurate, and was no doubt originally coined to show how "disgusting" mutual petting leading to climax was.

Even if petting to climax *did* consist of "mutual masturbation," what would really be wrong about *that?* Masturbation, as we have pointed out early in this book, is a good rather than a bad sex practice; and mutual masturbation, if there were such a practice, would be a *doubly* good thing! So let us not, please, be biased by the low-sounding tone of the term "mutual masturbation." This is definitely *not* what mutual petting to climax is; but if it were, what of it?

Genital Petting

Although some girls are averse to genital petting, even when they will allow you all kinds of other stimulation of their bodies, this aversion is usually psychological rather than physical; and it can be overcome, most of the time, by stimulating these females sufficiently with nongenital methods, so that they finally become greatly aroused and will permit, nay welcome, more direct contact. In the great majority of cases, girls who are correctly approached welcome genital petting and require some form or degree of it if they are to get fully aroused and to have an orgasm.

Males are prone to make huge errors in stimulating their female partners' genital areas, since they anthropomorphically tend to concentrate on the vagina, which is often relatively insensitive, rather than on the clitoris, inner labia, and introitus (entrance to the vagina), which are usually exquisitely sensitive. They evidently have difficulty in realizing that while the male has a single main sex organ, the penis, all normal females are supplied with three vulval parts; (a) the clitoris, which is at the very top of their sex oval and consists of a small pea-sized organ, normally the main seat of female sexual sensitivity; (b) the meatus, or entrance to the urethra, which is below the clitoris, and is a urinary outlet; and (c) the vagina, which is at the lower end of the female vulva, and is mainly a birth canal, an outlet for the menstrual flow, and port of entry for the penis in intercourse.

In addition, the female vulva is surrounded by the outer lips, which are fairly thick and usually not very sensitive, and the inner lips, which are much thinner and less easily definable, and which are frequently very sensitive to stimulation. Because of the multiplicity of the female sex parts, genital petting does *not* mainly consist of your inserting your fingers into your partner's vagina, and using them as a kind of substitute for the penis—although this will work very effectively in some instances, particularly if you focus on certain sensitive spots of the vagina such as the entrance (or vestibule), or the upper wall (which lies underneath the clitoris and the urethra and is sometimes quite responsive to excitation).

In most instances, proper genital petting of the female

consists of locating her clitoris and massaging it and the immediately surrounding area in such a manner as to fully arouse your partner and eventually, in many instances, give her a full orgasm. As Masters and Johnson have just recently discovered (1961, 1962), most females, when they masturbate do not specifically stimulate the clitoris itself, but seem to finger the surrounding region. They have also discovered that after the female has been excited for a while and is nearing her orgasmic phase, the clitoris tends to flatten out and be "lost" from sight and from direct touch. Continued stimulation of the surrounding area, however, will bring the female to her peak of arousal and satisfaction.

Techniques of stimulating the clitoral area are quite varied, and there does not seem to be any general method which works well in all cases. W. E. Parkhurst (personal communication, 1963) contends that a very rapid vibrato method of stimulation gives the best results with most women. But Masters and Johnson (1962) indicate that in intercourse females frequently achieve climax because the male's penis pulls rhythmically and regularly on the tissue of the inner lips, which in turn pulls fairly regularly at the clitoral tissue, thus producing orgasm. If this is true, then it would appear that slow, steady massage of the clitoris and its surrounding area is just as effective as more rapid manipulation; and with many females, no doubt, even more effective.

Open-minded investigation will show that female responsiveness differs greatly in this respect. Some girls seem to like slow massage and some more rapid movements; some enjoy firm pressure of the fingers, others seem to like only very gentle approaches; some require up and down or side to side movements, others want circular massaging around the outside of the clitoris; some women desire absolutely steady, rhythmic massage, while others seem to get more aroused by irregular, intermittent caresses. As usual, you should experiment as much as possible in this respect, to discover exactly what your female partner enjoys; and, as we previously noted regarding kissing and general caressing, *keep* experimenting, from time to time, to see if your partner changes her preferences or learns to respond to new methods of approach.

As we indicated above, oral stimulation of your partner's genital area is not only permissible but highly desirable in most instances, since the lips and tongue of the male are admirably designed to excite the female genitalia. This is partly because lubrication is often important in stimulating the various parts of the female vulva; and in manual excitation you frequently have to stop to moisten the clitoris or surrounding area with saliva, secretions from other parts of the girl's genitalia, K-Y lubricating jelly, or some other effective lubricant. In mouth-genital contact, however, such lubrication is ordinarily automatically supplied and need not be artificially added. Moreover, for females who enjoy light massaging of the genital area, the lips and tongue are again admirably equipped for this kind of excitation.

Although much thought has been given in sex manuals to the various positions of intercourse, very little has been published on the positions of manual or oral-genital petting. Obviously, if you lie directly on top of your female partner, as would often do in penile-vaginal coitus, you are going to block your access to her genital area and are going to impede your petting of this region. Even your lying side by side with your partner may prove to be ineffective in getting your hands—and certainly your mouth—in proper apposition to her genitals; and when you effect contact in such a position, your hands and arms may be uncomfortably situated, and tend to tire quickly.

Therefore a little thought must be given to correct or desirable genital petting positions. If, for example, you lie on your side, with your head facing your partner's genital area; or you lie below her (if the bed is large enough!) and look directly up into her genital region; or if you sit on a chair or on the floor, while she lies or sits with her legs apart on the edge of a bed or table—in such positions you are more likely to have convenient access to her genital area and be able to caress or kiss it more adequately. A little imagination and experimentation in this connection will invariably turn up several positions which will be most feasible for you and the particular girl you are with.

Genital petting, like other forms of sex play, should normally be two-sided. Girls are frequently loath, at first, to caress or kiss the male's genitalia. But if you consistently stimulate and satisfy them in this manner, and clearly demonstrate by your manner and attitude that nothing is wrong with such forms of sexuality, they will usually tend to reciprocate. This will especially be true if you ask them to reciprocate, after a time, and if you do so not necessarily in words, but by placing their hands or lips in the area you want to be stimulated.

Most girls, you will probably quickly discover, are very poor lovers as far as genital stimulation is concerned: since they are inexperienced at it, and (being females rather than males) just do not realize what kinds of strokings and manipulations are most satisfactory to the male. Thus, they will frequently tend to grasp the penis quite harshly, and to try to give the male an orgasm as quickly as possible. Even when this approach works, it is not entirely satisfactory to the male.

Take some time and effort, therefore, in teaching your female partner precisely what you would like to have her do sexually, and in helping her, at first, to do this. Tell her, frankly and openly with no resentment or hostility, what caresses and kisses you do *not* enjoy—or what procedures are, at times, *too* stimulating, since they tend too quickly to bring you to climax. Don't be ashamed to open your big mouth in this respect, and to try to get the form of stimulation you really desire!

The main points, then, that you should keep in mind in regard to petting are these:

1. Caressing and kissing, of almost any nature whatever, are good as long as you or your partner enjoy them, are not fetishistically or obsessively-compulsively attached to a particular mode, and are willing participants.

2. Petting should usually be continued up to and including orgasm, unless it is to end in sexual intercourse, which itself leads to climax. Petting without climax is all right for some individuals under some conditions; but it has mental and physical risks and should be engaged in with care.

3. Individual tastes in petting are widely varied, and the only way you can discover what both you and your partner maximally enjoy is to communicate openly with each other and to keep trying various modes of approach, until you find mutually satisfying methods. Both verbal and physical communication are important in this respect—as they are in all forms of heterosexual relations.

Chapter 10

What Every Young Man
Should Know About Bedmanship

Let us assume that you have a reasonably willing female partner, and that your aim is to arouse her sufficiently so that she will want, after a sufficient amount of foreplay, to have sexual intercourse with you. How should you go about arousing this girl to a maximum degree? and how should you go about having satisfactory coitus with her? Let us, in the present chapter, try to answer these questions.

Arousing a Female Psychologically

Even a woman who cares for you and has been to bed with you frequently has to be motivated again and again to have intercourse with you, since females are generally not so quickly and easily arousable as are males, and sometimes have to be "worked on" for a period of time before they are truly desirous. Some of the best psychological methods of inducing your girlfriend to be in the mood for physical love are these:

1. Show her that you are enthusiastic about going to bed with *her*, not with just any girl who happens to be around that night, and that *she* arouses you and is capable of fully satisfying you. Be *enthusiastic* about her sexual and non-sexual characteristics, and indicate that you are more than willing to ignore any flaws that she may have—or thinks she may have (Liswood, 1961).

2. Indicate to your partner, if you can do so with any reasonable degree of honesty, that you don't merely *want* her, but that you *love* her—and that, of course, you will continue to do so, and perhaps more so, *after* your sex appetites have been appeased (Bibby, 1961; Fielding, 1961; Mace, 1958; Watts, 1958). A loving relationship not only aids initial sex experiences, but often enables sexual compatibility between two partners to keep growing and expanding, as

Dr. Robert Harper and I have emphasized in our book, *Creative Marriage* (1961a), and as many other authorities on sexual adjustment have also stressed (Calderone, 1960; Eichenlaub, 1961; Gottlieb and Gottlieb, 1962; Hamilton, 1961; Hirsch, 1962; Rainer and Rainer, 1962; Robinson, 1962; Stokes, 1962).

3. Show self-confidence and keep taking the sexual initiative. If your partner thinks you really know what you are doing sexually, and that you have no hesitation about doing it, she will be inclined to go right along with you, and overcome many of her own doubts and hesitancies. The more inexperienced she is, the more she will tend to want you to be experienced and competent (Caprio, 1952, 1962). In order to show self-confidence, of course, you should really *feel* it. And this means, as I indicate in my writings on psychotherapy and self-help (Ellis, 1957, 1962a; Ellis and Harper, 1961b), that you must stop being perfectionistic, stop blaming yourself for your weaknesses and fallibilities, and stop thinking you *need* the approval and love of every desirable female whom you may encounter.

4. Effective verbal communication is probably the best way to put any woman in the proper mood for sex relations. As I note in *The Art and Science of Love*: "No man or woman is a mind-reader. Even individuals who are passionately in love frequently misunderstand each other; and husbands and wives certainly do. Your sex proclivities are necessarily so personal and unique that it is difficult for another member of the same sex to understand them. A member of the other sex, who is bound to be startlingly different in many ways, has even greater difficulty. The only sane way, therefore, to know what sexually arouses and satisfies your mate is, in unvarnished English, to ask her; and the only sane way to get your mate to understand what sexually arouses and satisfies you is to tell her (Harper, 1958; Katz, 1956).

"Shame, in this connection, is utterly silly—just as silly as a husband's being ashamed to tell his wife that he likes eggs scrambled instead of sunnyside-up, and then becoming angry because, somehow, she does not fathom this. Why the devil should she? And why on earth should he be ashamed to tell her?

"If, then, you like your sex with the lights on, with music playing, in front of mirrors, rolling on the floor, slow or fast, orally or manually, by land or by sea, for heaven's sake *say* so. And do your very best to discover, by *words* as well as deeds, what your mate likes, too."

5. Considerateness is the essence of bed manners, as it is of nonsexual manners. It is Utopian to expect that your girlfriend will want to do exactly the same sexual things as you want to do, and to do them at the same time. Often, she will require you to hold back when you want to rush ahead with some sex act; or to rush ahead when you want to hold back. Often, too, she will be much more easily aroused and satisfied if you vigorously caress her (when perhaps you feel like being more gentle and tender) or if you monotonously stick to one form of sex participation (when you would like to be more varied in your approach). If you can show your partner, therefore, that you *want* to do what she wants to do, that you *enjoy* pleasing her even when you are not necessarily doing exactly the thing *you* want to do, *she* will be more likely to want to do what you want *her* to do, too.

The good lover, in other words, *actively looks for* ways to please his inamorata. Without being masochistic, or surrendering his own pleasures, he really *desires* to find ways of satisfying her; and he communicates, by gesture and word, this desire to her (Rhoda Winter Russell, personal communication, 1960). If you can show your girlfriend that you are, in this sense of the term, a good lover, you will have a much better chance of fully arousing her than if you less considerately try mainly for your own satisfaction.

6. It is sometimes desirable for you to use special exciting psychological materials, such as pictures, films, or stories, to rouse your mate to the greatest heights of desire of which she is capable. The oriental peoples have, for many centuries, employed "pillow books," or illustrated erotic texts, to stimulate their mistresses and wives; and the famous seventeenth century erotic Chinese novel, *Jou Pu Tuan* of Li Yu, which has just recently (1963) been translated into English for the first time, shows in detail how the hero instructs one of his wives by reading with her the well-illustrated *Han-kung yi-chao*, or traditional portraits from the imperial palace of the Han dynasty, which leave nothing to the imagination as far as sex technique is concerned. In our own day, Kronhausen and Kronhausen (1959), Maddock (1959), and Sagarin (1962) have indicated how "pornographic" writings or the use of "obscene" language may sometimes be most stimulating to

females. Kelly (1961, 1963) has also recommended that sex partners place a fairly large mirror at the foot of their bed and watch themselves having intercourse by using this mirror (perhaps in conjunction with a hand mirror held by one of the partners). The main point is that whatever is found to be psychologically stimulating by you and your girl should be unhesitatingly and unabashedly employed.

7. Novelty is sometimes a help to sexual arousal. Many females become relatively jaded when sex is done in the same manner each time, and appreciate some kind of mild or radical change. If you will on occasion have sex relations at unusual times (such as in the mid-afternoon or early evening, instead of late at night); or at novel places (such as in the forest or on a deserted beach); or with different accouterments or materials (such as with your clothes partly on or while listening to symphonic music); if you will imaginatively arrange these kinds of novel performances, they will sometimes be rewarding in terms of high arousal and satisfaction for you and your partner. You can, of course, go to great extremes in this respect, and can—for example—arrange sex orgies, at which you have present persons other than your particular girlfriend. But, unless your girl herself is most unusual, these kinds of extremes will rarely pay off, and will frequently boomerang. But, while still keeping within the more usual range, you can often devise novel ways of having sex relations that will be especially stimulating to your partner.

Arousing a Female by Physical Means

Many girls, even when the psychological conditions are excellent, require a goodly amount of physical arousal before they are ready to have intercourse; and some of them, though easily aroused, require special physical techniques in order to help them come to climax. Some of the main physical methods of sex excitation that you can use are the following:

1. As noted previously, in our mention of petting, females normally have certain erogenous zones, and if these are properly stimulated, they will become fully aroused, and may even attain orgasm. The main female zones, in this connection, usually are the clitoris, the inner lips, the vestibule of the vagina, sometimes the vagina itself; and the lips, ear lobes, scalp, neck, armpits, breasts, buttocks, anus, thighs, small of the back, spinal column, and shoulders. No two women

are exactly alike in this respect, however: so that in each case you must experimentally determine exactly what your girlfriend enjoys and must endeavor to please her by stimulating her special erogenous zones in whatever manner she likes. Kissing, tonguing, caressing, kneading, massaging, and similar forms of activity are the usual methods of stimulating a female's erogenous areas.

2. It is often erroneously assumed that all women have very well defined erogenous zones and that you can only arouse them by manipulating these special areas. This is not exactly true, since some females are erotogenic in almost any part of their anatomy; and some of them are highly excitable in one area at certain times and in quite a different area at other times. Consequently, you will often find that brisk or light contact with your partner's skin in some of the most unlikely places—such as the calves or the back of the neck—will sometimes be quite stimulating to her. On occasion, especially after a female (or, for that matter, a male) has recently had an orgasm, the usual genital and erogenous zones are too exquisitely sensitive and painful to touch, and should not be employed for arousal. But at those times, areas of the body which are usually not particularly erogenous can sometimes be stimulated to good effect.

3. Coitus itself can in some instances be unusually exciting and arousing. If your girlfriend is not too excitable at a certain time, but is willing to engage in intercourse, she may become aroused through doing so, and may wind up by becoming intensely involved sexually, even though she was relatively passive when you first started to copulate. At such times, it may be necessary to use artificial lubrication, such as K-Y jelly, in order to start intercourse; but once it is under way, your partner's natural lubricating fluids may begin to operate and make very very satisfying relations.

4. There are various stimulants which can sometimes be used effectively to arouse a woman; and the best of these are often the natural sights and smells of your own body. Although females are less sexually aroused by sight than most males are, their partner's odors sometimes excite them. One woman I knew, for example, told me that she couldn't resist the smell of a man who had just awakened in the morning. If there is anything arousing about your sight and smell to your girlfriend, try to discover what this is, and do your best to capitalize on it—as by taking a bath (or *not* taking a

bath!) before you see her; using toilet waters or deodorants that she may like; being clean-shaven and well-groomed; dressing in a certain manner that is stimulating to her, etc.

5. Various foods and drugs are supposed to have an aphrodisiacal effect on some individuals; but, as many authorities have shown, true aphrodisiacs are practically nonexistent, and there is nothing that you can rely on in this connection (MacDougald, 1961). The few drugs, such as strychnine, cantharides, and yohimbine, which sometimes do have arousing qualities, are dangerous and should never be employed except under strict medical supervision (Kelly, 1957). Alcohol, when imbibed by a woman in small quantities, often serves as a sex stimulant, largely because it allays anxiety and minimizes sexual inhibitions; but, if taken in larger quantities, it usually deadens sexual excitability. Opium and its derivatives and the synthetic analgesics (such as demerol and methadon) may also *temporarily* reduce sex blockings and give the individual courage to have affairs that she might otherwise not have; but opiates generally reduce or obliterate rather than enhance sex desire, and drug addicts are normally fairly asexual (De Ropp, 1961; Mauer and Vogel, 1954; Nyswander, 1958). Tranquilizers and psychic energizers also make it easier for some sexually inhibited individuals to have intercourse; but none of them has yet proven to be a very effective and reliable sexual stimulant. On the whole, you should not, therefore, rely on any aphrodisiacal foods or drugs to help arouse your girlfriend, but should use less artificial means of attempting to excite her.

6. Occasionally females are sexually frigid because of hormonal deficiencies; and in these instances, they may be helped by hormone injections, particularly by treatment with the male hormone, testosterone (Benjamin, 1958; Clark, 1959; Dengrove, 1963; Kupperman, 1961). Hormones, however, frequently have serious side effects—such as a general masculinization of the woman who is treated with male hormones —and must only be used under strict medical supervision. In the great majority of instances, moreover, female anesthesia is not the result of a poor hormonal supply, but of antisexual attitudes on the part of the female, and poor sex-arousing technique on the part of her male partner.

7. Adequate lubrication is essential to sexually arousing many women. Under normal conditions, as the female becomes stimulated, her own secretions from her Bartholin's

glans and her vaginal walls start flowing, and her genitals become well lubricated. But frequently, for one reason or another, sufficient lubrication of this nature does not occur, and artificial supplementary means must be employed. Vaseline is not a particularly good lubricant for sex purposes, though it may be used in a pinch. K-Y jelly, saliva, and hand lotions are much better for this purpose (Kelly, 1963). Also, lubrication may be taken from one part of a female's genitals, such as her vaginal region, and transferred to another part, such as her clitoral area.

Techniques of Helping a Woman Achieve Orgasm

As can be seen by the foregoing sections of this chapter, there are many psychological and physical methods of exciting a woman physically so that she will be more than willing to have sex relations, and coitus in particular, with you. However, many females, even though they become greatly aroused, have a good deal of trouble in finally getting a satisfying orgasm; and if you leave one of these women stranded in mid-air, as it were, she often will be tense and frustrated, and will have little incentive to have repeated sex relations with you. It is necessary, therefore, that you know something about helping a woman come to orgasm when she has difficulty doing so.

This does not mean that *all* women do have such difficulty. A small percentage of women almost always achieve climax fairly quickly, with no trouble whatever. But a large percentage achieve it only after twenty minutes or more of active sex participation; and another sizable percentage achieve it on some occasions fairly quickly but at other times with some difficulty. When you are having an affair with a partner who has trouble coming to climax, here are some pointers that you can employ to help her achieve the greatest kind of orgasm of which she is capable, and to achieve it in a relatively brief period of time.

1. Some females only can come to orgasm through one special locus of sex sensation, such as the clitoral region, and they require steady, consistent, rhythmic pressure at this spot in order to achieve orgasm. If your girlfriend is one of these women, do your best to discover where her special seat of sensation is, and then do anything necessary to give her the kind of stimulation she requires in this area. If you can do this while having intercourse, fine. But always remember that it

is *not* necessary to satisfy a girl during coitus, and that millions of females will never, or rarely, be satisfied in this manner.

2. Some women require a few preliminary build-ups before they can go orgasmically over the top. In these cases, you should arouse your partner to a high pitch; then let her rest awhile; then arouse her again, then perhaps let her rest again; then go back to the arousing technique—until she is finally ready to have her climax. In other instances, a girl may have an orgasm easily enough, but may not be satisfied with this, and may require three, four, or more orgasms before she is satisfied, or before she finally has one (which may be bigger than all the rest) which she finds fully rewarding. In these instances, you should be able to bring your girlfriend to climax again and again—usually by digital manipulation of her clitoral area, but sometimes by various other methods—until she indicates that she is truly satisfied.

3. It is especially important that you not become irritated with or angry at your partner if she has trouble coming to climax. You must realize that innumerable women have difficulty attaining orgasm, and some of them (including some who have considerable sex pleasure) never do attain it. There is nothing unusual about this, since the female of the species is often considerably different from the male in this respect (Elkan, 1948; Havemann, 1962; Shuttleworth, 1959; Terman, 1951). If you fully accept the fact that your girlfriend may be one of those who does naturally have orgasm difficulties, and if you stop telling yourself that it is *terrible* and *awful* that she has them, you will be able to keep yourself from becoming angry with her, and will invariably prove to be a much better sex partner. The less irritated you are with a girl who has orgasm problems, the more relaxed she is likely to be and the more capable of finally being satisfied.

4. Some females require deep vaginal penetration in order to achieve climax. In such instances, you may be able to penetrate deeply with your penis, especially in certain positions—as when you are on your back and the woman is on top of you. Where it is not possible to give your partner sufficient vaginal stimulation through intercourse, you will still normally be able to do so if you use your fingers or hand—which can reach deeply into her vagina, and locate sensitive spots, and keep stimulating these spots, where the penis would almost certainly fail. The same thing goes for a female who

needs powerful contact with her clitoris or some other part of her vulva before she comes to orgasm. If your penis will not serve to stimulate such a woman properly, you can ordinarily do so with your knee, elbow, fist, palm of your hand, or other suitable parts of your body (Ellis, 1963f).

5. You sometimes can make effective use of multiple physical contact in sexually satisfying your girlfriend, and may stimulate two or more of her bodily parts simultaneously. Thus, you may kiss her on the lips or breasts while you are copulating with her; or massage her clitoris while also massaging her breasts or anal area with your other hand, or while kissing her breasts. All kinds of double and triple possibilities of stimulation may be devised, if you use your imagination and your various bodily appendages.

6. Don't over-emphasize the importance of simultaneous climax, since this will often distract your partner, and make her so fearful that she will *not* have her orgasm at exactly the same time that you do, that she will never have it at all. Show your girl, by words and by deeds, that you are most willing to give her an orgasm, either before or after you have had your own, and that you greatly enjoy her pleasure, even if it does not exactly coincide with yours. Let her know that you will not hesitate to satisfy her, manually or labially, even when you are not able to obtain or sustain erections, and therefore cannot literally copulate with her. Also show her that if she does not have a climax on any particular occasion, you will not feel horribly put out, but will gracefully accept the fact that this may just not be her night for this kind of satisfaction.

7. In recent years, for the first time in human history, there has become available a new kind of method of satisfying a female, and one that works especially well with many women who have difficulty in coming to orgasm: and that is the electric vibrator. Vibrators can either be attached to your hand, in which case they pulsate your fingers very rapidly, and allow you to give sensations to your partner that you could not possibly otherwise give; or they have their own rubber suction cup and other attachments which you can gently apply to your girl's sensitive areas, to arouse her greatly and often to bring her to orgasm. Dr. LeMon Clark (1949), one of America's foremost gynecologists and sexologists, reports that when a vibrator is used with a female who has never previously been able to have an orgasm, it can even

help create channels or pathways of nervous excitation which, once they are started, may thereafter help to bring on future orgasms, which may be had by nonmechanical means. Do not hesitate, then, to suggest the use of a vibrator or similar device if your girl has serious orgasm difficulties; and experiment with these kinds of instruments just as you would with the natural parts of your own body.

8. Occasionally, you and your girlfriend will find that nothing that you can do in the way of lovemaking will help her reach climax; and that therefore, while you simply hold her and perhaps kiss her, she will have to manipulate her own genitals to bring on her orgasm. If this is true, gracefully and manfully accept this fact, and do not think that it in any way proves that you are a poor lover, or that you are a weakling. It proves, instead, that you care for your girl so deeply that you are willing to do almost anything to help her achieve satisfaction, and that you will even temporarily take a secondary role in helping her come to fulfillment. Which is exactly what the best kind of lover is: one who will go to the most unusual lengths to encourage and abet his girl's achieving the greatest pleasure of which she is capable.

Techniques of Retarding Your Own Climax

Many women, as you might expect, find that active intercourse is the most arousing and satisfying form of sex relations they can have; and some of these women require the male to last for fifteen or twenty minutes or more during intercourse, so that they can fully enjoy themselves. Most males, especially young males, find difficulty in lasting this long, since they are fully aroused even before they start coitus, and often have not had sex relations for a considerable period of time before the current act. Consequently, they tend to last only a minute or two in active copulation, once entry has been made. While this does *not* mean that they are afflicted with premature ejaculation—which exists when they ejaculate even before they make vaginal entry or almost immediately after they do—it does mean that they have great difficulty in satisfying women who desire fairly prolonged intercourse.

There are many effective techniques that you can employ to retard your orgasm and to enable you to copulate for much longer than you ordinarily would. Some of the best of these techniques are as follows:

1. Have sex relations as *often* as possible, rather than too seldom. The less frequently you have sex orgasms, the *faster* you are likely to come when you do have intercourse. If, for example, you have coitus two or three times an evening, you may well last considerably longer the second and third times than the first. Don't assume, therefore, that you are through just because you have had a single climax, and you do not momentarily "feel" like continuing sex relations. Wait a little while, and then have your partner stimulate you sexually, while making an effort yourself to think of something exciting, and you will be surprised to find, in most cases, that you *can* have a second or a third or even a fourth perfectly good erection during the same sex session. If there is not going to be time for this much sex activity, then you can often obtain the same effect by masturbating an hour or two before you expect to have intercourse with your girl, and then seeing if you cannot last longer than usual even during your "first" copulatory attempt with her.

2. The main method of bringing on quick or premature ejaculation is to *worry* about coming quickly. For as I and my associates have shown in recent works on rational-emotive psychotherapy (Callahan, 1960; Ellis, 1957, 1962a, 1963b; Ellis and Harper, 1961a, 1961b; Hudson, 1961; Jacobs, 1962), worrying or catastrophizing about almost any act will interfere seriously with your performance of this act; and catastrophizing springs from the simple exclamatory internalized irrational sentences that you tell yourself. Thus, if you suffer from premature ejaculation, you are saying, first, a perfectly sane sentence: "I hope to hell that I don't come too quickly, since my girl wouldn't like that, and I wouldn't like displeasing her." Then you are following this with an utterly insane sentence: "If I have a quick ejaculation, and if my girl dislikes me for having it, that would be absolutely terrible: for it will prove that I'm a no-good slob who *always* will fail sexually and who could never *possibly* satisfy any woman."

This second, insane sentence has to be consistently and vigorously challenged, if you find that you are saying it to yourself, by your asking: "*Why* would it be absolutely terrible if I fail sexually this time? . . . *How* does it prove that I'm a no-good slob if I now fail and even if I *never* succeed at prolonging copulation? . . . *In what way* does my present failure, if it occurs, prove that I will *always* fall on my face while having coitus, or that I could not *possibly* satisfy my partner sexually, even if I did not ever last long at intercourse?"

If you forcefully and persistently challenge your catastrophizing, self-defeating sentences that drive you to premature ejaculation, you will soon see that they *are* nonsense, and that there *is* no real truth to them. For sex failure by no means proves that *you* are a total loss and are no good for anything; nor that you will fail *forever* because you have done so the last few times; nor that you could never be a good lover to your girlfriend even if you did keep consistently failing to copulate for a prolonged period. It only proves that *so far* you have shown no lasting power in intercourse—but that the chances are, if you stop worrying about your failure, desist from denigrating yourself as a human being for having failed, and keep practicing copulation at every opportunity, you will ultimately start lasting longer and longer.

3. Psychological diversion is perhaps the oldest and still one of the best techniques of delaying your orgasm. Sexual excitation is mainly mediated through your focusing directly on sexually exciting things and objects—such as the beauty of your partner, or how much you are going to enjoy copulating with her, or what a great pleasure it now is to be touching her fair skin, etc. The better you focus on such sex-inciting stimuli, the more aroused you will normally become, and the quicker you will tend to come to orgasm.

If, then, you take the opposite tack and focus, instead, on *non*exciting things, you will find that you are not able to focus on two things at a time, and that consequently, the nonexciting thoughts will drive out the arousing ones (Ellis, 1960; Kelly, 1961b; Street, 1959). Think, for example, of some business problem while you are engaged in active coitus; or about the political situation in China; or start adding figures (that is, *mathematical* figures!) in your head; or recall to mind some particularly *un*appetizing female you ran into recently. If you will divert yourself in this kind of fashion, you may be surprised how long you can maintain your erection during intercourse (or other modes of sex relations).

The danger of this kind of diverting activity is that you will be so effective at it, that you will not be fully related to the girl with whom you are having intercourse; and she may notice this and become upset. However, you may be able to think even of her in a loving, nonsexual way—focus, for example, on *her* pleasure rather than on your own—and you will thereby be able to divert yourself from overly high sex excitement, while at the same time getting yourself to feel even closer to her than ever.

4. Various muscular movements can be used, if you want to practice them, that will often help you in controlling your sexual excitement and keep you from ejaculating too quickly when you are fully aroused. You can, for instance, learn to tighten and relax your anal sphincter and perineal muscles (those you use to control defecation and urination), and thereby be able to ward off approaching orgasm. Or you can focus on breathing exercises, such as inhaling deeply at the point you think that orgasm is approaching, or taking a deep breath and, after holding it a moment or two, slowly and calmly exhaling. Certain leg movements, hand movements, and other movements can also be employed, if you experiment with them, to retard your orgasm.

5. You can often ward off your climax by performing coitus in a slow, unthrusting manner, taking care that your pelvic movements are mild and minimal rather than vigorous. When orgasm is approaching, you can stop completely for a while, and resume when your excitement has diminished. Or you can move your penis from side to side, or in a circular way, instead of thrusting it forward. Or you can press it against the upper wall of your partner's vagina, instead of the lower wall, thus avoiding exciting contact with the underside of your penis, which tends to be its most sensitive area.

6. You can try certain coital positions, such as the one where your partner mounts you instead of your mounting her; and you will often find that you are able to control your coital movements better and last longer in these positions than in the more conventional male surmounting female method of intercourse.

7. The use of nerve-deadening ointments, such as Nupercainal or Xylocaine ointment, will be found in many instances to be excellent for retarding orgasm (Kelly, 1957, 1961, 1963). If a small amount of this ointment is applied to the genitals a half hour or so before you expect to have intercourse, and is allowed to set and sink into the penis by your covering the ointment with talcum powder, it can be very effective in allowing you to maintain an erection for a much longer than usual time (Dezso Levendula, personal communication, 1962). The same effect can sometimes be

attained if you wear a condom or two to partially deaden penile sensation during intercourse.

8. Some authorities, such as Hirsch (1951, 1957), recommend daily massaging of the penis for ten to fifteen minutes a day, sometimes with desensitizing creme, in order to make this organ less sensitive to stimulation. Semans (1956) has developed a technique for teaching males how to become less sensitive genitally by having their partners play with their penises without, at first, having intercourse. When the male is able to take considerable friction of this sort, the female then repeats the process, using cold cream or hand lotion on her hands, thus simulating the lubricated internal environment of the vagina. Once the male is able to tolerate a good deal of penile friction under these conditions, Dr. Semans finds that he is also able to last much longer in actual intercourse.

9. Dr. G. Lombard Kelly (842 Greene Street, Augusta, Georgia) recommends and distributes the Loewenstein (1947) coitus training apparatus—a device that the male can attach to his penis when he has trouble sustaining an erection, and which enables him to have intercourse whether or not his penis is flaccid. There are many such devices, many of them impractical or unwieldy; and most of them requiring the full cooperation of a sex partner.

10. Alcohol, taken in moderation, or quick-acting barbiturates (such as nembutal and seconal) may at times be useful sedatives that will calm down an individual who is very tense and whose premature ejaculation is related to his tenseness. Tranquilizers also sometimes work in this connection; but all such drugs and concoctions should only be taken under strict medical supervision.

11. Psychotherapy is especially helpful in many instances wherein the individual obviously has nothing physically wrong with him, and can get and maintain erections in several different kinds of circumstances, but is impotent or afflicted with premature ejaculation when he attempts intercourse with a female partner. Psychoanalysis is frequently the method of choice in such cases; but my own experience has been that any Freudian-type analysis not only is likely to be useless in cases of impotence, but frequently will do the patient more harm than good (Eysenck, 1961; Phillips, 1956). This is because males are rarely rendered impotent by their childhood sex experiences or their Oedipus com-

plexes (as the Freudians doggedly and wrongheadedly keep contending); but they almost always are sexually inadequate because of the *present* irrational, self-defeating philosophies of life which they firmly believe, and which they vigorously (and unconsciously) keep indoctrinating themselves with.

Having been trained as a fairly classical psychoanalyst, and having found by experience that this method of psychotherapy is *not* truly depth-centered or effective, I have developed during the last decade a system of rational-emotive psychotherapy which is designed not only to show individuals how they originally became disturbed, but to demonstrate how they are *sustaining* their disturbances by continually, right in the present, reindoctrinating themselves with all kinds of nonsense about their sexual and nonsexual performances (Callahan, 1960; Ellis, 1957, 1962a, 1963b; Ellis and Harper, 1961a, 1961b; Harper, 1959; Hudson, 1961; Jacobs, 1962; Rockberger, 1963; Wagner, 1963).

Rational-emotive psychotherapy is based on what I call the A-B-C theory of personality disturbance, which was originally posited by Epictetus, Marcus Aurelius, and various other Stoic philosophers who lived and wrote some two thousand years ago (Hadas, 1961). This theory states that whenever you get upset or disturbed over something that has happened, it is not the stimulus or occurring event, A, that makes you upset at point C; rather, it is your interpretation or *what you tell yourself* at point B about what happens at point A that really disturbs you. Thus, in regard to sexual inadequacy, it is not your early sex experiences with your parents or the fact that your girlfriend is now being difficult and critical (at point A) which make you impotent (at point C). Rather, it is the claptrap you are telling yourself (at point B) *about* these early or later experiences.

You may, for example, be saying to yourself at point B: "Because I lusted after my mother when I was a young child, and thereby proved myself to be a worthless person, I don't deserve to succeed now with this lovely girl I am in bed with; therefore, I might just as well resign myself to failing with her." Or you may be telling yourself: "I only will be a worthwhile individual if I can show my girlfriend that I can satisfy her in intercourse, and thereby prove that I am a real man. But since there is a good chance of my failing and not satisfying her, and thereby showing her that I am a weakling, and since it would be absolutely terrible if she thought that about me, I'd better keep worrying about my sex performance with her, and concentrate on pleasing her rather than on enjoying the sex act." Or you may be convincing yourself: "Alice's last boyfriend, from what she has told me, could last for a full hour in active intercourse, and that is why she kept going with him for so long. If I can last for only a couple of minutes, she is going to hate me and soon leave me; and that would be perfectly awful, and show that I am never going to be able to satisfy *any* girl like Alice. Therefore, I'd just better be able to last for an hour—or else!"

By telling yourself such irrational, self-defeating, catastrophizing sentences at point B, you are almost certain to interfere with your sexual adequacy at point C. If you want to become more adequate sexually, you must see clearly that you are telling yourself these sentences, must forcefully challenge the philosophies that lie behind them, and must do something, in actual practice, effectively to contradict the nonsense that you are telling yourself.

In rational-emotive psychotherapy, therefore, the patient with a sexual (or any other kind of) problem is shown not merely the facts and psychodynamics of his own behavior but his underlying philosophies or ideas which lead to and flow from these historical facts. A concerted *attack* is then made by the therapist on the patient's irrational beliefs that are disclosed in the course of therapy. Unlike what occurs in psychoanalytic treatment, emphasis is placed far less on the disclosure of his unconscious drives or feelings than on revealing his unconscious and irrational *attitudes* which create these drives or feelings.

In addition, in rational therapy the therapist literally *teaches* the patient how to observe his (unconscious) illogical thinking and how, instead of thinking crookedly, to change his internalized sentences so that he can think straight. Finally, the patient is usually encouraged, urged, or helped to engage in emotionally reeducating *activity*, and is often given specific homework assignments to facilitate this kind of activity.

If, then, you are having real difficulty in obtaining or maintaining erections, or in ejaculating either too quickly or too slowly, and if all the techniques outlined in this chapter fail, you should seriously consider getting some psychotherapeutic help—preferably from a rationally-minded therapist who will literally *work* with you to help you overcome your sex (and other) problems.

Techniques of Sexual Intercourse

Man is not born with the kind of sex instincts that enable him to have intercourse automatically, without learning, in a successful, pleasing manner. Even some of the lower animals, such as many monkeys, must learn by a trial and error process how to make correct intromission and to carry out coitus. Man can only learn by his mistakes in this connection, since only rarely does he do exactly the right thing from the start.

If you are having intercourse with a virgin, you have to exert special skill and care in many instances, since both physically and psychologically she may hardly be ready for coitus, and she may be traumatized if you rush in rashly, on the assumption that she is an experienced partner. The general rule is to be as considerate and kind as possible, to take things slowly and easily, and frequently to explore your partner's vagina with your fingers before you do so with your penis, and sometimes to stretch, break, or push aside her hymen (assuming that she has one) by digital manipulation.

Usually it is best to insert your penis in the upper (or anterior wall) side of the vagina, since the hymeneal opening is likely to be larger there. But vigorous penetration in this area may also push against the anterior vaginal wall itself, which may contain nerve endings from the underside of the clitoris and the urethra, and thus be sensitive to pain (Hans Lehfeldt, personal communication, 1960). Although a slow, gentle entrance of the penis into the virgin's vagina is usually preferable, there are some instances, particularly where the girl is frightened, where a bold stroke that quickly breaks through the hymen proves to be more practical and less pain-provoking.

Where your partner has a thick or inelastic hymen, or has a small vaginal entrance, it may be better if she herself stretches or breaks her hymen by using her fingers or that you do so with your fingers. An analgesic ointment, such as Nupercainal ointment, may sometimes be used in conjunction with such stretching (Cauldwell, 1958). If your partner is unusually nervous or there is great difficulty in having initial intercourse, it may be best that she visit a physician several weeks before you attempt to have coitus, and that she have her hymen surgically deflorated or be supplied with a series of graduated cylinders, which she may wear until a wider vaginal entrance or canal is effected.

Usually, the more highly you can arouse your girlfriend before initial intercourse, the more likely she will be to lose herself completely in the heat of passion and not mind the tearing of her hymen even if it brings her some pain. This is not to say that defloration of a virgin is always uncomfortable for her, for in many cases it isn't. But you should be prepared for difficulties in case they occur. Have artificial lubricants, such as K-Y jelly, handy if they are needed; and a towel or wads of cotton to stop any bleeding that may occur. If you use a condom for initial intercourse, see that it is a well lubricated one.

The best coital position for initial intercourse is generally the face to face position, with the male surmounting the female, and her legs raised quite high, sometimes over his shoulders, thus making as wide as possible a vaginal opening. Intromission should proceed slowly, after the hymen is breached, since the girl may have a narrow or shallow vagina which will react painfully to vigorous and full penetration.

After initial intercourse has ended, try your best to make your partner feel as comfortable as possible. Show her that it is a good, and not a bad, thing for her to surrender her virginity; and if she is in the least guilty, do your best to dispel her guilt. Make every effort to show her that, as a nonvirgin, she is a valuable and worthwhile person to you, and that now that initial intercourse is over you both can go on to even better sex satisfactions.

If you are having regular intercourse with a nonvirgin, conditions are generally easier and better. But there are still some psychological and physical rules that you may find it well to follow. For example:

1. Try to have intercourse under conditions that are most satisfactory to your girlfriend. Although you yourself may be relatively insensitive in this connection (and may be able to copulate successfully on a park bench, or even in Macy's window!), she may be quite sensitive. You should therefore discover her preferences and sensitivities and try to cater to them to some extent (Beigel, 1953). You, for example, may prefer having coitus in a lighted or semi-lighted room; but if she, for even silly or neurotic reasons, prefers it in the dark, you may be wise to give in to her prejudices.

2. Look for signs of readiness in your partner and try to regulate your coital relations according to these signs. She may feel more sexually desirous at certain times of her monthly cycle, particularly before, during, or immediately after menstruation. Or she may prefer copulating during the day, rather than at night; or on weekends, instead of during the week. Try to arrange whatever times or conditions she finds peculiarly satisfying.

3. Regulate your coital and noncoital relations to fit in with your, and your girl's, special anatomic and mechanical preferences. A slim, wiry, and acrobatically inclined partner, for instance, will like certain positions which a fatter, stumpier, and less acrobatic partner will not necessarily enjoy. A girl with a large mouth will probably like certain kinds of oral-genital relations in which a girl with a small mouth will suffocate while trying. Some girls are constructed so that they love anal-genital relations; and some so that they absolutely abhor such sex acts. Discover your particular partner's coital and non-coital preferences and behave accordingly.

4. If your girlfriend has great difficulty in coming to orgasm, you may have to favor certain copulatory positions and preliminary modalities that help keep her (in more ways than one!) coming. Thus, the male surmounting female position may be great for you, since it may enable you to come quickly and efficiently to orgasm. But if your partner wants prolonged intercourse, you may have to favor a female surmounting or a side by side coital technique.

5. Although you may prefer to get to intercourse quickly, and even to get through with coitus as soon as possible, you may find that in order to please your partner you must take a much more patient and relaxed attitude in this respect. One girl may actually find your imperiousness and quick, savage copulatory movements very exciting and pleasing to her; whereas another girl may find this kind of copulation disturbing and may require much slower-paced, gentler movements.

6. Variety may or may not be pleasing to your girlfriend. Some females get bored with a single coital position, and demand continual change in this respect. But still other females are able to have maximum satisfaction in only one conventional manner, and simply do not enjoy doing it differently. If you can induce your girlfriend to try a number of positions, and to try them for a sufficient length of time to give

both of you a chance to perform them adequately, the chances are that both you and she will discover at least a few variations that you will want to keep returning to from time to time.

7. As we have noted previously, numerous females do not greatly enjoy coitus itself, since they are so constructed that they do not achieve sufficient clitoral or labial stimulation while copulating. Some others enjoy intercourse, but simply find it impossible to come to orgasm while it is going on. For females in these classes, it is usually best if you somehow manage to stimulate their clitoral regions while engaged in intercourse. Kelly (1961) and Hirsch (1951) recommend that you do this by "riding high" during intercourse, so that the shaft of your penis is bent over against your girl's clitoris and you are maintaining pressure against the clitoral area during coitus. But this is not an easy method for most partners to assume and sustain during active copulation, and is often downright impossible.

Another technique of clitoral stimulation during intercourse is that recommended by Greenblatt (1957), who advocates the man's pressing the head of his penis against his wife's clitoris prior to intercourse, and withdrawing his penis entirely from time to time to reapply it to the clitoris. This technique is workable; but you and your partner may not feel like interrupting penile-vaginal contact frequently.

A preferable method is for you to manipulate your girl-friend's clitoral region with your fingers or knuckles during intromission. This can easily be done when she is surmounting you in the face to face position or when she is seated or standing and you are sitting on the edge of a bed or table. It can perhaps best be done when you achieve vaginal entry while you are lying behind your partner, and you put your arm around her and stimulate her clitoral region with your hand.

8. Once you have entered your partner's vagina with your penis, your strokes may be gradual or sudden, shallow or deep, depending on her and your desires. Sometimes you can begin with short strokes and slow movements, and then work up to longer and more rapid ones. You may find that powerful, penetrating thrusts are more exciting; but may also find that they are painful to your partner or that they bring on excitement and orgasm too soon for either one of you. As ever, experimentation and open communication between the two

of you is necessary to discover the most pleasing pattern of coitus.

9. There is no reason why other related activities should stop during active intercourse, and good reason why kissing and caressing should continue at this time. In the conventional male-surmounting-female position, you may not be able to caress or kiss your partner very easily during coitus; but if you are lying on your back or side, you will find that your hands and lips are quite free to engage in additionally stimulating activities while you are copulating.

10. Intercourse, as we have noted before, should normally not be started until your partner is adequately lubricated, although there are exceptions to this rule. If she has trouble lubricating, or has a narrow vagina, or complains about painful sensations during intercourse, artificial lubrication is often desirable. This is best done by using saliva, K-Y jelly, most contraceptive jellies, or other water-soluble jellies or creams. Petroleum jelly (Vaseline), hand lotions, cold creams, and soap may all be used at times, but tend to have distinct limitations. If intercourse is prolonged, new applications of lubricants may have to be made. If a condom is employed, it should preferably be of the lubricated variety, or else lubrication should be placed on its outside.

11. There are no special rules regarding the frequency of intercourse, since this varies widely from couple to couple. In general, you should have coitus as often as you and your partner are arousable and truly enjoy it. Having it too frequently is almost impossible for the male, since he cannot get an erection when he is sexually satiated; and when a woman has it too frequently, she normally loses desire and is not able to continue to have orgasms (if she is capable of having them during intercourse). Physical irritation of the genitals may sometimes stem from frequent copulation; and if so, lubrication may have to be used, coital frequency cut down, or more gentle methods of penile stroking be employed.

12. Sex relations by no means necessarily end with coitus and orgasm. Some couples prefer to drop off to sleep immediately after sex congress; but others are wide awake, and are eager to repeat intercourse again, or talk, or do something else. Females, in particular, often want to be loved and appreciated after coitus, and resent the male's lack of interest in them at this time. Also, females who have not had an

orgasm during intercourse are often left unpleasantly hanging. So be sure that after you have copulated with your partner, you show her that you still care for her, and you manage somehow to give her an orgasm by extra-vaginal means if she has not already had one.

Positions of Intercourse

Theoretically, there are almost innumerable positions of intercourse, but actually most of these boil down to minor variations on a few major themes. The main positions of coitus with their special advantages are these:

1. *Face to face, man on top.* Your partner lies on her back, spreading her legs and flexing her knees or (sometimes) placing her feet on your shoulders. Her buttocks, if necessary, may be raised by putting a pillow under them. You lie *over* (rather than *on*) her, supporting the weight of your body on your own hands or elbows. She may keep her legs apart and flat; or keep them between your knees; or put one of her legs between your legs; or bend her thighs backward toward her chest; or raise one of her legs while keeping the other flat; or wrap one or both legs around your legs; or wrap her legs around your waist.

This face to face, male surmounting position makes for easy entry; allows you to set the pace and to slow or hasten your orgasm; facilitates other intimacy between you and your partner; enables you sometimes to continue intercourse after you have had an orgasm; is most convenient if you and your partner enjoy your making vigorous pelvic thrusts.

2. *Face to face, woman on top.* You lie on your back and your partner squats over you and guides your penis into her vagina; or she sits down in an astride position on your erect penis and loins, resting her back against your flexed knees and raised thighs; or you achieve penetration in some other position, such as a side position, and then gently roll around until she is on top. Once entry is effected, your partner can keep squatting, or can sit astride, or straighten out her legs and lie between or outside your legs. You can lie prone, or can raise yourself on your hands or elbows, or raise your knees on the side of or in back of your partner.

The face to face, woman on top position gives your partner maximum freedom of action and allows her to rub the sensitive parts of her vulva directly against your genitals. It enables you to rest quietly, without too much movement, so that you may last longer in coitus and it frees your hands so that you can caress your partner and manipulate her clitoris if this is found desirable. It enables your mate to experience deep vaginal contact with your penis and to arouse herself, if she wants to do so, with strong pelvic thrusts.

3. *Face to face, side by side.* You and your partner lie on your sides, facing each other. You may both have your lower legs on the bed, with her upper leg over both of yours; or her lower leg may rest on your lower leg and your upper leg may rest between her legs, so that you are interlocked. As Hirsch (1951, 1962) notes, in the so-called "side" positions, either you or your mate are mainly on your back, and the other partner is partly supported on the chest of the one who is on his or her back.

You will often find the face to face, side by side position quite restful and less strain inducing; it may enable maximum contact between your genitals and your partner's clitoris; you can easily regulate your pelvic thrusts and sometimes last longer in intercourse; both of you have relative freedom of movement and may attain a steady coital movement; withdrawal and reinsertion can often be done without a drastic change in your positions; and you and your partner can sometimes go to sleep after coitus while still remaining sexually interlocked.

4. *Rear entry, man's face to woman's back.* In this position there are several main possibilities: (a) You may lie on your side behind your girlfriend's back (she, too, being on her side), with her buttocks somewhat above your penis and her body slightly curved inwardly, her legs bent at her hips. You may enter her vagina between her legs and after intromission she may press her thighs together, providing additional friction for the penis and preventing it from slipping out of the vagina. (b) She may kneel on her hands and knees, with her head and breast almost on the bed or sofa, with you kneeling behind her. Again, you enter her vagina between her legs and press your pubis against her buttocks. (c) She may lie on her stomach, with her pelvis raised and you lying on top of her. This is an awkward and not too useful position for most couples. (d) You may sit on the edge of a bed or a chair, while your partner, with her back to you, sits down on your penis and your lap (or lower part of your stomach). You open your thighs somewhat and lean back

while she opens her thighs as wide as possible and leans forward.

In the rear entry positions, you have the advantages of being able to feel your partner's gluteal region with your legs, scrotum, and pubic area—which may be particularly stimulating to you or her. You also can easily put your hands around your partner during copulation and play with her breasts or clitoris; and you will find, in this position, that her vagina is foreshortened, which may be advantageous if she has a wide and slack vagina or you have a relatively small penis and you both desire closer vaginal-penile friction.

5. *Sitting positions.* Several major sitting positions of coitus may be attempted, including these: (a) You sit on a chair or on the edge of a bed, with your partner facing you, her legs astride yours. With your legs apart and her legs around your waist, you can pull her toward and away from you, and raise and lower her pelvis, thus effecting copulatory movements. If you have a chair or bed that is suitably high, you can sit on it while your partner, facing you with her legs somewhat apart, can stand. You can pull her hips back and forth to you, in between your spread thighs. (c) You can squat between your partner's thighs, while she is lying on her back facing you, with her legs on your hips. You can then make pelvic thrusts or pull her pelvis back and forth toward you. Or your partner can squat between your thighs, while you are lying on your back with your legs apart, and she can move her pelvis in a circular fashion, making churning movements around your penis. (Haire, 1951; Malinowski, 1929; Robinson, 1936). (d) You can sit on a bed or chair, while your girlfriend bends over, in a doubled-up position, with her back to you. You can then, using the rear entry position, pull her pelvis back and forth over your penis.

Some of the advantages of the sitting positions are that both partners may have maximum freedom of movement with their hands; you can sometimes retard your orgasm more easily, especially if you pull the female to and from yourself, rather than using sharp pelvic thrusts in your own right; you can effect deep penetration of the penis past your partner's cervix if you want this kind of penetration, but can also employ shallow penetration if that is what you and your partner enjoy; the sitting positions are often quite restful and relatively free from exertion; and in these positions you can easily stimulate the female's clitoral region if, when you are face to face, she leans over backward and gives you manual access to this region.

6. *Standing positions*. If your partner has long enough legs or you have sufficiently short legs, you may sometimes stand and face each other and thus have intercourse. Or she can lie with her legs dangling over the edge of a table or bed while you stand between them. Or you can stand while she, with her arms around your neck, clasps your hips between her thighs. The standing positions are usually quite difficult to achieve and maintain, and generally are not recommended, except in special instances. They do, however, have some advantages, since they may be varied and exciting at times, just because they are not routine; they usually leave your or your partner's hands free for caresses; and they can be combined with dancing, taking showers together, and other standing pursuits.

A final word on sexual intercourse: Technically speaking, as I have shown in an article on "Coitus" in *The Encyclopedia of Sexual Behavior* which I edited in collaboration with Dr. Albert Abarbanel (1961), the word *coitus* is derived from the Latin term, coitio, made up of *co-*, together, and *ire*, to go. It therefore does not consist merely of penile-vaginal copulation, but of any coming together of two sex partners, so that the genitals of one are sufficiently stimulated by the body of the other to bring on orgasm. If we speak of coitus only as penile-vaginal intercourse, then we should also use the more general term, coital relation, or what Brian Heald (personal communication, 1961) calls the coital complex, to describe other forms of male-female sexual coming-togetherness. And we should not deify coitus in the limited or restricted sense, but should fully accept *all* forms of coital relations as being good and proper.

Coital relations, in this broader aspect, include the male's penis having orgasm-inducing contact with the female's vagina, external vulva, anus, mouth, thighs, stomach, breasts, armpits, and other parts of her body. And in regard to the female's interpenetration with the male coital relations include the female's vagina engaging in orgasm-inducing relations with the male's penis, tongue, hand, elbow, toes, etc., while her external vulva and clitoris may engage in contact with his penis, hand, foot, knee, arm, lips, tongue, etc. If we are to employ the more usual, Latinized terminology, coital relations may consist of "regular" intercourse, fellation or irrumation, cunnilinctus, anal intercourse, analinctus, femoral intercourse.

All these forms of sex are good and proper, as long as the man and woman participating in them find them mutually satisfying, and no force or coercion is involved in their relationship (Ellis, 1963a). Coitus in the more limited sense of the term is fine, wonderful, and glorious. But coital relations in the more unrestricted sense are also great and beautiful, and should be practiced to your and your partner's fullest enjoyment.

Chapter 11

Birth Control Is the
Better Part of Valor

If birth control is an important part of marital sex relations, it is a still more important part of non-marital relations, since it is most important, in the great majority of instances, that these relations do *not* lead to pregnancy. No matter how much you may love children, it is unlikely that you and your girlfriend are going to take care of them very adequately when you are unmarried; and one of the very poorest reasons for getting married is because you have carelessly impregnated her and you do not want to see her bear a so-called illegitimate child.

Although there is much to be said in favor of legalized abortion when a child is conceived outside of marriage and its parents do not want it to be brought into the world, there is also much to be said against abortion on any ground, particularly under the illegal conditions that it is generally performed in the United States at present. At best, abortion is something of a major operation, which may have unpleasant and occasionally fatal consequences; and it frequently interferes with a woman's subsequent ability to carry a child to full term. There is no sense to this operation's being performed, if it can be avoided; and obviously, the best way to avoid it is to prevent the woman from becoming pregnant in the first place—preferably through the use of adequate contraceptive technique.

Actually, from several hundred thousand to perhaps as many as a million abortions are performed every year on American women, with many authorities being inclined to accept the larger figure (Calderone, 1958; Clark, 1963; Guttmacher, 1963; Rubin, 1959). Moreover, well over a million women in this country every year resort to mechanical methods of self-abortion before they think of attempting "criminal" abortion. Thus, they use hot baths, strenuous exercise, horseback riding, violent coitus, hormone injections, laxatives, massive doses of quinine or ergot derivatives, and other possible abortifacients, none of which are particularly effective and some of which are dangerous. Some women, with terror born of desperation, even resort to self-induced abortions, which they perform with long needles, skewers, hatpins, and other instruments, frequently with tragic consequences to themselves and their embryos (Mozes, 1959).

Other women are sometimes able to get therapeutic abortions, which can be done in hospitals under proper surgical conditions. But it is very difficult to get permission for this kind of abortion in most parts of our country, and consequently few of these are performed (Lehfeldt and Ellis, 1959). This is all the more reason why anyone engaging in premarital sex relations should carefully employ correct contraceptive methods.

Your use of birth control, moreover, is likely to be one of the best assurances of your having sex relations with a girl, in the first place, and your being able to carry on such relations in a sustained satisfactory manner, in the second place. Because one of the main reasons—and a perfectly good reason at that—why so many modern girls refuse to have intercourse with males is that they are afraid they will become pregnant; and if you assure a girl, by your words and by your manner, that you are most careful about contraceptive technique, and that there is virtually no likelihood of her becoming pregnant if she does copulate with you, you have an infinitely better chance of getting her to bed than if you are not able to give her this kind of assurance.

Moreover, even if your girlfriend does not happen to be much concerned about her becoming pregnant, there are still good reasons why you should be. Once she is impregnated, she may become terribly upset: she may insist that you marry her; she may need a great deal of extra attention; and if she does insist on having an abortion, you will amost certainly have to pay for it. It is therefore to your clearcut advantage, on several counts, to see that she does not get pregnant.

Birth Control Methods

No known method of contraception is absolutely, perfectly, one hundred per cent foolproof and easy to use. Such a method is still sought and will probably be found one of these years. But, as yet, the proper use of birth control devices largely falls upon the female, and has to be worked out by her in consultation with a physician (Lehfeldt, 1960 Tietze, 1962). You, as a male, should know, however, about the available contraceptive techniques, and should be adept at playing your part in their use and be psychologically attuned to employing them and seeing that your partner does also. A fairly complete listing of the various birth control methods and how they are normally employed is given in my sex manual, *The Art and Science of Love*. More of an outline presentation will be given in this chapter.

Oral contraceptives. By far the most effective birth control measure ever invented is the steroid pill which goes under several trade names, the best known of which is *Enovid*. This pill, when taken regularly for twenty days in a row, will regulate the menstrual periods of the female who is taking it, and will render her sterile for as long as she takes it; yet just as soon as she stops taking the pill she not only will be able to become pregnant again, but will actually tend to have increased chances of being impregnated. The difficulties with Enovid and similar birth control pills are that they create unpleasant side effects in some women, at least for a period of time; they cannot be taken by every female; they tend to bring on an increased menstrual flow for a short period; and they must be taken absolutely regularly, day after day, if they are to be effective. When taken by normal women, they have no other proven side effects or disadvantages; but since they have only been in use for a limited period, it is possible (though highly unlikely) that they may eventually affect some women adversely.

Although married women can easily take birth control pills regularly, and single women who live alone or with suitable roommates can also arrange to take them, they of course have disadvantages in the case of bachelor girls who are living at home and who do not want their parents or other relatives to know anything about their sex life. They also are inconvenient for disorganized women who cannot keep to any regular schedule. On the whole, however, they seem to be unusually efficient, unbothersome, and psychologically uncomplicating for most women to take; and if you are having regular sex relations with a girl, you should seriously consider encouraging her to use this new, and so far very superior, contraceptive method.

Male instruments. The main method of birth control used by the male is the condom, or sheath, or "rubber," which is a sleeve-like jacket of rubber or animal skin that is first rolled up and then rolled onto the penis. It is usually placed on an erect penis, but may at times be rolled onto a flaccid organ before love play starts, thus enabling the user to be ready for intercourse without interrupting this play to don the condom. Condoms come plain or lubricated, and often have a small tip at the end for collecting the ejaculated semen, so that there is little danger of their breaking.

Condoms may be used alone, but are much safer when employed with spermicidal jelly on the outside or just inside the tip. They can also be used in conjunction with the safe period (explained below) or with other chemical methods, and preferably should be, since they can break, have pin-holes in them, or slip off during intercourse. Condoms are found by some males to reduce pleasure and to be a nuisance to use. Other males, however, find that they prolong ejaculation time and therefore are a double boon. They should be removed with care, after intercourse, to make sure that semen does not leak over their tops and lead to impregnation.

Female instruments. The rubber diaphragm is the main female instrument which is employed for contraceptive purposes. This is placed in the woman's vagina, fits over the entrance to the uterus, and prevents the semen from entering the womb. Plastic or metal caps are sometimes employed instead of rubber diaphragms. In all instances, they should be fitted by a medical specialist, so that the woman is given exactly the right size diaphragm and is given proper instruction as to using it. When used in conjunction with spermicidal jelly or creme, diaphragms are quite good contraceptive measures; but recent research by Johnson and Masters (1962) has shown that they can be pushed out of place during violent intercourse and that they have their hazards.

Many women get fitted with but soon stop using their diaphragms because they find that they are unesthetic, or too troublesome to keep putting in place and later removing, or because of similar objections to their steady use. Some women even find that they interfere with their coital pleasure.

Instead of a diaphragm or a cap, women sometimes employ tampons, sponges, or wads of cotton which can be steeped in contraceptive agents and then placed in their vaginas prior to intercourse. This method is not considered very safe and is not usually recommended by birth control authorities.

Another contraceptive device which is now being used fairly widely is the intra-uterine ring, which may be made of plastic, metal, or silk, and which, when inserted into the uterus may remain there for a year or more and provide excellent protection against pregnancy (Tietze, 1963). As more experimentation is done with this method, it may become one of the most popular female techniques.

Chemical methods. Women often find it convenient to douche with plain water or chemicals immediately after intercourse; or to use various kinds of vaginal jellies, pastes, cremes, suppositories, and foam tablets which contain chemical substances to kill sperms and block the cervical opening. Douching is not a very effective method of contraception, because it often is done too late; and chemical tablets and foams are fine when employed with a condom or diaphragm but are not too effective when employed alone (Tietze, 1959, 1962).

The so-called safe period or rhythm method. It has been known from the early part of this century that women usually ovulate around the middle of their menstrual cycles and are fertile for only a few days around this time (although some very recent research has tended to show that many women ovulate toward the earlier part of their cycles). Consequently, if a female who has regular periods and ovulation refrains from having intercourse from about the eleventh to the eighteenth day of her 28-day cycle, she will not become pregnant. Tietze and Potter (1962) show that *if* a woman's menstrual cycle is absolutely regular, and *if* she and her partner never make a mistake and are never careless in using the rhythm method, the theoretic effectiveness of this method is roughly comparable to that of the diaphragm or condom. On the other hand, other authorities point out that it is still not possible to pinpoint the exact ovulation time of any given woman, and that other difficulties involved in using the rhythm method make it in practice far from a totally safe technique (Davis, 1963; Hartman, 1962; Nelson, 1963).

Withdrawal. Although physicians and sexologists have inveighed against the method of withdrawal or coitus interruptus for almost a century now, it is still one of the most popular methods of contraception. This is because it consists merely of the male's withdrawing his penis from the vagina just prior to his ejaculation, and is therefore the simplest and cheapest of any method ever invented. Withdrawal, however, tends to create anxiety in those who employ it, since they are never sure that the male *will* withdraw in time, and must keep worrying about this and thus distracting from their satisfaction.

Other disadvantages of withdrawal as a contraceptive method include these: (a) The male's precoital lubricating fluid, which sometimes flows copiously even before entry of the penis into the vagina, may contain some sperm; and he may possibly impregnate the female with this sperm even if he does not have an emission in her vagina. (b) The male can easily misjudge his timing and fail to withdraw his penis before he ejaculates. (c) If the male withdraws in time, but ejaculates near the entrance to the female's vagina, he may still possibly impregnate her. (d) If they try intercourse a second time, live sperms may remain in his urethra from the first ejaculation, and he may impregnate his partner with this sperm.

Coitus reservatus. At various times and places in America, certain groups—such as the Oneida colony in New York during the nineteenth century—have practiced coitus reservatus, with the male's having intercourse with no orgasm or ejaculation whatever on his part. This has never been shown to be a very effective method of contraception, and it may well have other disadvantages, even though a few fanatic groups have practiced it for a period without obvious adverse effects.

Combined methods. The only fully safe method of birth control—aside from abstinence, which is highly impractical in most instances—that has yet been invented is the regular use of the steroid birth control pill. As Guttmacher (1961), an outstanding authority on contraception states, "The pill offers 100 per cent protection against conception if taken as prescribed." The next best methods, the diaphragm and the condom, offer high rates of protection; but they are really combined methods, since the diaphragm is almost always used in conjunction with a spermicidal jelly or creme, and the condom is theoretically supposed to be used in the same manner.

In premarital sex relations where, as we emphasized before, the avoidance of pregnancy is even more desirable than it generally is in legal marriage, the employment of a thoroughly safe contraceptive method is exceptionally important. Consequently, if the birth control pill is not used, it is wise to employ two birth control measures simultaneously. Thus, you can use the condom or the diaphragm technique—but use it in conjunction with the rhythm method, so that intercourse is avoided when the female is highly fertile, or else extra care is taken to avoid conception at this time.

Although it may appear redundant, there is no reason why *both* diaphragm and a condom cannot be used simultaneously—particularly, as just noted, when a woman is at the height of her fertile period. Similarly, withdrawal, if it is to be used at all, can be employed in conjunction with the safe period. If extra care is taken in this connection, your partner is much more likely to feel secure in having coitus and to be able to relax and enjoy it fully; and you, too, are more likely to be able to let yourself go sexually, because the possible unpleasant consequences of your act are thereby avoided.

The main thing that you have to guard against in employing any contraceptive techniques is carelessness. It is most easy, because you are tired, or under the influence of alcohol, or simply annoyed at taking proper precautions, for you or your girlfriend to rationalize and to think, "Oh, to hell with it! There's not much chance of anything happening *this* time." Maybe, statistically, there isn't: since, even without the use of any contraceptive whatever, it may take from fifty to a hundred copulative acts to get the average girl pregnant. But there still *is* a chance that *this* time will be it; and if you *keep* being careless, there is an increasingly good chance that *one* of the times you make up excuses for not employing full contraceptive protection will be the time that you later regret.

So let's have no nonsense about this contraceptive thing. If you are going to employ birth control at all, you'd better employ it efficiently and regularly. Sex without marriage can be one of the most beautiful things in the world—when it is *sanely* and *cooperatively* performed.

Chapter 12

How to Avoid Venereal Disease

The public generally thinks of venereal disease as including only syphilis and gonorrhea. Actually, there are several other major and minor diseases which are spread mainly or exclusively by sexual contact, including granuloma inguinale (which is rather widely distributed in tropical and subtropical regions), chancroid (or soft chancre), and lymphogranuloma venereum. Vaginitis in the female and urethritis in the male can also be spread venerally, since a tiny parasite, the trichomonas, may pass between the male and female's sex organs and infect one or the other. However, as Guttmacher (1961) points out, such ailments as vaginitis can also be acquired in nonvenereal ways and are therefore not, strictly speaking, venereal diseases.

The two most prevalent and serious manifestations of V.D., syphilis and gonorrhea, are the ones against which you should normally be on guard. Although syphilis seemed to be well on its way to being eradicated just a few years ago, largely as a result of the widespread use of the new antibiotics, there has recently been a reversal of this trend; and from a low figure of 6,200 new cases of syphilis reported in the United States for the year 1957, the figure has recently risen to 20,000 reported cases. Gonorrhea rates, while never falling as rapidly as the syphilis rates, did diminish for a while, and lately have also risen.

Yet, as Rubin (1963) has pointed out about syphilis, "the germ which causes this havoc (spirochete) is one of the weakest germs known; is easy to detect and diagnose in its infectious stage; is one of the easiest diseases to cure now; and is 10 per cent preventable." Why, then, has there been a recent upsurge in venereal disease rates?

For several reasons, including these:

1. Just because the V.D. prevention program in the

United States was becoming so effective several years ago, barriers were relaxed in regard to the control program, much less money was appropriated to back it up, and consequently educational and other preventive measures which had been vigorously taken previously were no longer being as effectively pursued.

2. Many private doctors, because of their own hesitancy and embarrassment in discussing sex matters with their patients, do not investigate to discover if they are venerally diseased; and when they do, by routine examinations, discover that these patients are infected, they do not see that the persons from whom they contracted the disease are followed up and treated.

3. There is a great deal of pussyfooting in regard to giving proper sex education, including venereal disease information, to young people. An attempt is made to frighten youngsters into not having any kind of premarital sex relations; and this attempt usually fails. A sane attempt to teach them what to do about the prevention of venereal infection when they do have premarital relations is rarely made in our schools and other institutions.

4. A great deal of venereal disease exists because the individuals acquiring it are too emotionally disturbed to take the proper precautions that would enable them to avoid getting diseased. This is particularly true in regard to lower-class, delinquent populations in our large cities. Members of these groups are usually so mentally ill, and consequently so careless about taking any sexual precautions, that they frequently become diseased and pregnant. Society does very little, in the meantime, to prevent or to treat the emotional disorders of this large segment of the population.

5. Much of the recent increase in venereal disease in this country has been the result of increased promiscuous homosexual rather than heterosexual relations. As Dr. Ralph R. Sachs, Los Angeles health officer, has noted in this connection: "Unquestionably, the white male homosexual has replaced the female prostitute as a major focus of syphilis." Homosexuals are prone to become venereally diseased because, not having to take contraceptive measures, they rarely take any other kind of prophylactic measures, and consequently sooner or later become infected when they are (as they most frequently tend to be) promiscuous. Moreover, because homosexuality is legally and socially beyond

the pale in our country, no formal campaign is ever waged to teach homosexuals to use prophylactic means against venereal disease.

All told, the main factor in sustaining the still relatively high rates of venereal infection is our basically puritanical attitude toward sex. If we viewed sex-carried diseases, such as syphilis and gonorrhea, as objectively as we do other infectious diseases, such as measles or smallpox, it would be relatively easy to eradicate them within a generation or two. But every time effective methods to this end are suggested by medical or military authorities, public opinion tends to sabotage the suggested solutions, and they never quite materialize. Syphilis and gonorrhea are still fairly widespread not because of heterosexual or homosexual intercourse but because of the antisexual, negativistic attitudes we still mainly take toward these kinds of intercourse. When our attitudes finally change, serious venereal disease will almost certainly become extinct.

In the meantime, since you live in a benighted age where syphilis and gonorrhea do exist, you would be wise realistically to accept this fact, and to take all possible personal precautions against becoming infected. These precautions include the following:

1. Try to avoid sexual contact with individuals who are likely to have syphilis or gonorrhea. At the present time, you will generally find that such veneral diseases are rare among nonpromiscuous persons from middle-class, college-level, professional-type backgrounds. On the other hand, they are much more common among promiscuous persons from lower class backgrounds and among severely disturbed individuals. If, therefore, you usually restrict your sex activities to fairly well educated girls who you know, in their turn, limit their sex participation to relatively few partners, you will have little chance of contracting any venereal disease. I find in my own psychotherapy practice that, although many of my male patients are quite promiscuous themselves, as long as they keep going with girls of the type just described, they practically never acquire venereal infections.

2. When you do have intercourse with a girl who is not well known to you, and who might possibly be a carrier of gonorrhea or syphilis, it is always best to employ a condom—even though she may be using a diaphragm, birth control pills, or some other effective form of contraception. It is vir-

tually impossible for you to catch gonorrhea when you are using a condom, and it is difficult, though possible, for you to be infected with syphilis when you are employing one.

3. After you have had sexual contact with a girl who may possibly be a carrier of venereal disease, it is always wise to wash your genitals thoroughly with soap and water. If, under medical supervision, you can manage to take a penicillin tablet or other suitable drug prior to sexual contact, that will be fine, since under military conditions this kind of prophylaxis has been found to work well (Blau, 1961). But wherever you are, you should at least be able to make liberal use of soap and water, which is one of the best preventives known in the case of venereal infection.

Assuming that you have taken all possible precautions, or have been careless and have failed to take them, and that you do acquire syphilis or gonorrhea, how are you to recognize these ailments? First, in regard to syphilis, the primary lesion, or chancre, normally develops at the point of inoculation within two to six weeks after the individual has been infected. This chancre usually starts as a small red capsule that later becomes eroded and moist and is painless. There may also be a painless, swollen lymph gland in the groin if the chancre is on the penis. This primary chancre heals and goes away by itself, without treatment.

The symptoms of the secondary stage of syphilis develop from two to six months after the initial infection has occurred, and take on a great many different forms. They include malaise, persistent headache, nausea, vomiting, deafness, hoarseness, low-grade fever, and sore throat. These symptoms usually disappear within a few weeks or months; but they may persist for about a year.

A latent period occurs about two years after the initial infection, and for the next eight years or so the infected individual may be without symptoms, although his blood serum will be positive, if tested. Then, around the tenth to thirteenth year after infection, late or tertiary symptoms occur and may take a large variety of forms. Late syphilis may result in the involvement or destruction of many different parts of the body, including the skin, the cardiovascular system, the skeletal structure, and the central nervous system. When neurosyphilis occurs, it generally takes the form of general paresis and tabes dorsalis; but it may also result in meningitis, cerebral hemorrhage, brain tumor, deafness, blindness, mental disturbance, and epilepsy (Blau, 1961).

Syphilis, of course, cannot be self-treated, but usually medically supervised use of penicillin or other antibiotics is effective. If syphilis is caught in its early stages and properly treated, a biological cure is possible in the vast majority of cases.

Gonorrhea, or the clap, is an even more prevalent disease than syphilis. In the male, it first shows itself as a burning on urination and a thick, greenish-yellow discharge from the penis. It may also result in a continual desire to urinate and in painful erections. These symptoms start from two to seven days following intercourse that has resulted in the infection.

In the female, gonorrhea usually leads to a vaginal discharge, a sensation of pain and burning in the vagina, and sometimes frequent urination accompanied by burning sensations. It is frequently accompanied by bartholinitis, an infection of the vulvovaginal glands, and by salpingitis, an infection of the uterine tubes. Sometimes gonorrhea in the female goes beyond the genito-urinary area and may result in various other ailments, such as arthritis, conjunctivitis, and skin infections.

If it is caught in its early stages, gonorrhea may be easily treated with various antibiotics, such as penicillin, the sulfonamides, the tetracyclines, streptomycin, and chloramphenicol. But if it is not treated until its later stages, when infection has become more widespread throughout the genito-urinary system or other parts of the body, treatment becomes more complicated and may require special surgical procedures. Gonorrhea, while not as unpleasant a disease as syphilis can be, is a serious ailment, particularly in females, who are sometimes rendered sterile as a result of its complications.

As emphasized at the beginning of this chapter, both gonorrhea and syphilis could be totally eradicated, if our society as a whole were sane enough to use all proper medical preventive and therapeutic approaches to it. But it is most unlikely that these venereal diseases will be eliminated during the next several decades, because of our general queasy, puritanical attitudes toward sex. Consequently, you must assume that you, personally, are in some danger of acquiring these diseases, and must take all possible precautions not to become infected with them.

Moreover, in regard to venereal disease, as in regard to matters of pregnancy, the more careful you indicate you are, the more confidence you will likely inspire in female partners. If you indicate to your girlfriend that you are duly cautious and wise in this connection, she will tend to feel safer in having sex relations with you; and if there is any question in her mind between choosing between you and another male who is likely to be careless and liable to venereal infection, the chances are that she will favor you.

Moreover, the attitude that your girlfriend takes in regard to pregnancy and venereal infection may be indicative of her general attitudes toward life, and may give you some valuable insights. If she is unusually careless in these respects it may well indicate that, even though she is lucky and has no unfortunate experiences leading to pregnancy or disease, she will be equally careless, after marriage, about such matters as budgeting, raising the children, organizing the housework, and so forth. You may be wise, therefore, to observe her sexual behavior, if you are seriously considering living with her as a marital partner for many years to come.

If you have great difficulty in protecting yourself against pregnancy or venereal disease, even though you have full knowledge of the dangers involved, this means that you have some kind of serious self-discipline problem, and are almost certainly acting on the principle of short-range rather than long-range hedonism. You are telling yourself, in other words, sentences along the following lines:

(a) "I don't like the trouble that I have to take in order to protect myself fully against getting a girl pregnant or becoming infected with V.D." (b) "Therefore, it isn't worth this trouble, and I'll just take my chances of getting into these kinds of difficulties."

Although the first of these sentences is perfectly sane, the second simply doesn't logically follow. Instead, you should be concluding: "No matter how much I dislike taking the trouble to protect myself in regard to pregnancy and V.D., it *is* worth taking this trouble, in view of the serious disadvantages that could easily occur if I refuse to take it."

If, therefore, you are goofing in regard to certain sexual precautions which *are* important to your happiness, you should face the fact that you definitely are telling yourself some nonsense at point B; determinedly look into your own heart and mind until you discover exactly what this nonsense is; and then concertedly keep tackling it and challenging it until it is replaced by more sensible views. If you find that you do not challenge your own self-defeating sentences in this manner, then you need psychological help, and should seek it as soon as possible. But you *can* challenge and question your own nonsense—if you really try.

Chapter 13

Consumer's Guide to Prostitution

Young males, these days, do not patronize prostitutes to anything like the degree that was common in the early part of this century, largely because they can have sex relations easily and frequently with female companions who do not ask to be paid for their favors. Nonetheless, a surprisingly large amount of prostitution still exists in the United States and in other parts of the world. The facts still show that about two-thirds of white American males have some experience with prostitutes at some time during their lives (Kinsey, Pomeroy, and Martin, 1948; Benjamin, 1961; Rubin, 1959; Rutledge, 1963).

Not all males who patronize prostitutes, of course, are single. Innumerable married males, some of whom even have reasonably satisfying sex relations with their wives, still resort from time to time to prostitutional affairs; and many authorities are convinced that a large part of the income of various kinds of call girls and whores is derived from the patronage they receive from married men (Ellis, 1959). But single males are probably still the main customers of females who sell their love; and the question is continually being raised: Is it right for these males to be resorting to this kind of sex activity?

Reasons for Patronizing Prostitutes

Before we attempt to answer this question, let us take a look at some of the main reasons why contemporary bachelors tend to use prostitutional sex outlets. Dr. Harry Benjamin and I examined this matter some years ago (Benjamin and Ellis, 1954) and found the following motives for patronizing prostitutes:

1. Male sex drives, for both biological and social reasons, are frequently imperious and of high intensity. Conse-

quently, when no girl is around who will go to bed with him on a voluntary basis, the highly sexed male will easily be tempted to resort to prostitutes in spite of the disadvantages involved in doing so.

2. Many males, for various good or bad reasons, do not wish to become emotionally involved with their female partners. Out of neurotic or nonneurotic motivation, these males merely wish to relax in female company and, as Havelock Ellis (1936) noted, "to add an element of gaiety and variety to the ordered complexity of modern life, a relief from the monotony of its mechanical routine, a distraction from its dull and respectable monotony." These males prefer to associate with harlots.

3. A goodly number of males—and, indeed, perhaps the vast majority—have (like most other animals) distinctly varietist or promiscuous sex urges. In a "monogamous" nation like our own, where even a girlfriend usually demands that her lover be faithful to her, it is most difficult for these males to satisfy their varietist desires except by resorting to prostitutes.

4. Just because monogamous marital and premarital mores, which are prevalent in our part of the world, give the husband or the steady boyfriend something of a strict monopoly on the favors of his mate, bachelors who are without steady girlfriends are sort of left out in the cold, with relatively few truly available girls to choose their sex partners from. Consequently, they find it most convenient to have a special class of girls, prostitutes, who are always available to them in a nonmonopolistic way.

5. A great many males are too shy or emotionally or physically handicapped to compete successfully with other males for heterosexual favors, even when these are non-prostitutionally available. Still others are—or consider themselves to be—too stupid or ugly to attract female attention. In addition, many males who were once sufficiently capable or attractive to compete for female favors are now too old to be looked upon approvingly by most women, and especially by the ones whom they would find desirable. Such males, many of whom have powerful sex drives, are often on the lookout for prostitutes, and would consider themselves seriously deprived if such girls were not available.

6. Some males are semi-impotent and cannot normally find unremunerated sex partners who will bear with their

sexual inadequacies. Still others have special kinds of sex fetishes or deviations, and cannot easily find females who will accord them the sex satisfactions they desire. Such males, again, must often resort to prostitutes to have their particular urges gratified.

7. Many males in our society have perfectly natural (though sometimes socially tabooed) sex desires—for example, desires for mouth-genital relations. They find that these desires are looked upon with prejudice by a considerable number of females; and they consequently begin to resort to prostitutes who will engage in such acts with them.

8. Some males object to our existing courtship amenities, and feel that they do not have the time nor the desire to go with a girl for a long period before she will allow them copulatory favors. Still other males find that courting American girls, and wining, dining, and entertaining them in the course of such courtship, is actually more expensive than patronizing prostitutes. Both these types of males find resort to prostitution a more satisfactory solution to their sex problems.

9. A number of males are afraid of impregnating a girl, and of the possible consequences of an abortion, illegitimate paternity, or a forced marriage. They consequently prefer to visit prostitutes, with whom none of these dangers normally exists.

For various reasons, then, a good many males in our society prefer to patronize prostitutes; and although many do so only occasionally, others do so for most of their lives (Kahol, 1963). As can quickly be seen, some of the reasons why single men keep resorting to prostitutes are quite sane—for it *is* often difficult for them to get sufficient sex satisfaction without their becoming more involved than they would prefer to be with nonprostitutes—and some of the reasons for their patronizing call girls or whores are relatively insane. Particularly, males who irrationally *fear* becoming involved with girlfriends, or who obsessively-compulsively are *driven* to ladies of pleasure, are usually giving up on their first choices for sex partners, and are neurotically winding up with second- and third-rate choices; and these males are obviously defeating their own ends.

When, therefore, the question arises of whether a man *should* patronize prostitutes, it is wise to retranslate this into the question: Would such patronage on his part be truly wise—or self-defeating? For this seems to be the real issue at hand, rather than any moralistic measure which is irrelevantly introduced by many religionists and social reformers.

Is there, then, nothing immoral, per se, about patronizing prostitutes? It is difficult to see how there is. For, in our country at least, girls freely choose to be or not to be harlots, and no one normally forces them to be. And if they choose to be so—even for all the wrong reasons—they are presumably getting distinct gains, monetary and otherwise, from their trade. Males, too, choose to patronize or not to patronize prostitutes; and if they choose to do so, they presumably feel that they are getting their time and money's worth. Since, on both sides of the fence, there seems to be a regular, above-board business transaction going on, and both parties derive their own kinds of satisfaction from this transaction, it is rather ridiculous to talk about the "immorality" of the bartering arrangement.

Moreover, as we too often fail to admit, sexual prostitution is only *one* form of prostituting oneself, and is probably a much lesser form than many other prevalent modes. For prostitution, in the broadest sense of the term, means doing an act that you do not want to do in order to receive some form of payment for it; and in this sense, anyone who works at an unsatisfactory job, or lives with his family only because it is cheaper, is prostituting himself. Also: any female who has sex relations with her husband mainly to get mink coats and other forms of remuneration is also prostituting herself. And although all kinds of prostitution are probably undesirable, since it would be far better if human beings did not sell themselves in any way for monetary gain, they are hardly immoral, as long as the individual who is prostituting himself or herself, as well as his or her patron, knows perfectly well what the score is, and is willing to enter this kind of business transaction.

The main immorality involved in being a prostitute or in patronizing one, then, is the possible unfairness to oneself that may be involved. For prostitutes may well sell themselves short, and may get lesser gains than they would otherwise get from their prostitution; and patrons may well have poorer (even though more easily arranged) sex-love relations with call girls than they might otherwise have with girls who truly care for them and do not charge for their favors.

Do prostitutes normally harm themselves by engaging in

their profession? No, not necessarily. There is a large school of psychological thought, such as that exemplified by Greenwald (1957), which insists that virtually all prostitutes are self-destructive, and that they are necessarily very neurotic. It is questionable whether the existing evidence supports this contention, although it does seem to indicate that *most* prostitutes (like, alas, most nonprostitutes in our society) are pretty severely disturbed, self-blaming individuals. There are, however, several sensible reasons why girls may, especially temporarily, resort to harlotry of one kind or another.

Thus, the economic rewards of prostitution are in some cases far higher than those of most other female occupations. The prostitute's life may be more adventurous and rewarding than that of an ordinary office worker. Some prostitutes actually enjoy their work, from either a sexual or a social viewpoint. And many girls who are psychologically inadequate or physically weak find it almost impossible to hold any kind of regular job other than prostitution. It is therefore rash to assume that being a whore is a totally inappropriate, self-destructive life for everyone who engages in such a profession; for this is certainly not true.

Reasons for Avoiding Prostitutes

Granting that patronizing prostitutes is not truly immoral, and that one is not thereby contributing to the self-destruction of his sex partners, are there still good reasons why you should normally avoid having prostitutional affairs? Yes, there are; and these include:

1. There is some real danger in resorting to prostitution. The place you visit may be raided; or you may be robbed; or possibly blackmailed; or otherwise placed in jeopardy.

2. Prostitutes, even when they take care of themselves hygienically, are normally promiscuous, and therefore can spread venereal infection. The girl who was medically examined a couple of days ago and found to have a perfectly clean bill of health may since that time have become infected, and may pass on a venereal disease to you. You may partially protect yourself against infection (as we showed in our previous chapter), but there is no guarantee that you will not somehow acquire V.D. from *any* promiscuous woman.

3. In most instances, prostitution affords you a low-level kind of sex-love satisfaction. The prostitute usually is not in-

terested in you as a sex partner, but in the money she will get from you. Rarely can she spend any amount of time with you —since that would be too expensive. Only occasionally can she permit you to satisfy her sexually, since she has too many partners a day for that sort of thing. Most of the time you will have little opportunity to know her as a person and to develop any lasting relationship with her. The pleasure you receive with her, therefore, while not necessarily minimal, will not tend to be the kind of deeper and more lasting pleasure you may be able to obtain on a nonprostitutional basis with a girl who cares for you and for whom you also care.

4. Resort to prostitution tends to be so distracting and sexually satiating that it sometimes takes away a great deal of your incentive to find yourself a regular girlfriend. Patronizing prostitutes is generally made so easy that you will tend to keep taking sexual things this easy way and not to go toward more difficult and more rewarding life experiences.

5. As Rutledge (1963) points out, the kind of sex relations that you are likely to have with prostitutes, which emphasize only *your* sex satisfaction and not theirs, are not particularly conducive to your learning how to satisfy a woman sexually and to cooperate with her in various ways. Consequently, patronizing harlots does not give you a good background for adjusting to a marital situation, no matter how much purely sexual practice you may have with such girls.

6. Kirkendall (1961) found that college level males who patronize prostitutes frequently have unsatisfactory sex experiences with them; and that they then may overgeneralize to other forms of sex activity and may stay away from or make poor adjustments to nonprostitutional heterosexual affairs. Some non-college level males probably react in the same unfavorable manner to their less than satisfying contacts with prostitutes.

All told, it can be seen that there are distinct disadvantages (as well as advantages) to employing prostitutional sex outlets, even when there is nothing strictly immoral about doing so. Consequently, you are better off, in most instances, when your contacts with prostitutes are minimal, and when they are made because there are no nonprostitutes available or because other unusual circumstances exist. If you find yourself steadily patronizing prostitutes rather than "amateur" girlfriends, there is a possibility that you have either a sexual or a general personality problem, and that you should try to determine what your problem is, and perhaps get professional help with it. It is possible that you may hold women in low esteem; or be afraid to risk sex failure with a regular girl; or be able to have sex satisfaction only when the woman you are with is not a "nice" girl; or have some other neurotic reason for sticking exclusively or mainly to whoremongering for your heterosexual affairs.

Prostitution, in other words, just like any other sex act, *may* become a deviation: if you are fetishistically, fixatedly, fearfully, or obsessive-compulsively attached to this kind of sex behavior, and can never or rarely enjoy other aspects of sexuality. Prostitution itself is not a perversion; but in any particular case it may be made into one. If so, the deviant who is fetishistically attached to prostitutes may be psychologically treated just like any other deviant, and maybe helped to overcome his problem.

Should Prostitution Be Banned or Legalized?

One school of thought, as expounded for years by the American Social Hygiene Association, strongly feels that prostitution should be absolutely banned, and that prostitutes (and perhaps their patrons as well) should be arrested and jailed as public offenders, in order to stamp out this evil. The adherents of this school are generally authoritarian minded individuals who fail to see the significant difference between vice and crime.

Granted that prostitution is not the best possible kind of sexual arrangement, and that (as we noted above) it includes some distinct dangers and disadvantages, this hardly seems any reason why it should be legally banned. We must sanely distinguish, in this connection, between vice and crime (Benjamin, 1931, 1961; Harding, 1938; Vollmer, 1936). An individual is vice-ridden when he engages in activities, such as gluttony, smoking, and excessive drinking, which may be harmful to him, and which he may self-defeatingly and stupidly perform, but which nevertheless are his human *right* to do. For every human being *does*, once he is an adult and has been given a reasonably good education, have the right to defeat or destroy himself; and to try to take away this right from him is to rule him in a high-handed, fascistic manner. Children, mental defectives, and a few other individuals often have to be protected from their own ignorance or stupidity. But a nondefective adult has to be permitted to engage in various kinds of vices—or else the worse vice of tyranny is inflicted on him by the powers that be.

Crime, on the other hand, consists of activities which needlessly and concretely harm *other* human beings, and which therefore have to be socially and legally barred. If John Smith drinks himself to death, he is vice-ridden; but if he forces others to drink, or brings up his children as alcoholics, or sells booze without paying a state liquor tax, he may well be a criminal. Criminal activity may rightly be legislated against, and the individual performing it may be penalized (though preferably not devalued as a human being, or blamed and punished) for engaging in it.

At worst, then, performing prostitution or patronizing prostitutes is a vice, and should not be legislated against and considered to be a crime. If the right of the prostitute to ply her trade is taken away from her, the right of the wife to be married to, and sleep with, the man she doesn't love may be the next to go—and the right to smoke, drink coffee, and chew gum may follow soon after. If you happen to be opposed to any vice, you can refrain from engaging in it yourself, and legitimately try to induce others to desist from it by using education, advertising, propaganda, and publicity with these others. But if you try to legislate it out of existence, you are essentially a fascist (Ellis, 1958).

How and Where to Find Prostitutes

Prostitution is illegal in most American and Western cities, even though it still tends to be widespread and is patronized by literally hundreds of thousands of males every day in the year. If you want to be addicted to the vice of patronizing prostitutes, it is not too difficult for you to follow your bent, except in any given region immediately after there has been a "cleanup." For, somewhat periodically, the police or some other reform agency gets moving against prostitutes in different areas, and for a while it is difficult to locate even a high class call girl. But sooner or later conditions return to their "normal" state, and all kinds of prostitutes are usually to be had for the buying.

In the old days, prostitutes did a good deal of literal streetwalking, and you could easily find one by walking the streets in certain neighborhoods, and waiting for one to make an overture to you. Or you could ask almost any cabbie where the nearest brothel was, and very probably (since he collected a commission on all the guests he brought) he would take you to it. Today, conditions have changed in this respect in most areas, so that street-walkers are likely to be nonexistent, and brothels hardly to be found.

Instead, in a city like New York, bar-girls and call girls seem to be prevalent. The bar-girl is to be found, as you would expect, at various bars, many of which tend to be not of the most respectable variety. The bartender and the other patrons of the place know who such girls are, if you want to ask them for their help. Or if you just look around yourself, you can pick them out as they hang around the bistro.

Strip-tease night clubs and taxi dance halls are also favorite hangouts of prostitutes. At the strip-tease clubs, the girls who are doing the stripping are usually required to drink with the patrons, when the patrons desire them to do so; and frequently, in a back room or even in the dimly lit club itself, they will have masturbatory or other sex relations with these patrons. At the taxi dance halls, where the patrons pay a dollar or so for each dance, the girls are also more willing, in most instances, to engage in heavy petting with the customers—for a price. Many of these same girls, as well as other hangers-on at these places, are all-out prostitutes, with whom regular assignations can be made.

Call girls, who may or may not belong to an organized syndicate, are usually available through bartenders, bell hops at hotels, taxi drivers, night club doormen, and other members of the service professions. They are sometimes also available from model agencies, theatrical agencies, sleazy employment agencies, and similar sources. Call girls are frequently used in our large cities as "entertainers" at parties thrown by business concerns for out of town buyers and other potential customers. In fact, modern investigations have shown time and again that some of the largest business deals are consummated largely because of the effective use that is made of call girls in putting them over.

Prostitutes are also usually to be found among the criminal elements in any community, particularly among the alcoholics and heroin addicts. This is because a habit such as drug addiction is very expensive to maintain, and therefore many addicted females must resort to prostitution fairly regularly in order to keep themselves in funds.

If, therefore, you are looking for a "respectable" source of information about call girls, you can usually find such sources in the business community, especially among the whole-salers; and if you are looking for less respectable sources, you can find them in the low-level theatrical enterprises, the bars, and among the hotel and cab-driving people. You may have difficulty, these days, in finding a brothel where you can go regularly, or even a girl who keeps living at the same address, since the professionals find it safer to keep moving a lot of the time. But if you keep looking, and *asking*, you will soon be able to locate something along the lines you want.

The main question still remains: should you patronize prostitutes or not? And the general answer is that, even though it is not terrible immoral or awful to do so, you would normally be better off if you didn't—and if you found other kinds of outlets instead. Even the experience of *failing* sexually with a nonprostitute is often much better, so long as you learn by it, than that of "succeeding" with a whore. But there are exceptions, naturally, to every rule. And if you do feel constrained to patronize prostitutes, either temporarily or permanently, there is nothing for you to be guilty about in this connection. You are not a worthless slob for doing so. You are, at worst, a self-defeater. And you can always keep *working* against your self-defeatism.

Chapter 14

How to Avoid Becoming
a Sex Pervert

Literally millions of American males today are sex perverts or deviants; and the percentage of deviants tend to be much higher among the single than among the married males. Homosexuals, exhibitionists, and voyeurs, who constitute a sizable proportion of existing deviates, are generally single; though some of them, of course, are or have been married.

Is it a holy horror and disgrace for anyone to be a sexual pervert? Absolutely not. Sex deviants are, as I have stoutly contended for a good many years now (Ellis, 1952, 1958, 1960, 1962b, 1963a; Ellis and Brancale, 1956), nothing but emotionally disturbed individuals, just as are nonsexual neurotics and psychotics. And there is no reason why they should in any way be blamed or devalued as human beings because they are sick in their particular kind of way. So even if you were sexually deviated, you would not automatically be a louse or a rat; you would merely be a disturbed individual. It would be most unfortunate if you were sick in this way; but it would hardly be, unless you made it so, catastrophic.

Why would it be most unfortunate if you were a sexual deviate? For many reasons, including these:

1. Sexual perversion, as we have just noted, *is* a form of emotional disturbance; and it is no great bargain being disturbed—as I, for one, can attest, after spending most of my working time during the last twenty years with severely disturbed, and usually desperately unhappy, people.

2. Even apart from its connection with mental aberration, sexual deviation is a tragically *limiting* state in which to exist. Human beings, by inborn inclination, are normally labile, varietist, and amazingly flexible in their sex interests and behavior. Their sex desires and practices cover an enormous potential range; and when they are healthy, they take in a good deal of this range at some times during their lives.

When they are sexually neurotic or perverted, however, they usually restrict their potential circle of sexuality and narrow it down to a small sliver of the potential pie. They consequently throw out numerous kinds of enjoyment and remain fixated on a few relatively unswinging aspects of sex.

3. Sexual deviation is, almost by definition, involved with the deviated individual's either (a) fearing to engage in some kind of sex acts (e.g., fearing to have sex relations with females and therefore restricting himself exclusively to males); or (b) obsessively-compulsively attaching himself to a given form of sexuality (e.g., being obsessed with peeping, to the virtual exclusion of all other form of sex activity); or (c) angrily excluding some form of sex behavior (e.g., refusing to have intercourse with women over thirty because he hates his mother, who was in her thirties when he first began hating her); or (d) disorganizedly and unselectively engaging in all kinds of sexual participation, including bizarre acts (such as copulating with corpses), because he is unable to focus his time and energy on maximally enjoyable and nondestructive modes of sexuality. If this is so, then it is clear that the main motivations behind perversion are serious states of anxiety, obsessive-compulsiveness, hostility, and personality disorganization. Even if the sex acts that these states lead to are themselves at times quite enjoyable, the general personality aberrations from which they flow are invariably crippling and self-defeating.

4. It unfortunately happens that, in our antisexual society, many perversions are socially and legally proscribed, and often severe punishments are leveled against those who perpetrate them. Thus, homosexuals, voyeurs, and necrophiliacs are condemned and persecuted in almost all parts of the contemporary "civilized" world (Cory, 1961; Fonzi, 1963; Gervis, 1963). This persecution of deviates is eminently unfair, since it is not consistent (for example, the heterosexual pervert who is hostile toward all women over thirty is rarely scorned or jailed, while the homosexual who is hostile to all women of any age and who consequently copulates with males is often hounded and penalized). Moreover, persecuting an individual because he is emotionally disturbed makes no sense whatever, hinders rather than helps his treatment, and frequently induces him to look down on himself and thereby become more compulsively disturbed. Emotional disturbance is almost always connected with an individual's

severely castigating himself for being less than perfect; and if society blames him for being deviated, he will only tend to blame himself and become more rigidly deviated. For if he is *no good* for being a deviant, how can a no-goodnik like him possibly change and become nondeviated?

5. Most deviants are severe goofers, or avoiders of serious issues. They learn, usually fairly early in life, to enjoy a limited and disadvantageous form of sexual behavior; and then, once they see how self-destructive this behavior is, they refuse to go through the onerous process of retraining themselves. Unlike many other individuals who work their way out of their neurotic or deviated problems, fixed deviates give up, tell themselves it's no use, frequently rationalize that they were born the way they are, and in one way or another refuse to change. But their sexual goofing is normally mirrored in other aspects of their lives as well; and they only rarely achieve what they otherwise could achieve in life because they insist on remaining *short-range* hedonists. Their sexual disorder, in other words, is part of, and in turn reinforces, a much more generalized neurotic or psychotic illness.

There is little doubt, then, that overt, fixed deviation in our society is generally disadvantageous; and that, as I have pointed out in previous writings (Ellis, 1958, 1960, 1962b) and as many other authorities have also indicated (Adler, 1917; Ansbacher, 1958; Allen, 1949; Caprio, 1962; Cory, 1958, 1963; Harper, 1959b; McReynolds, 1959), virtually all fixed, exclusive deviants are severely neurotic. These deviants, including the homosexuals, were *not* born the way they are, as so many of them prefer to think; and they definitely *can* be cured by various kinds of psychotherapy (Allen, 1949; Buckle, 1949; Creadick, 1953; Deutsch, 1954; Ellis, 1962a; Fink, 1954; Foster, 1947; A. Freud, 1951; Gurvitz, 1957; Hadfield, 1958; Karpman, 1956; Lewinsky, 1954; London and Caprio, 1950; Nedoma, 1951; Poe, 1952; Robertiello, 1959; Rubinstein, 1958; Shentoub, 1957; Srnec and Freund, 1953; Stekel, 1930).

Let us suppose that you, personally, are worried about becoming a sex deviant. Is there actually much chance that you may become one, considering how worried you may be in this connection?

No, there actually isn't much of a chance—because the great majority of males who are concerned about becoming a homosexual, an exhibitionist, a fetishist, or some other kind of deviant are more concerned about being *thought of* as a pervert than they are about the *content* of the particular perversion they are worried about assuming. That is to say, they deem perversion a horrible state of affairs, and would view themselves as totally weak and incompetent if they were deviated; and it is this *weakness* or *incompetence* of which they are truly afraid: just as they would be similarly afraid of weakness or incompetence in business, or athletic, or social affairs.

Sigmund Freud (1924-50) believed that homosexuality was an invariable concomitant of severe emotional disturbance, particularly of paranoid schizophrenia. Kurt Freund and his associates (1953, 1960, 1961a, 1961b) at the Sexological Institute at Prague have found, however, that paranoid schizophrenics are *not* usually homosexual, but that they almost invariably are *worried about* becoming perverted. This is what happens in most cases of severe disturbance, particularly where the male holds himself in low esteem. Even though he is not in the least homosexual, and may be quite obsessed with heterosexual pursuits, he frequently is severely anxious about the mere *possibility* of his becoming homoerotic; and *this*, perhaps more than almost anything else, is what bothers him.

So the mere fact that you may be suspicious of and anxious about your own sexual perversion by no means proves that you are a pervert, though it may indicate that you have serious emotional problems. True deviants tend, like as not, to be somewhat *unconcerned* about their deviational tendencies, and to rationalize about these to such a degree that they even come to think of themselves as superior to nondeviants. The fact remains, however, that some people who worry about becoming deviated actually do become so upset that they take themselves out of normal fields of sexuality and end up as perverts; but this tends to be the exception rather than the rule.

Warding Off Sexual Deviation

Are there any things you can specifically do to prevent yourself from becoming a sex deviant? Yes, there definitely are.

First of all, you must understand how sexual perversion arises. It does not—as the Freudians unfortunately keep contending, and as many other schools of psychology agree—

merely arise from childhood upbringing. True enough, the manner in which you are reared as a child has *something* to do with prejudicing you in favor of homosexuality or some other form of deviation. Thus, if your parents deliberately raised you as a girl; or if they were exceptionally puritanical about their teachings and induced you to believe that premarital intercourse is a horrible business; or if you became over-attached to your mother early in life; or if you had a very weak father, who was not very "manly," and who perhaps neglected you; or if you had a very negativistic mother, who prejudiced you against most females—if any of these kinds of things happened to you during your childhood, you may well have been influenced against heterosexuality and against viewing yourself as a strong male, and you may therefore have been an easy convert to homosexual activity.

Nonetheless, it is definitely *not* a child's early learning that automatically makes him homosexual, even though it may *encourage* his ultimately becoming so. Rather, it is the *philosophy* about himself and his sexuality which he partly absorbs from his elders (and also from his peers) and which he then *makes* his own by self-indoctrination. Thus, if the child's parents teach him that heterosexual premarital relations are wicked, he must, as he grows into adolescence and manhood, *continue* to tell himself similar nonsense if he is to keep himself afraid of women and prejudiced in favor of homosexuality (which no one may have warned him about or excoriated as being wicked when he was young). Or if he thinks, when he is a child, that he must have a strong male with whom to identify, and that since his father is not this kind of person he must get an older, homosexual lover to make himself worthwhile, he must still continually *reinfect* himself with this silly belief if he is to remain homosexually attracted to supposedly stronger males.

Perversions, then, do not arise from early childhood experiences, but from the philosophy one *evolves and sustains* as a result of these experiences. Consequently, no matter what the early experiences are, it is quite possible, albeit admittedly difficult, for an adolescent or an adult to *reassess* his philosophic conclusions and assumptions, and to *change* them. If he does so, he will eventually overcome any tendencies toward homosexuality or other sex deviations that he may have originally acquired.

In particular, the homosexually inclined male must see,

reevaluate, and change the following kinds of philosophies: (a) that *something terrible* will happen to him if he has sex relations with females; (b) that he is a dead duck if he cannot get a strong or handsome or competent male to love him; (c) that he just simply was born the way he is and therefore *cannot possibly* succeed sexually with a woman; (d) that assuming masculine responsibilities for courtship, marriage, and child-raising is just *too hard* for him, and that he cannot live happily in such overly difficult circumstances; and (e) that because he has been homosexual for a number of years and is fetishistically attached to the idea of having sex relations with males, he cannot possibly work against his past behavior patterns and become equally attracted to and sexually satisfied with female partners.

If any fixed homosexual will consciously and consistently *think* about these kinds of philosophies that he has vigorously espoused for years; if he will then keep *questioning* and *challenging* such viewpoints; and if he will particularly *act against them* in practice, by taking out girls, forcing himself to have sex relations with them, thinking about how desirable they are while he is masturbating, and so on, he will almost certainly find his deviation-sustaining views disappearing and discover that they are being replaced, gradually or quickly, by much more normal sex thoughts, feeling, and behavior. Usually, it will take him some amount of *time* to undo the old thought and action pathways and to replace them with new, heterosexual paths. But, by the same token, it takes time to change one's stroke at tennis, or the way one fingers the piano, or one's style of writing, or almost anything else one wants to modify. But, given this time and enough determined effort, the change almost always will occur.

The same thing is true with other sexual deviations than homosexuality. Naturally, the exhibitionist or the voyeur *enjoys* his sexual pattern—for the simple reason that unconsciously, over a period of years, he has literally worked very hard to *make* himself enjoy this kind of sex activity. He has kept telling himself, for example, how thrilling and delightful it would be to exhibit himself in public; how exciting it is not to get caught at doing so; how arousing it is for him to see a girl who might possibly be a good victim; how he will be able to recall a particular exhibitory act, and to re-excite himself all over again, perhaps while masturbating, by thinking about it; etc., etc. And he has also worked very hard, in the dyed-in-the-wool cases of exhibitionism, by looking for suitable victims, hunting out places where he can get away with his perversion successfully, getting the actual practice of exhibiting himself, running like hell away from the scene of his crime when there is danger of being arrested, and so on. It is this very hard and consistent *work* that he has done which has established his exhibitionistic pleasure and then kept it alive, perhaps for years, even in the face of the great disadvantages that are attached to it.

If, then, the deviate will fully see and admit the vast amount of effort he has undertaken over a period of time to originate and sustain his deviation, and if he will determinedly work, in thought and in action, just a fraction as much as he has previously done to become a pervert, he will almost always get good results and will begin giving up his deviated activity. In most cases, it is wise for a fixed deviate to go for psychotherapeutic help while he is trying to overcome his perversion. But in many cases, I am sure, such individuals have successfully fought against their abnormal tendencies by continually thinking and working against them without going for formal therapy. Certainly, if self-help fails, the deviate should go for treatment. But there is no harm in his trying, at least for a while, to overcome his nonsensical beliefs and the emotions and actions to which they invariably lead.

The Prevention of Sexual Deviation

Obviously, any unhealthy form of sexual (or nonsexual) behavior is better prevented from the start, than first performed and later attacked. Human beings who become emotionally disturbed almost never become completely cured, and are usually subject for the rest of their lives to an occasional return of their symptoms (Ellis, 1962a, 1963d; Solomon and Wynne, 1954). It is therefore preferable that they not become disturbed in the first place.

What are some of the techniques which you may employ to keep yourself from becoming seriously sexually deviated? These:

1. Make sure that you are as unpuritanical as you can possibly be about all aspects of human sexuality. Convince yourself that sexual relations between consenting adults are invariably good, or at least not immoral, no matter what various individuals or social groups may think. Never allow yourself to be authoritarianly persuaded that premarital

heterosexual relations, masturbation, petting, or any other harmless form of sexual participation is wicked or sinful.

2. By remaining unpuritanical and open-minded, allow yourself full leeway for engaging in a variety of different kinds of sex relations, both with the same and with diverse partners. Never conclude that any particular form of sex activity is wrong or unsatisfying for you until you have at least unprejudicedly *tried* it a few times, and have pragmatically convinced yourself that it is just not your onion.

3. Observe and forcefully combat your general or nonsexual anxieties and hostilities. If you are terribly afraid of what people think of you, or about doing the wrong thing, or in regard to failing at any task, ask yourself what there is *really* to be afraid of, and show yourself that there practically never *is* anything that is truly fearsome, other than physical pain or injury. No matter how much satisfaction you may temporarily receive from hating others, show yourself that this kind of satisfaction is simply not worth it: since your hatred ultimately must impinge upon *you*, and turn up as a pain in *your* gut. Realize, moreover, that sexual fears, compulsions, and hostilities normally stem from nonsexual philosophies of life, and do not merely arise full-blown in their own right. If, therefore, you can manage not to be anxious and hostile about practically *anything* and *anyone*, you will be able to steer clear of the negative thinking and emoting that invariably lie behind and cause sexual perversions.

4. Particularly watch out for the signs of, and immediately set about combating, your own serious forms of evasion or goofing. Sex deviates, as we noted above, are almost always goofers, who take what seems to be the easiest pathway to satisfaction, but what is actually in the long run an overly hard and needlessly self-sabotaging path. If you find, therefore, that you are avoiding normal heterosexual participations because they seem too difficult or too time-consuming or too expensive, ask yourself whether they are *really* that onerous, or whether you are not grossly exaggerating the difficulties attached to them. And, before you have become seriously neurotic or deviated, deliberately force yourself to do "the hard way" many sex-love aspects of living. Force yourself, that is to say, to date girls, to make passes at them even when you may possibly get rejected, to try to win them for your steady girlfriends, and so on.

5. If you think that you are becoming even mildly fetish-

istic or deviated, vigorously work in the opposite direction to open more flexible lines of communication for yourself. Thus, if you find that you are enjoying heterosexual relations only when your girlfriend uses a black negligee or engages in mouth-genital contacts with you, deliberately work at becoming aroused and satisfied with her when she is *not* dressing in this manner or engaging in this particular kind of sex with you. Similarly, if you find that you are becoming attracted only to small girls, or red-headed girls, or to good-looking boys, force yourself, if necessary, to have sex relations with some *other* kinds of partners, and make sure that you adequately focus when you are with such partners so that you enjoy them *too*. Don't allow yourself to give up too easily and to keep desperately looking for the narrow kind of sex satisfaction that *easily* arouses and gratifies you. Keep after different sexual approaches, ideationally and actively, until they too begin to become satisfying.

This does not mean that you must compulsively try *all* methods of sex and *all* kinds of partners—for that kind of frantic varietism, too, can become a sexual deviation. But try to manage your sexual life so that a somewhat wide *range* of techniques are found to be satisfying, just as you might try to arrange your eating habits so as to include a fairly wide range of enjoyable foods. Sex deviation for the most part consists of a *rigid narrowing* of sex outlets; and this kind of narrowing can be avoided and worked against.

6. As noted above, if you become deviated in some particular manner, this does not mean that you were necessarily born this way, nor that you must remain similarly perverted for the rest of your life. Either by your own efforts, or preferably with psychotherapeutic aid, you can definitely overcome virtually any kind of serious sex deviation—as long as you will take sufficient time and energy to attempt to do so. Always remember, especially, that you are not *to blame*, are not a *louse*, for being mildly or seriously deviated. You are merely, in those circumstances, emotionally disturbed. And almost any kind of emotional disturbance, if you blamelessly accept it at first, can be calmly fought against and overcome.

Chapter 15

Adultery, Anyone?

The Ethics of Adultery

Adultery is a form of sex activity that has, at least in our society, distinct disadvantages—many of which I have listed in my books, *Sex Without Guilt* and *If This Be Sexual Heresy* . . . These disadvantages, however, apply mainly to married individuals who are unfaithful to their mates. For marriage is, at its best, an exceptionally trusting kind of relationship; and it is most difficult, when a man is born and raised in a civilized community in the Western world, for him to maintain full trust and honesty with his mate when he is at the same time engaging in adultery.

But how about the single man? Why should *he* not engage in an adulterous relationship with a woman who is already married to someone else?

Well, you may object, would not the single man who is an adulterer be a homebreaker? And would he not be behaving reprehensibly toward the husband of the woman with whom he is carrying on an affair?

The answer is no on both these counts. The married woman who has adulterous relations with a bachelor usually has no particular home to break up; since in most instances, she considers her home life already very poor, and that is the main reason she is engaging in adultery. And even if she does, on account of the affair she is having, finally break up her home, that is obviously *her* problem, and not that of the individual who is having the adulterous relationship with her. For he, the adulterer, generally has no contractual or other obligation to this married woman's husband; only *she* has. And if she negatively impinges on this obligation, that is her responsibility.

Similarly in the matter of your behaving reprehensibly toward the husband of your adulterous partner. As I have noted elsewhere (Ellis, 1963a), although a married woman obviously has a contractual and presumably trusting relationship with her husband, and although she tends to be false to and disrupt this relationship with him by engaging in adultery without his consent, her lover, unless himself a close friend of her husband, has no such trusting relationship. This lover is essentially in the same position as a business man, whom we shall call Smith, who makes a deal with another business man, whom we shall call Jones. As it happens, Jones is actually in partnership with Brown, and is making the deal with Smith behind Brown's back.

In this event, Jones is unquestionably acting unethically toward his partner, Brown. But Smith, of course, has a perfect right to make any kind of a deal that he wants with Jones, as long as he is not also a friend or partner of Brown's. And no matter how much Jones may be harming Brown by engaging in the deal with Smith, Smith is definitely *not* acting unethically toward Brown, as long as he has no special kind of contractual or other relationship with him.

So you, of course, are not behaving immorally toward Mr. Brown if you are carrying on with his wife—even though she, by the very same copulatory act which she engages in with you, may be highly unethical in her relationship with her husband. You are, in a sense, helping her be unethical. But, obviously, if she is going to behave this way with you, she could easily do so with half a dozen other males; and you would hardly be putting a stop to her behavior if you simply refused to be an adulterer with her.

As long, then, as you are not in any way friendly to the husbands of your adulterous inamoratas, and as long as you are quite honest and aboveboard with these women themselves—and do not, for example, induce them to go to bed with you because you falsely tell them that you love them madly or are going to marry them after they divorce their husbands—you can be a most moral, and practically straitlaced, adulterer. The society in which you reside may not particularly approve your behavior, and in some instances it may even legislate against it; but except by some fairly arbitrary social or religious definition, it is difficult to see how your extramarital sex activity is truly immoral or iniquitous.

Advantages and Disadvantages of Adultery

Are there, then, no particular disadvantages in regard to your engaging in an affair with a married woman? Oh, yes: there usually are. *All* heterosexual affairs, in fact, would appear to have *some* distinct disadvantages; and adulterous relations are no exception to the rule. Some of the obvious drawbacks to adultery are these:

First: even though you are truly not harming the husband of your sex partner, *he* may erroneously assume that you are. And if he is of a particularly quarrelsome or jealous disposition, he may well go after you with a shotgun; or may give you a physical beating; or may try to level economic sanctions against you, or may blacken your name in the community; or may otherwise attempt various sorts of reprisals against you —all this, of course, assuming that he discovers what is going on between you and his wife, and takes a dim view of your sexual compatibility with her.

Second: married women are sometimes not the most convenient kinds of sex partners, especially as far as availability is concerned. They may not be able to meet you when you want to see them. You may have to sneak around the town with them, and avoid various public places. You normally will not be able to call on them in their own homes, or stay the entire night with them when you do get together. They may well have children, parents, in-laws, and other relatives who seriously interfere with their affairs with you. And assignations with them may, for a variety of similar reasons, be curtailed.

Third: very often you cannot go as far as you might like to go in your intimate relations with an adulteress. If you want to marry the girl, she may well not be available. If you want to live with her under the same roof, in an unmarried state, that is usually impractical too. If you want to have children by her, serious complications generally ensue. If you want to give her gifts, or money, or take her away on a trip, none of these things may be arrangeable.

Fourth: in most circumstances, you will have to share your married inamorata with her husband. In some cases, she may manage to have sex relations only with you, and never with him, but in most instances, she will still have to keep going to bed with him, at least from time to time; and neither you nor she may be enthusiastic about this kind of plural sex-love affair on her part. The sexual monopoly that you would get if you were married to this woman, and that you would usually even be able to arrange if she were your steady girl-friend, is just not likely to be obtainable when she is sharing the same household with another man to whom she is legally married.

Fifth: you may, actually, not be able to leave your married lover if you want to do so, since she may threaten you with exposure, or otherwise be in a position to blackmail you to stay with her, just because you have been carrying on a clandestine relationship. Where a single girl with whom you are having an affair may or may not have some unusual hold on you, a married woman (particularly if you are yourself weak or vulnerable) may actually have a greater hold, and consider you more obliged to sustain this affair when you no longer wish to do so; and all kinds of unpleasant complications may therefore possibly occur.

It can easily be seen from the foregoing reasons that carrying on an adulterous affair is not all gravy, and that it may have distinct disadvantages. On the other hand, of course, it has several obvious bonuses. If a bachelor carries on a relationship with someone else's wife he is not likely to be forced to get too close to her or to marry her, if he does not wish to do so; he will probably save a good deal of time and money that he would have to spend if he courted a single girl; he obtains a sex partner who is presumably somewhat experienced and may possibly be more sexually adequate than many single girls would be; he does not literally have to live under the same roof with his inamorata; he avoids responsibilities for raising and providing for children; he sometimes doesn't have to be as concerned about the risk of pregnancy as he would have to be if he were having relations with a bachelor girl; there is usually very little chance of his acquiring a venereal disease; and he can often get rid of his sex partner fairly easily if he wishes to do so.

The main point is, of course, that there are *both* advantages and disadvantages if you engage in adulterous affairs, just as there are if you participate in fornicative or marital sex affairs. Consequently, you must not expect to derive only the joys of such adventures without any concomitant drawbacks (English and English, 1963).

Obviously, too, whether or not you should take part in any

particular adulterous relationship depends on the circumstances involved. Is the woman with whom you are considering such an affair sufficiently mature to have one without involving you in unnecessary hassles? Is she likely to open her big mouth and let her husband (or other interested individuals) know what is going on? What are the chances of her becoming so emotionally involved with you that she will insist on divorcing her husband or even abandoning him and her children and running away with you? Are the restrictions that will probably be placed on your relationship with her worth the price of giving up relationships with single girls, that may well have to go by the board if you carry on an affair with her? These and similar questions are the ones that you have to ask yourself before you rashly rush into an adulterous involvement.

If you do engage in adultery, there are usually rules that it would be much wiser for you to keep, in order to protect yourself and your inamorata. Keeping your *own* mouth tightly shut, for example, and not even informing most of your closest confidants what you are doing, or who is your ladylove. Taking extra-special contraceptive precautions. Being careful not to be seen too openly in public, unless you have a good excuse for being seen with her. Watching closely what you say to her over the phone or—especially!—in any written communications. Such precautions as these are usually quite necessary.

In some states, depending on the particular marriage and divorce laws, there may even be legal penalties for adultery. You may, for example, be sued by a husband for alienating the affection of his wife; or may be unpleasantly named as a corespondent in a divorce suit. You might do well to check the laws of your state in this connection, to see what genuine risks you may be running, and to do your best to minimize them.

However, the main point is, to use the terminology of the general semanticists (Korzybski, 1933, 1951), that adultery$_1$ is just not the same as adultery$_2$, and it is false to generalize in this connection. To say that you should never commit adultery would be foolish, even though there are usually many disadvantages to doing so. To say that you should eagerly enter almost any kind of an adulterous affair is also silly, even though such affairs frequently have great advantages. Whether you should enter a particular adulterous relationship depends very much on you, the kind of life you generally lead, the community in which you live, your sex-love goals, etc.; and, of course, it depends just as much on the partner you select, what kind of person she is, how she is likely to react to an affair, and so on. As Thomas Watson of IBM fame used to say: THINK—and then, in each individual instance, act accordingly.

Chapter 16

Marriage Isn't For Everyone

Some people enjoy marriage, tight-rope walking over a deep canyon, or garlic. Some don't.

To assume that marriage is absolutely either a good or a bad state is to hold that you must either decline its heaven or plumb its depths of hell without any true knowledge of what you are doing. Mating is a gamble in which the odds are weighted for or against you: depending on whether you and your chosen partner are or are not compatible with the marital institution and with each other. Which means that it is just about as safe to generalize about the joys of marriage as it is to talk, in the abstract, about the delights of eating, working, or listening to jazz. One man's meat, in this respect, is another's ptomaine poisoning.

There are, however, some common benefits and difficulties of marriage; and before you decide to plunge onto or cautiously avoid the marriage-go-round, it might be better if you gave these two sides of the coin a little closer attention. First, let us look at some of the assets and the liabilities of most marital unions.

The Advantages of Marriage

In our theoretically monogamous but actually monogynous (that is: one mate at a time rather than one-for-a-lifetime) society, marrying has distinct advantages for many men and women. The most important of these seem to be:

1. *Steady sexual relations*. Whether we like to admit it or not, numerous males and females in our culture marry chiefly because only by so doing can they legally obtain a steady sex partner. Monogamous society does its best to make nonmarital sex relations difficult, and forces many individuals to lead relatively abstinent lives unless they are

legally wed. In marriage, moreover, both mates are led to feel some kind of *obligation* to satisfy each other sexually; and in many instances they at least partially fill this obligation, whether they are personally interested or not in having regular intercourse.

This means, of course, that the man who has trouble in getting girls to bed on a steady basis, or who does not feel like continually competing with other males for female favors, or who dislikes the usual dating routine (including the dining, wining, dancing, etc.) which often precedes premarital intercourse, may find it advisable to barter his freedom and *its* advantages for the safety and security of *knowing* that he is going to get laid fairly regularly after he and his wife sign up "for life" at the license bureau. The sexual monopoly that he thereby gains may be more fancied than real, since his wife may easily find many ways of getting out of her side of the erotic "bargain." But, in theory at least, and usually to some degree in fact, the legal husband carves out for himself a *steady* piece of vulvovaginal pastry; and this may be all that he is really asking in his erotic life.

2. *Children.* Modern society bans the procreating of children outside of marriage and tends to viciously penalize "illegitimate" children and their mothers. Some people manage to bear and raise children outside of legal mating, and thereby are not deprived of having progeny even though they are not formally married; but these individuals are few and far between. The average person who wants to have and to raise children of his own has to marry in order to do so, and the state of marriage therefore gives him an advantage in this connection.

3. *Economic convenience.* Women derive clearcut economic conveniences from marriage, particularly when they have children, since they are usually more or less supported by their husbands, and sometimes are enabled to live very well without doing any kind of onerous vocational activity. But men, too, sometimes benefit economically from marriage. They may marry women who have considerable money and who help set them up in business or contribute to their incomes; or may marry wives who, themselves, work, and who significantly add to their economic status; or may have wives who help them, directly or indirectly, in their business affairs (e.g., by doing bookkeeping for them, entertaining business associates, attracting customers, etc.). In some oc-

cupations—as when a man is a clergyman or a marriage counselor, it is almost mandatory for him to get married or to stay married. And in business positions, even if his marriage is a holocaust, and largely exists in name only, a married man is frequently preferred over a bachelor.

4. *Social status.* Women frequently acquire a high degree of social status from marriage, and are sometimes scorned by their friends and relatives if they remain spinsters. Men, though to a lesser degree, also may acquire social status from marrying. Thus, a man may need a hostess for the parties he throws; or may gain in prestige by marrying a woman who is in the social register; or may be able to maintain social relations with certain solid citizens of his town only if he is respectably married; or may gain the "right" kind of friends in certain communities because his children are friendly with other people's children; or may be considered to be a much more mature and solid person by others just because he is married.

5. *Domestic advantages.* Women, by dint of marriage, may obviously gain the kind of home they want and may be able to engage in domestic routines that would be quite impossible if they were to remain single. But men, too, frequently gain domestically by marriage—particularly because they are often raised, in Western countries, so that they are not very efficient at shopping, cooking, sewing, and other domestic tasks, and consequently require a woman to do these things for them. When a man works eight or more hours a day, it may well be a good thing if he can arrange a division of labor, so that his wife does most of the housework while he spends his time at the office. Even if he is quite capable of doing such housework himself, he may not like to do so or may find it advantageous to see that his wife takes care of it. Most men, moreover, do not seem to be as interested in household affairs as are Western women, and they therefore derive benefits by getting rid of most household tasks, even when they have to work harder at the office in order to support their wives and children.

6. *Ensured companionship.* Many people in our society hate to be alone, and can easily stand sexual starvation better than deprivation of steady companionship. These individuals are frequently better off married, since marriage usually provides for domestic togetherness, and for a highly conventionalized type of fellowship. Thus, a wife is *supposed*

to accompany her husband to dinner, to the movies, to parties, and to other social functions; and he is *supposed* to stay at home with her for a good part of the week. If either or both of the mates have a strong desire for steady companionship, this desire is likely to be at least partially met by the mere fact of their being married.

High-level companionship or intense love between a husband and wife are, of course, not in the least assured by their being married. Indeed, romantic love is often sabotaged by the dull routine of domesticity. But conjugal or companionate love is generally fostered by marriage, since even unrelated roommates who live together for a long period of time tend to become attached to each other and to stay together in spite of the disadvantages their domestic sharing may have. Just as people become attached to dogs, cats, and other animals in the household, which are often a real bother to care for, so do they become attached to their marital housemates. Marriage, therefore, does in many cases create or cement a companionate love relationship—even when it seriously interferes with more impassioned or "higher" forms of loving.

The Disadvantages of Marriage

Granting that modern marriage has many potential or actual benefits for the average man (and woman) who enters this "blissful" state, surely we must admit that it has distinct disadvantages as well. Some of its obvious limitations are these:

1. *Sexual restriction.* Legally and socially, the married man is supposed to have sex relations exclusively with his wife; and he faces serious trouble—especially *with* his spouse —if it becomes known that he is carrying on adulterous affairs. This kind of enforced sexual monogamy may be fine and dandy for some reasonable low-sexed or perfectly mated husbands; but both statistical surveys and common observation prove that it is a pain in the testicles to a very high percentage of married men—who seem to have, in spite of the fact that they may love their wives and regularly enjoy copulating with them, highly varietist inclinations. Monogamic sex restrictions are an even greater bother to millions of males who have lost virtually all sex desire for their spouses and enjoy intercourse with these spouses about as much as they would with the original Queen of Sheba in her present sadly decomposed state.

Even husbands who have not lost desire for their wives are frequently—in fact, usually—seriously restricted in their sex lives if they remain totally faithful to these wives. For the average married woman in our society is sexually hors de combat a great deal of the time because of her menstrual periods, various forms of physical illness, fatigue, sexual disinclination, hostility toward her husband, absorption in the children, interest in some other man, fear that she will not achieve orgasmic release, general neurotic tendencies, vital absorption in outside vocation or avocation, and literally a hundred other reasons. Moreover, when she is quite interested in copulating with her mate, *he* may temporarily be in no condition to enjoy bare-assed felicity with her because *he* is momentarily too tired, ill, worried, hostile, externally absorbed, etc., etc., etc.

Because of this highly prevalent tendency of both the average husband and wife in our culture to be frequently unavailable for satisfying sex relations and often for any sex contact whatever, the *usual* copulatory rate of a couple that has been married for five or more years is appallingly low. In fact, if the true figures were ever fully realized, it is doubtful if a large fraction of the males who now marry would ever do so: since great numbers of these males obviously offer themselves as sacrificial lambs upon the marriage altar largely because they expect steady sex satisfaction after the return from their honeymoon; and in any reasonable sense of the term, *steady* satisfaction is exactly what they do *not* get. In fact, many of them were considerably better off in this respect before being married; and a certain proportion of these sexually deprived husbands find that they can regain their premarital level of sex fulfillment only by resorting to regular adultery.

2. *Difficulties with children.* Many of the people who marry primarily to have children find that when they do have them the children are far from the delight they expected them to be. Aside from requiring a great deal of time, trouble, and expense in their rearing—which most children, especially these days, do—human offspring can commonly be quite unrewarding to have around. Even the best of them are prone to sickness, temper tantrums, stubbornness, and various kinds of preadolescent and adolescent rebelliousness; and the worst of them may be as lovable as surly porcupines, and many literally end up in institutions for the mentally

deficient, in mental hospitals, in reform schools, and on the gallows.

Whereas, in the old days, children were a kind of social insurance, could be sent to work at an early age, and would often support their parents in the latter's old age, this is no longer true. More often than not, children are an economic drain, and may have to be supported through graduate school as well as through college, and even provided for during the first several years of their marriages. Occasionally, they in turn help with the parents' economic support when these parents get along in life; but this tends to be the exception rather than the rule.

Many married couples, moreover, do not really care for children, and could easily live without them. If they had remained single, they would have done just that. But, being married, they often feel socially obligated to bear and raise at least a couple of kids—often to their later sincere regret. Men, particularly, can live most happily without having any progeny. As Pearl S. Buck has noted, "A surprisingly small number of men are natural fathers, the ancient Chinese found. Far too many have fatherhood thrust upon them." The ancient Chinese obviously had no monopoly in this respect, for to marry, these days, still means almost inevitably to have fatherhood (or even motherhood) thrust upon one. This may be great for mankind (assuming that it does not strangle to death with overpopulation); but it is hardly conducive to the greatest good for the greatest nmber of reluctant parents.

3. *Economic inconvenience.* Only the rare husband these days gains economically by marriage, in spite of extra tax exemptions, the possible business help of his wife, and various other financial advantages he may sometimes gain by marrying. For two can not, in this day and age, live as cheaply as one: even, in many cases, when both are working and producing income. For one thing, the economic *expectations* in regard to married couples are much too high. Whereas the single girl or fellow can live respectably in almost any kind of low-level apartment or neighborhood (and can often, in fact, live most economically with his or her parents, while paying practically nothing for board and room), this is not normally allowable for married couples. They must live under conditions wherein they can properly entertain friends, show off their house or apartment, drive a fairly new car, be in a

neighborhood that is suitable to raise children in, have the right kind of address, and so forth. Therefore, even if their family income is reasonably high, they may easily find that they are falling in debt in order to keep up with the other married Joneses near whom they live or work.

From the standpoint of the male, marriage is almost always economically onerous, since not only must he spend more money to support his wife and family than he would ever spend to support himself, but he also tends to be quite restricted in his choice of jobs and the way he can go about working at them. The single man can take a position almost anywhere in the world, if he wants to do so, and can work all hours of day and night if he thinks that is the best way to get ahead at it. But the married man must consider where his wife and children want to live, and must frequently give up certain kinds of jobs or refuse to work long hours at them because these jobs and hours of work would not fit into the schedule of his family. Moreover, just because he is married and must spend practically all his income, in most instances, to support his wife and children, he finds it almost impossible to build up capital which he could use to go into his own business, or buy into a firm in which he would like to work. Eventually, if he keeps working very hard and saves avidly (often at the expense of constant quarrels with his wife), he may be able to accumulate capital and be able to go into business for himself. But the chances are about nine out of ten that it will take him much longer to do this when he is married than if he had remained single.

This is not to say that males are the only ones in our society who are economically inconvenienced by marriage, for sometimes women are even more handicapped in this respect. Thus, wives may give up good positions to live off the meager bounty of their husbands. Or they may be unable, because of their child-rearing chores, to finish school and prepare themselves for the kind of professional positions they would like to assume. Or they may be forbidden to work, by their husbands, and thereby deprived not only of income but of a vitally absorbing occupation that might only add appreciably to their happiness. Or they may wed niggardly husbands who never give them proper allowances for things they want to purchase. Or they may sometimes find themselves forced to work at poor jobs in order to support their husbands and families. So, although many women do gain economically by marriage, many do not; and there are numerous instances wherein both husbands and wives wind up in a much poorer socio-economic position by marrying than they would have got into had they both remained single and perhaps carried on an indefinitely prolonged affair with each other. As one of the pioneers in the study of marriage and family relations, Ernest R. Groves (1925) has written:

"Both man and wife may feel that married life entails too great a cutting down of personal expenditures. . . . Marriage was once a decided economic advantage for both the man and the woman. It is now for many, especially for city dwellers, an enterprise that cuts down the former income of the two and at the same time increases expenses. . . . It does not necessarily help the young fellow in business that he has recently married. Family cares and worries may even handicap him in his competition with those who are carrying no home burden."

4. *Social inconveniences.* Although marriage often gives increased social status to its participants, it also has it social drawbacks. A married man, in particular, cannot do many things that an unmarried man can do. He is supposed to drag his wife with him wherever he goes. He is restricted in his visiting. He may be hampered in his social-business contacts. He is likely to receive fewer social invitations to parties, dinners, and affairs than he was wont to receive when he was single. He may have to drop many of his premarital friends, especially his female friends. He often cannot easily, when he wishes to do so, play poker with the boys, or go to a ball game, or sometimes even take a walk around the block. As the noted playwright Arthur Wing Pinero wrote (1924): "You know a marriage often cools friendships. . . . In nine out of ten cases a man's marriage severs from him more close ties than it forms."

5. *Domestic disadvantages.* Marriage is a domestic inconvenience to numerous husbands and wives. Thus, there are men who like to live by themselves, and who find that marriage seriously infringes on their privacy. There are others who at most want to share their living quarters with one or two others, and who find themselves seriously handicapped living with larger families (including, often, their in-laws!) after marrying. There are still others who prefer to eat in restaurants rather than at home, or like to play their hi-fi equipment at full blast, or who prefer to stay up half the

night reading, or who want to throw their clothes on a chair or sofa (or even the floor!) instead of neatly hanging them up all the time. These individuals, and many more with other kinds of idiosyncrasies, find themselves terribly confined by domestic sharing, even though they may truly love their mates and enjoy steady sex relations with these mates. Domesticity, though greatly desired by some spouses, is anathema to others, and often turns out to be the worst bane of marital living.

6. *Companionship and love restrictions.* Many people find that, oddly enough, there is both too much and too little companionship in marriage. On the one hand, they become irked by *always* having to live under the same roof and attend the same affairs with their legal mates, when they may very well frequently want their own privacy or may prefer to go out with *different* partners. On the other hand, they find that the "companionship" that they realize in marriage is on an exceptionally low level and is far from intense, absorbing, or amusing. It usually keeps them from having more vital companionable relations with nonmarital partners, especially those who are members of the other sex.

In the field of love, or even intense friendship, conditions tend to be worse in the vast majority of marriages. Although a man may quietly and consistently care for his wife, the chances are that the intensity of his love for her will decrease over the years and that this kind of conjugal love will not by any means fill all his amative desires. But, of course, if he dares to become emotionally involved with other women in addition to his wife, and she becomes (as she often will in such circumstances) aware of his outside involvements, there will almost always be hell to pay, and he will have to surrender his extracurricular emotional relationships—or else seek a divorce. Even if he becomes intensely absorbed in a friendly (and presumably nonhomosexual!) relationship with another man, his wife and children are likely to be jealous of this kind of involvement and to discourage him from perpetuating it.

This means that the sexual, amative, and companionable advantages that one frequently derives from the monopolistic character of marriage tend to be double-bladed; and one of the blades, the restrictive one that discourages outside affairs and friendships, can be viciously cutting, and can emasculate a married person's affectional propensities until he engages in only a pitiful fraction of the intense human involvements of which he is theoretically capable. This is perhaps one of the most serious, and least observed and acknowledged, disabilities of modern monogamous marriage.

7. *Restrictions on action and adventure.* Many married individuals become notoriously tamed after they have entered holy—or, as the case may be, hellish—wedlock. Being mated, and having children in most instances to tie them down, they tend to lose much of their courage, determination, and energy, and are often no longer in any mood to embark upon activities and adventures to which they may previously have looked forward. Sometimes their entire careers are muddied or ruined because they feel they must settle down to conventional marital routines which limit them and deprive them of creative energies and imagination, and which dissuade them from risking their all for an absorbing cause. At other times, they do well enough in their business or professional interests, but find themselves forced to forego most of the adventures and pioneering forays—which may range all the way from climbing Mt. Everest to working for a political or social organization—that they would eagerly attempt if they did not feel chained to their marital menage.

As John Stuart Mill (1869) noted in this respect: "Whoever has a wife and children has given hostages to Mrs. Grundy." And Romain Rolland (Maurois, 1940) concurred: "A married man is no more than half a man."

8. *Legal bondage.* Legal marriage is, to some degree, a kind of enforced entrapment: since, without the specific consent and collaboration of one's mate, it is difficult to get a divorce in most Western lands. Although it is doubtless just that a man should be in some way legally bound to his wife, since he may have children by her and these children have to be supported whether or not he cares to continue the marital relationship, it is indubitably unfair for this man to *have* to stay with his mate, whether he likes to do so or not, long after he has ceased to care for her in any way. Yet, that is precisely what he will have to do, in certain instances, if he wants to break the marital tie and cannot induce her to cooperate.

Marriage is also a kind of imprisonment or constraint in that, even when spouses do not have any intention of divorcing each other, they are often forced to undertake various obligations for which, especially at certain times, they have no stomach whatever. Thus, a married man is frequently obligated, whatever his current personal inclinations may be, to take his children to the circus, to be nice to his monstrous in-laws, to accompany his wife to the ballet, to have intercourse when he feels as sexless as a paramecium, and to do a host of other things which leave him mightily unenthusiastic. Most married people somehow manage to tolerate these kinds of inconveniences—just as most prisoners somehow manage to tolerate an extended incarceration. But the mere fact that some people gracefully lump, and at times even enjoy, imprisonment does not mean that they would not be much happier outside the bars. The bonds of marriage, even when they may be "adjusted" to in a sensible way, are frequently irksome to most married individuals.

Max O'Rell (1901) half-humorously noted: "When you are dead, once said a cynic, it's for a long time; but when you are married, it's forever." H. L. Mencken (1924) agreed: "No man, examining his marriage intelligently, can fail to observe that it is compounded, at least in part, of slavery, and that he is the slave." And Samuel Butler sang in *Hudibras*:

> "So men are by themselves betray'd,
> To quit the freedom they injoy'd,
> And run their Necks into a Noose,
> They'ld break 'em after, to break loose."

9. *Marital difficulty and unhappiness*. Marriages may, as has sometimes been alleged, be made in heaven; for certainly only angels could be happy in most of them. It may be more realistically contended that marriages, all right, are *made* in heaven—and then slowly or quickly wend their way down the path to hell.

Far from being a necessarily happy affair, marriage is an exceedingly difficult and miserable business for many couples. About one-third of the people in our own society who wed end up, sooner or later, in the divorce court. Many other spouses never resort to actual divorce, but quietly and extra-legally separate from each other and live apart for the rest of their lives. Still many more—in fact, millions upon millions, of husbands and wives—continue to live together until death mercifully doth them part, but are woefully mated all their married lives. If ten per cent of all the people who marry are truly happy with one another during the rest of their days, this would be a surprisingly high percentage. From three to five per cent would probably be closer to the mark.

It may be realistically observed, therefore, that once there's a solution in marriage, there's often none of it; and one of the great risks that all married persons take is that they will find blisslessness in their domestic venture and will live scrappily ever after. To such persons, who fail in their marriages but still continue, for one reason or another, to remain tied to their mates, marriage is mainly a huge discomfort and disadvantage. Said some of the sages and authorities on marriage:

Ai-Damiri, Hayat al-Hayawan (Mathers, 1930): "Someone said to a philosopher: 'Your enemy is dead.' 'I had much rather you had reported,' answered the philosopher, 'that he was married.'"

Robert Louis Stevenson (1909): "Marriage is like life in this—that it is a field of battle, and not a bed of roses."

Oscar Wilde (1935): "Men marry because they are tired; women, because they are curious; both are disappointed."

Samuel D. Schmalhausen (1930): "I give it as my sober and most thoughtful judgment that an insane asylum is a place of peace and repose and sweet reasonableness compared with the institution of marriage as generally practiced."

Edward Westermarck (1936): "Marriage is not made for everybody, not attractive to everybody, nor good for everybody who embarks on it."

Havelock Ellis (1952): "Marriage has always been difficult. It perpetually involves trouble and injustice among savages. It does the same among ourselves. In the middle of the seventeenth century Dorothy Osborn wrote that it was a miracle if two couples in ten lived in agreement. Today it is said that no more than one marriage in four is happy, while even that is sometimes regarded as an optimistic estimate."

In many different ways, then, marriage is almost inevitably restricting and freedom-destroying. This is not to say that it usually doesn't have distinct advantages and compensations; for it often does. But anyone who believes that he is going to attain all the joys of marital existence without giving up a good deal of his independent *self* has huge rocks in his head. The game may—yes, *may*—be well worth the candle. But the candle invariably costs *something*; and the comfortable light it sometimes sheds is often gloriously expensive—as well as, all too frequently, a frightful expenditure of glory.

Westermarck, then, was right. Marriage definitely *isn't* for everyone. And no matter how much you may think you need marriage, you actually don't. You may *prefer* it over the single state, and very much *want* to enter it; but the *need* that you think you have is merely your own irrational idea that you *must* have it, and will practically drop dead unless you are married. The chances are, to say the least, you won't.

You don't *have* to marry, then; and you should give the most careful consideration to doing so. As Leo Tolstoy (1919) said: "Above all, think twenty times, a hundred times, before marrying. To join one's life with that of another by the sexual link is for a moral and sensitive person the most important act and the one most pregnant with consequences, which it is possible to commit. One should always marry in the same way as one dies: that is, only when it is impossible to do otherwise." And, in even more serio-comic vein, there is the famous century-old line from the English magazine *Punch:* "Advice to those who are about to marry: 'Don't!' "

Of course, there is always the more experimental approach. Marriage *is* a unique life experience, and it seems a shame for anyone to miss this experience—even when it turns out to be somewhat trying and miserable. My own advice to single people tends to be: "Everyone should marry—at least once!" And this, I think, is excellent advice—assuming that any given marriage is not taken as necessarily final, and you can somehow arrange to get out of it, if you later want to do so, without too great a hassle.

In other words, if you want to *try* marriage, with a particular girl, largely because you want to see what the marital situation is like, and because you also think that you may (but also may *not!*) have a chance at a good relationship with her, then you can enter into a legal bond with this girl with a reasonably experimental attitude, hoping that the marriage will work out but fully facing the fact that it just may possibly end in an amicable divorce.

Of course, you must know your customer, and know her very well, if *this* is the kind of an approach to marriage that you take. For women are funny creatures. They tend to become exceptionally attached to even a poor marital relationship; to desperately want children; to feel that once they have been supported by a man for a number of years, they can't possibly make it economically on their own thereafter; and to want to stay indefinitely, for a number of status-seeking and other poor reasons, in a bad marriage.

So before you try any experimenting with marriage, discuss this matter thoroughly with your prospective mate. Determine, beyond all reasonable doubt, that she is something of an experimentalist herself; that she has no mystico-religious reasons for remaining in a low-level relationship; that she has sufficient self-respect to want to get out of a poor marriage herself and to go on to something better in life if she doesn't get along well with a given husband; and that she is most unlikely to demand, out of vindictiveness or severe personal insecurity, unreasonable economic support in the event of a divorce. If, moreover, you know full well that your marriage may not last forever and a day and are nonetheless willing to give it a good try, it is far wiser, in most instances, to put off child-rearing until you and your wife have been together for a few years and are fairly certain that you *want* to continue the marriage on a long-time basis.

Whether or not your approach to marriage is experimental, give the entire matter active cogitation and due consideration. Sex is a ball; love is a joy; but marriage is a hell of a serious business. Think before you leap—and get the thickest foam rubber you can find to cushion your potential fall!

Chapter 17

If Marry You Must:
How to Pick a Suitable Wife

Never marry until you have known at least a score of women intimately. Then you may not want to!

More seriously: never marry until you first know *yourself* —know what *you* tend to like and dislike about women. And the only safe way to know yourself in this connection is to know a good many women intimately and to spend as much time with them as possible. For *you*, essentially, consist of your basic preferences and dislikes. You, for example, may greatly enjoy coitus, solicitude, or constant companionship. Or you may *not*. But how the devil are you going to *know* whether you want a woman to be highly sexed, incessantly affectionate, or always intent on being in your company unless you try her, and preferably try a couple of other women quite unlike her, and see?

You may, of course, prefer *one* woman to be sexually avid —and want another female to stay a hundred miles away from you in bed. Or you may want to be with a certain female companion practically all the time—and wish that another female, who continually wants *your* companionship, would permanently reside in China, and perhaps visit you for one weekend a year. But the chances are that you have some preferences and distastes that apply to practically *all* females; and that the only way you are actually going to discover what these are is to be sexuo-amatively intimate with several of them. If, by being attached to four or more women, you discover that you practically *never* want to have sex relations more than twice a week, or that you almost *always* feel much happier when your partner is a well-ordered, housewifey type of individual, then you may be pretty certain that moderate sexual participation or well-ordered domesticity *is* your oyster, and that you'd better seek, in a permanent mate, one who *also* likes the same kind of seafood.

189

Know, then, thy marital *self*. And by *marital* I mean precisely that: for your courtship or premarital self may be significantly different from your domestically mated self. You may, for example, be a real sexual firebrand when you see a girl once a week, and think of little more than getting her into the sack thirty seconds after you meet her every Saturday evening, and keeping her there until at least the early morning hours. But once you actually live with this same beauty, and crawl between the sheets with her literally every night in the week, your sexual ardor may remain exactly as it was before marriage: that is, red-hot on Saturday night and ice-cold for the rest of the week. This kind of bed behavior may or may not be satisfactory to her, even though she may have been highly pleased with your premarital lustfulness. Similarly, you may miss your girlfriend terribly when you see her once or twice a week, and may think of her almost constantly when she is not around. But once you live with her, you may thank your stars that you leave to go to the office every day, and may give her hardly a thought (and perhaps a negative one at that!) until you return home in the evening.

How, then, can you possibly tell before marriage what it will be like to see your inamorata constantly and to share many significant aspects of life with her? The answer is: You can't. If you are sane about your premarital relations, you can get a good approximation of what your life with her is likely to be after the legal knot has been tied; but you can never precisely tell how it will be, since legal mating *itself* frequently changes the nature of a relationship and makes things important that were previously of little or no consequence.

Is the case for marital prognostication hopeless then? No, not quite: since you can, even during fairly conventional courtship in our society, see a considerable amount of your girlfriend, go on long camping or other trips with her, spend a good many weekends together, visit friends and relatives, plan various cooperative ventures, and do a good many other things that you may well have to do after you are married. And, by observing how both of you spontaneously enjoy or gracefully adjust to the things that you do together before marriage, you can at least get some idea of how you are likely to make out in similar ways after marriage.

This means, of course, that you should *not*, during courtship, do what a great many couples normally do: namely, see each other once or twice a week for a few hours at a time, and in artificial, and usually entertaining, circumstances. For if you habitually call for your girlfriend, take her out to eat, go with her to a show or movie, and then smooch for a while when you take her home, you are going to discover relatively little about her, in most instances—and especially about her day-to-day *living* habits. Only, in some manner, shape, or form, by your steadily *being with* her, are you going to get to know her.

Would, then, a kind of trial or companionate marriage—such as Judge Ben Lindsey (Lindsey and Evans, 1929) espoused over thirty-five years ago—be a good solution to the problem of finding someone who is truly suitable for you in wedlock? Yes, I think it would be; and I have said so publicly on several occasions (Ellis, 1958, 1963a), much to the horror of several radio and television audiences that I addressed. And I stand by my publicly stated opinion. The very best way to get to know an individual to whom you are not yet married is to live with her as closely as possible under truly marital conditions. If, therefore, you can induce your girlfriend to live under the same roof with you, and assume all the usual functions you would expect a wife to assume, for at least a year before you legally marry her, that would usually be an excellent idea for both of you. For you could thereby get a real inkling of what both of you are like when married. And you might be quite surprised!

I have had a number of people who have come to me for marriage counseling, who have sadly noted that if they had lived with their mate under the same roof for even a couple of weeks, they would have never married him or her. Let's not have this happen to you! If you can sample marriage, on some sort of a trial basis, before you actually take the legal plunge, by all means manage to do so.

Naturally, this cannot always be done so easily. Females, in particular, are usually loath to live together with you under the same roof, because then your premarital relationship becomes quite public; and they are ashamed to let their friends and relatives know that they are not truly married. So don't be surprised if the girl you think is just for you, and who is sane and stable in most ways, refuses to go into a trial marriage relationship with you. And don't necessarily think that therefore she would not be a good wife for you. The cards are so stacked in this regard in our society that it is surprising how many girls actually do live in the unwedded state with their partners, and how few qualms they feel about doing so. If you can locate one of these girls, great! But if you cannot, then you will just have to go back to less efficient forms of trial marriage—and, as we noted above, get as close as possible to living together with a girl before you marry her without literally sharing domestic arrangements with her.

Whether or not you live with a girl before marriage, and whether or not you get sufficient experience about yourself and what you are likely to require for a satisfactory mating relationship, there are some traits which have been found most desirable for a wife to have; and however much an individual you may be, the chances are that you should seriously consider these traits and the degree to which your beloved possesses them, before you wend your way to the altar. We shall now list and discuss some of these traits which, in the great majority of cases, it would be desirable for you to seek in a potential mate.

Emotional Stability

Emotional *instability* is often a fine thing—for sweethearts and mistresses to have. For the real kooky, or far out, woman may be fascinating, charming, lively, and incessantly changeable. Never, with her, is there likely to be a dull moment! And the more such women you can—for a time!—relate to, the more exciting will your life and your memoirs tend to be. I, myself, have had some of the greatest times of my life with some of the zaniest women I have known; and although the price I have paid for such times has often been steep, I have never considered it exorbitant. In many ways, I loved every minute of the hell they gave—or at least did their best to give—me.

Nutty women, then, are often wonderful. But not for marriage! Never, if you can possibly help it, *marry* a serious neurotic or psychotic. No: never. Highly disturbed women are almost always too confused, too self-centered, too inhibited, too self-destructive, and often too hysterical even to have satisfactory sex relations on a steady basis; and they rarely have good marital relationships.

Many neurotics—and especially many neurotic women—actually marry because they erroneously look upon marriage as a refuge, and believe that they will magically find emotional safety in it. But since their main trouble is that they cannot adjust to the comparatively simple problems of single life, they are hardly able to adjust satisfactorily to the even more difficult situations of marriage. Consequently, their neurotic condition frequently becomes aggravated in wedlock.

If either you or your partner, then, are seriously disturbed, do everything *but* marry. Love each other, if you wish. Have all the sex relations you like. But do not tie your hands with the legal bonds of marriage. In your own case, go for psychological help, and work at overcoming your neurosis before you marry. In the case of your partner, try to help her become less disturbed; and if possible, see that she goes for psychotherapy.

Can you yourself treat a woman with whom you have an intense sex-love relationship? Yes, you sometimes can. As I show in my book, *How to Live with a Neurotic* (1957), there is much that one mate can do to help another mate overcome her disturbance. Not that married partners are the best therapists for each other. Usually, they are not: since they are hardly objective, are themselves involved with the partner, and are apt to be viewed in a prejudiced, and somewhat negativistic light by their mates. But if you do happen to be married, and your wife simply will not go for the professional help that she could well use, then you might just as well try to help her yourself before you run off to the divorce court.

You can, for example, frequently help a neurotic mate by taking a thoroughly non-blaming attitude toward her; accepting her *as* a neurotic while she is still disturbed; showing her by your own calmer example that she doesn't *have* to be exceptionally anxious or angry when various unpleasant situations arise, being warm and supportive even when she does palpably wrong things; and actively teaching her a saner, less self-defeating philosophy of life. You can also help a girlfriend or a fiancée in much the same manner. The main point is, however, that you would be far wiser if you tried to help your disturbed partner *before* rather than *after* marrying her; since if she absolutely insists, as well she may, on remaining disturbed, you then have a much easier way out of the relationship. And if a woman insists—as, alas, many of them do —on being anxious and angry, and will not do much to help herself overcome her basic neurosis or psychosis, you are almost invariably better off without than with her. In a neurotic marriage, as Kubie (1936) has noted, "where only one of the two consents to be treated, or if only one succeeds in achieving health, separation may be the only healthy solution." In a neurotic nonmarital relationship, separation is obviously much easier—and cheaper!

Compatible Interests

Being married, even in this liberal day and age, still mainly means being together with your partner day after day, year after year, for a good many hours at a time. It should therefore be obvious that unless you and your wife have many interests and ideologies in common, you are not likely to get along well together for any long period.

This usually means that you and your potential wife should enjoy some of the same pastimes, see eye to eye on a good many important questions of philosophy, religion, politics, and economics; be interested in similar fields of endeavor; have many harmonious recreations; and otherwise be able to appreciate each other's interests, if not actually to engage in them together. For if one of you despises the vital absorptions of the other, trouble will inevitably follow (Ellis and Harper, 1961a). And if one of you has some abiding interest or hobby, and the other incessantly tries to drag this mate away from this vocation or avocation, a happy marriage is most unlikely to ensue.

"This is not to say," as Lichtenberger (1931) sagely points out, "that a married couple must go through life together like a pair of Siamese twins, nor does compatibility involve identity. Qualities may be complementary or supplementary as the very condition of their congeniality, but they cannot be irreconcilably combative if marriage is to endure."

Sexual Compatibility

There have certainly been a few—albeit damned few—marital relationships where the couple involved have been happily mated though they have been completely incompatible sexually; but the question is whether such individuals are truly married. *Marriage*, even in its legal sense, implies some kind of sexual involvement between the husband and wife; and it is often possible to obtain an annulment if no such involvement exists. Although sex is not technically an absolutely necessary part of marriage, few individuals go to the trouble of becoming legally wed without contemplating having sex relations; and those who do are to be suspected of having rather peculiar motives!

Happy marriages, moreover, are rare when the partners are having poor sex relations or none at all. Sexual incompatibilities literally lead to serious dissatisfaction in innumerable relationships and, very frequently, divorce or separation ensues mainly because the husband and wife just cannot manage to satisfy each other's sex drives. Ira S. Wile (Hutton, 1938) has noted that "no one knowing the facts can deny that most of the serious difficulties in marriage arise from sexual maladjustments." And Levy and Munroe (1938), reporting on the unhappy married couples they saw, stated that "every couple has its own story of sexual disharmony. The details are not important. The fact that some form of maladjustment in the sexual field occurs in almost every case of disturbed marital relationship is very striking."

It has to be admitted, of course, that just as sexual disharmony leads to general marital disagreement, so does nonsexual bickering usually lead, sooner or later, to sexual incompatibility. It is often difficult to decide, in these cases, which is the chicken and which is the egg. The fact remains, however, that there is such a thing as sex difficulty itself; and when it occurs, it is likely to flavor and discolor many of the other aspects of marriage, and cause some otherwise compatible couple to dislike each other intensely, and finally to contemplate divorce.

One of the obvious solutions to this problem of sex incompatibility—and one which the books on marriage almost always overlook—is for the potential husband and wife, before they become legally tied, to test their sex harmony in the only true way that it can be tested: in bed. By their having steady sex relations for at least several months before they marry (and preferably, as we noted in the last chapter, in the course of their actually living together during this time), they will not absolutely, beyond all possible shadow of a doubt, prove whether or not they are sexually compatible. For it is quite possible for a couple to get along wonderfully in sexual respects for some period of time, and later to be quite undesirous of each other. It is also possible for a couple to be poor sexual partners for a year or two, and then reach a point where they thoroughly enjoy each other's sexual company.

These, however, are exceptions that tend to prove the rule. The average husband and wife who seriously try to achieve sex satisfaction with each other for a period of months, and who still get little out of their sex relations, are rarely going to overcome their incompatibility later. They may very well achieve a better kind of harmony than they ever had before; but the chances are that they just don't "send" each other sexually, and that they never will. Similarly, the average man and wife who get along beautifully with each other in bed, and who at the same time maintain good nonsexual relations, are going to continue to enjoy sex with each other for many years to come.

Therefore, although there is no certainty that a premarital sex trial will ensure your discovering whether or not you are sexually compatible with a given partner, there is a near-certainty that such a trial will give you sufficient salient information about her and your own sex inclinations and co-operativeness that you will be able to predict, with a pretty high degree of success, whether she is likely to make a good bed partner for you. The more you experiment with your girlfriend before marrying her, the greater likelihood there is that you will see whether the two of you have a good measure of sex compatibility. If, especially, you are the kind of person who does his best to try out a car, a television set, or any other complicated piece of apparatus before you purchase it, the least you can do is to try out your sexual partner before you purchase a wedding ring and a marriage license!

Amative Compatibility

Most people in our society marry for love. Perhaps they shouldn't. Perhaps it would be wiser if, as happens in many cultures, their marriages were arranged for them by their parents or some social agency. But the fact is that they do, in the Western world, generally marry for love; and they have, of course, several significant affectional expectations when they marry. Since you are almost certainly one of those people who, if you decide to enter the state of wedlock, will want a definite kind of love relationship in your marriage, you'd better actively seek love compatibility as well as sex compatibility while you are still in the courtship stage. For in many instances you will find that a given woman, however much you may be physically or intellectually attracted to her, is amatively incompatible with you.

Your potential wife, for example, may be so attached to her parents that she cannot truly love anyone. Or she may be so self-centered that she cannot love at all. Or she may be obsessed with having children, and with giving practically all her love and attention to them. Or she may be quite capable of loving a male—but that man may not happen to be you.

On the other side of the fence, your beloved may be utterly mad about you and more than willing to devote considerable time and effort to being with you and making you happy. But *you* may not, yourself, be particularly interested in overt displays of affection. Or you may be over-attached to your family and want to spend considerable time with them instead of with her. Or you may be utterly devoted to your work, and find that continual and violent affectionality only gets in your way.

For many reasons, then, you and your potential wife may be amatively out of tune. If this is so, then the chances are that at least one of you, and perhaps both, will be miserable after marriage; since the one thing most people can stand even less than sex incompatibility is a day-to-day relationship with a mate who loves them much too much or much too little. Millions of husbands and wives, in fact, who manage to make surprisingly good adjustment to a perfectly miserable sex relationship are unable to adjust to a mate who is not meeting what they consider to be their rightful amative needs.

The solution to the problem of affectional compatibility in marriage is not easy or obvious. For although, as previously noted, once sex compatibility is attained it is not too likely to change very much, this is not true of love harmony. It is exceptionally common for a man and woman to fill each other's emotional desires satisfactorily during their courtship and early marital years—and then to become most incompatible in this regard. Women, for example, frequently become more and more attached to their husbands as the years go by; while men often are madly in love with their wives for a year or two, and then find less and less emotional satisfaction with them. Other women are utterly devoted to their husbands—until they have children, when their interest in their mates may seriously wane. Still other women become so relatively (if at times falsely) secure as a result of the status and social position they gain by marrying, that they have little subsequent need of emotional support from their husbands, and consequently become interested in Mah Jong, club activities, and everything else except their mates. Similarly, many men become so successful in their business or other enterprises after a few years of marriage that they no longer have need of the bolstering that they formerly required from their wives, and lose many of their amative ties to these wives.

If human love preferences and requirements are so changeable, what can you do about selecting a wife with whom you are likely to be amatively compatible? Sometimes, very little; since you can only do your best to predict the future, and then hope that things will come out the way you predicted. Most of the time, however, you can at least look keenly into your own heart and determine what your present and future emotional drives are likely to be. Are you, for example, the kind of person who is generally warm, affectionate, and interested in return affectionality? Do you enjoy hand-holding, tender kissing, and whispered sweet nothings? Or are you very little interested in this type of thing, and much more absorbed in objective problem-solving or in cool-headed conversation? If you are in the warmly affectional class, the chances are you will want one kind of wife; and if you are in the other class, you will probably be much happier with a wife who is also not too overtly affectionate, and who enjoys a calmer kind of relationship. If you can manage to be *both* warm and objective, then a similarly rare type of girl may be your ideal mate.

So look into your own heart, and try to determine, at the same time, what kind of person, in regard to love, your potential wife really is. Mere words may be misleading in this respect; for your chosen girl may *say* she is interested in warmth and affection, and actually be so amatively inhibited that she feels most uncomfortable when you act warmly toward her. Or she may *say* that she does not need much attention from you, and even truly believe what she says. In actual fact, however, you may note that she has little ability to stand on her own feet and to go about the business of living when you are not paying attention to her and catering greatly to her emotional needs.

As usual, the best indication of both your own and your

potential wife's affectional urges and requirements is the way you actually feel and behave toward each other on a fairly long-term basis. Know her, therefore, for a good many months, and preferably at least a year, before you marry her; and know her in the most intimate circumstances, for days at a time when you are living in close quarters. If you can literally live with her for a period of time before marriage, fine! If you cannot do this, then get as close to doing it as circumstances allow. The best way to know yourself and her is in practice rather than in theory; and affectional practice is just what it implies: being with her and acting affectionately (or, for that matter, nonaffectionately) to her for some period of time—and *then* seeing how both of you respond.

Mutual Interests and Companionship

Modern marriage usually demands pretty constant companionship between husband and wife; and only certain persons can be adequately companionable with each other over long stretches. Either you and your potential mate can get along beautifully together when you are continually by yourselves; or you cannot. For heaven's sake, find out!

Thus, either you or your girlfriend may want a great deal of privacy, and resent having to be with anyone on a steady basis. Or either of you may be unable to be alone for even a relatively short period and may mightily resent the other's absence. Or both of you may be quite companionable—but not with each other. As Robert Louis Stevenson (1909) remarked: "It is more important that a person should be a gossip, and talk pleasantly and smartly of common friends and the thousand and one nothings of the day and hour, than that he should speak with the tongues of men and angels; for a while together by the fire, happens more frequently in marriage than the presence of a distinguished foreigner to dinner."

If there is any serious companionable incompatibility between you and your hoped-for wife, do your best to discover it *before* you marry her. Then, you can either work hard to remove the incompatibility; or you can avoid marrying each other. How can you work at becoming more companionable? By seeing exactly what the differences between you are in this respect; by openly discussing them with each other; and by making energetic, mutually planned moves to remove or ameliorate some of the most serious differences.

Thus, if you are a chess bug, your potential wife may study chess, to see if she, too, can become enthusiastic about it. Or if you desire a great deal of privacy, or lead the kind of life where you will leave her to her own resources even if you don't prefer to do so, she is going to have to find some vital absorptions that she can enjoyably throw herself into when you are not around. Similarly, if your girl really is the kind of person who simply must have a steady companion if she is to lead a happy life, then either you have to arrange to be with her a good deal of the time, or else some other suitable substitute companion will have to be made available when you are not able to be with her.

Naturally, if you want a great deal of solitude or occupation away from home and your potential mate requires your almost constant companionship, things are not going to work out very well. Or if you are largely interested in attending political rallies and lectures, and she is only interested in music and art, you will soon tend to grate on each other—or else be happier apart. This is too bad; but it is far better that you find out this sort of thing before rather than after marrying. Just because you are sexually and amatively compatible —which you are quite likely to be at the time you are seriously contemplating marriage—does not mean that you have *enough* in common to make for a good, continuing relationship. Husbands and wives inevitably have much more to do with each other nonsexually and nonamatively than they do while they are copulating or holding hands. Think of these nonsexual, and generally time-consuming, aspects of marriage before you rush off to the license bureau! Those who cannot amicably keep steady company with their potential mates should not keep company with marriage.

Child-rearing Compatibility

If battles over child care ceased to exist in modern marriage, the battle of marriage itself would be considerably diminished. Innumerable couples squabble endlessly over how their children should be reared; and their ensuing frays are lost by husbands, wives, and—above all—their battle-grounded offspring.

If you have any intention of having children—and you should realistically face the fact you will probably have them sooner or later in marriage, whether you at first intend to or not—you should make a concerted effort to marry a woman who has ideas similar to yours concerning children, who wants approximately as many or as few as you do, and who is willing to rear them in a manner that is satisfactory to you. Otherwise, it is almost certain that your offspring—or even your lack of them—will be a constant source of irration and disagreement between you and your mate.

In respect to having children, you cannot too easily experiment before you marry. For once you decide to bring progeny into the world, the state, social groups, and other institutional pressures virtually force you to become legally wedded. Moreover, even if you have a child or two with a woman of your choice without technically marrying her, you are still liable for the moral and economic support of these children; so, in effect, you *are* married by the mere act of bringing them into the world.

You can, however, have a great many long-winded discussions with your potential wife about children. You can discover fairly easily how many she would like to have; what her ideas are regarding their religious upbringing; what kind of a disciplinarian she is likely to be; how attached to the children she will probably become; and how disappointed and surly she is likely to be if you later disagree with her over some points in the rearing of any children you may have. The more discussions of this sort you have, the better; for although both you and your girlfriend cannot be expected truly to *know* how you will feel about many aspects of child-rearing (especially if neither of you has helped bring up any children previously), you may still both have strong feelings in this connection that are likely to be continued if and when you marry and have offspring. By all means, then, try to get these feelings completely out in the open, and see how probable it is that you will later clash head-on about child-rearing.

As in other marital areas, conflicts about bringing up children can often be minimized through prolonged discussion and compromise. You may decide that, even though you can well live without children, your wife would be so unhappy without them that it is far wiser to have one or two than to remain childless. Or your girlfriend may agree that even though she would like to rear your children in some orthodox religious manner, she can well dispense with that kind of rearing if it makes you too uncomfortable. The main thing is that both of you see, long before you actually marry and get your wife pregnant, what serious child-rearing differences actually exist between you and what are the chances that you can make a satisfactory compromise in relation to these differences. Otherwise, both of you might be better off cultivating your own gardens—and marrying and having children with someone else.

Temperamental Compatibility

Though it is exceptionally hard to measure, there does seem to be a thing called human temperament; and to some degree it even seems to be inborn. Thus, one individual has one kind of biorhythms, and another individual has quite another kind. Without being seriously neurotic or psychotic, a man can be a "night person" and his wife can be much more alive and happy during the day. One mate can be exceptionally calm and almost bovine; and the other can have emotional flare-ups almost continually. A wife can be unusually industrious and hard-working; and a husband interested mainly in doing a minimum of work and in pleasure-seeking activities.

This does not mean that mates with different temperaments cannot make out well together or complement each other. As Winch (1961) and others have pointed out, sometimes people are distinctly attracted to each other because of their temperamental differences; and sometimes they make out well in marriage because one brings to the other certain aspects of living which, by his own temperamental ways, this other is not likely to experience.

Sometimes! But most of the time, probably, the result is just the opposite. People with clearcut temperamental differences tend to irritate each other a good deal of the time; to misunderstand the other's motives; to pull in acutely differing directions; and to have one hell of a hard time adjusting in marriage. This is not to say that they *can't* allow for their dispositional dissimilarities and make effective compromises. But they frequently don't. Or they do adjust, and then find that it is hardly worth making such adjustments— since they both could, of course, divorce each other and find mates with whom they were *naturally* more compatible.

As usual, therefore, you should do your best to find out what your own basic temperament is. What do you like and dislike? What easily and normally motivates you? What are your natural inclinations? It is most important that you know yourself in regard to your basic personality leanings before you think of marrying.

Similarly, of course, it is important that you know as much about your mate as you can possibly know in this regard. Does she really *like* the kind of things you do? Is her energy level somewhat akin to yours? Do her moods fluctuate greatly or is she relatively consistent in this respect? Is she a rapid mover or a slowpoke? Does she function best by day or by night? Is she largely a homebody, or is she incessantly looking to find things to do outside the home?

Question your girlfriend in these respects. Observe how she actually behaves. Be with her as much as possible, on a truly intimate and sharing basis, to see how she bears up temperamentally under close association with you. And if you have any reason to suspect that, no matter how beautiful she is, nor how good in bed, nor how bright and charming, she just has the kind of basic dispositions that are alien to yours, think seriously, before you marry her, of finding another beautiful, sexy, bright girl who is much closer to you temperamentally. Each of us is, to some considerable degree, what he basically is; and no amount of wishing, or sometimes even working, will make us too different. This may be sad; but it is still sadder if you ignore this fact when you marry.

H. G. Wells (1934), describing the relationship between himself and his wife (whom he later divorced), noted: "We both wanted now to be honest mates and adapt ourselves to each other completely. We were both perplexed and distressed by our failure to do that. We were in love with each other, quite honestly and simply desirous of being 'everything' to each other. But there was an unalterable difference not only in our mental equipment and habits, but in our nervous reactions. I felt and acted swiftly and variously and at times very loosely and superficially, in the acutest contrast to her gentler and steadier flow." Here were two people who very much *wanted* to think and feel together, but simply could not. So it is with many other initially loving couples.

Mutual Respect

Love, as has often been said, is not enough for a good marriage: usually there must usually also exist mutual respect. You can easily love a child, a mentally deficient person, or a criminal; but it is not likely that you will be happily married to a person for whom you have warm feelings but whom you cannot respect, admire, or cooperate with on an adult level.

This particularly goes for a member of the other sex. For it is very easy to love a girl who is beautiful, who does everything possible to satisfy you sexually, and who perhaps is an excellent cook and housewife, and caters to many of your material wants. But it is most difficult to stay happily married to such a girl if she keeps behaving childishly, cannot intelligently discuss many life difficulties with you, and is unable to keep up with you intellectually or esthetically. For in this event, you will not respect her; and even if you manage to keep from despising her (which is difficult, considering the way most of us are reared), you will become irritated or annoyed by a considerable amount of her behavior and will wish she would pack her things and leave.

Look, then, for a girl you can respect as well as love. If you can find one whom you genuinely admire—who has, for example, talents or traits which you like in practically anyone and which make it more enjoyable for you to be in the presence of the person who has such traits—that is great; and you have perhaps selected an almost ideal mate for yourself. But even if you cannot truly admire your potential mate, you should be able at least to respect her: to like many of her characteristics and to feel a quiet, steady pleasure in being with her or thinking about her when she is not present.

Naturally, again, you will only discover whether you truly respect a woman when you have a great deal of personal contact with her, and preferably when you see her in difficult as well as favorable circumstances. This means that the closer you get to living with her before you marry her, the better it is. But without such actual domestic sharing, you can see enough of her, and observe her with her relatives, friends, and even business associates to such a degree that you will be able to see how much you truly respect her character and her talents

Physical Attraction

Physical attractiveness in a mate is often most important, even quite apart from sexual compatibility. For it is possible for you to be sexually compatible with a girl who looks like a gargoyle—especially if you normally copulate with her in the dark, and if she has the kind of a body that you like to *feel* if not necessarily to *look at*. But it may not be possible for you to be happy sitting across the breakfast table every morning from a wife who is a nice person, intelligent, and a good mother, but whose face would tend not only to launch a thousand ships—but to send them crashing in despair upon the rocks.

This is not to say that it is most desirable that you seek a very beautiful wife. Beauty, as I indicate in *The American Sexual Tragedy* (1962b), has its distinct limitations, and in our society it is linked with all kinds of neurotic attitudes. The mere fact that you are greatly enamored of physical attractiveness may mean that you yourself have unthinkingly absorbed some of the idotic, Madison Avenue-inculcated ideas of our day, and that you are trying falsely to raise your self-esteem by showing everyone what a beautiful mate you can acquire. And the beauty that you go for, if you are thus neurotically motivated, may not have any functional value. For example, what can you do with a beautiful ankle in bed? And even a gorgeous face may have little real value, if it happens to be mounted on an unusually lean and bony figure that is just not comfortable to copulate with.

There are, moreover, several cogent reasons why you should think twice before you marry a very beautiful woman, including these:

1. Female beauty gives little indication of other desirable traits on the part of the woman who possesses it, but instead tends to blind you to defects which would otherwise be obvious.

2. Physical beauty almost always fades with amazing rapidity, despite all efforts to keep it extant. To be charmed by a beautiful flower is commendable; to vow to cherish it for your lifetime, idiotic. No matter how lovely a young woman may be, it will be phenomenal if she retains her youthful contours by the time she reaches her middle thirties. The women's magazines may blithely say otherwise; but O, 'tis false, 'tis false!

3. Many beautiful women have been so spoiled by adulation that they tend to be conceited and undisciplined and to make poor wives. Less handsome females, on the other hand, know perfectly well that they must have something besides their looks in order to get along successfully in life, and therefore they are more likely to work hard at changing themselves for the better and to act in a kindly manner toward their male friends and lovers.

4. The man who marries an exquisite woman may have much difficulty in keeping other men away from her; and, if he is notably jealous, he may experience much difficulty on this account. If he is sufficiently sane, he will not be terribly jealous (Harper, 1963). But the fact still remains that the competition for his wife is likely to persist long after he marries her, and he may consequently have to work harder to keep her favor than he would have to work if he were married to a less gorgeous creature.

5. Beautiful women are sometimes so obsessed with keeping their looks that they avoid certain tasks, such as bearing children or properly taking care of a house, because they are so busy keeping up with the newest beauty aids. Even sexually, they may sometimes avoid certain kinds of participations for fear of *looking* disheveled or unlovely when they are highly involved. Their philosophy of life is sometimes primarily one of *beautifying* rather than of *living*; and such a philosophy can be an awful pain in the rear end to live with.

Beauty, then, has its distinct drawbacks in marriage. As Thomas Carew noted a good many years ago:

> "He that loves a rosy cheek,
>   Or a coral lip admires,
> Or from star-like eyes doth seek
>   Fuel to maintain his fires;
> As old time makes these decay,
> So his flames must waste away."

So much is true. And yet!—there is quite another side to this fence. If you are, for one reason or another, greatly enamored of physical beauty, and if your esthetic propensities do cause you enormous pain when you are in the presence of a homely female, let's face it: you do have a problem in regard to marrying, and you'd better frankly acknowledge it. For no matter whom you marry, the chances are that she will, within ten or twenty years after the wedding, look quite different from the way she did when you first met and fell in love with her. And what can you then do about *that*?

Very little—at that time. But there are prophylactic measures you can take. You can, for example, realistically live with your love of female beauty by making sure not only that you marry a comely woman, but also one who is ten or more years younger than you. For the chances then are that her physical charms will last into your late middle age; and that by that time you may not be as needful of having a dazzling young thing for your marital companion as you previously were.

Or, if you want to be even more drastic, you can always marry a handsome woman—and get a divorce every ten or twelve years for a newer and younger replacement. Or you can refuse to marry at all, and content yourself with a succession of beautiful mistresses. Or you can remain married to an aging and not so lovely woman—and still content yourself with a series of younger paramours.

Whatever you do, be honest with yourself in this regard. If beauty is your particular desire, squarely face the fact that this is true. Then you can either work to reduce this desire or accommodate it. But if you have a great yen for feminine pulchritude and you do not face up to the realities that exist in this connection, the chances are that you will marry a lovely young wife—and then live most *un*beautifully with her, in more ways than one, for a number of years to come.

Economic Compatibility

Man does not live by bread alone—unless, one is tempted to say, he is married! For it is surprising how many husbands have to keep slaving away to make money, not because they have much need of it themselves, but because their wives and families seem to consume almost endless amounts.

It should go without saying that you would be most unwise to marry a woman who is primarily interested in having you support her after marriage; but to be on the safe side we'd better say this right here. The main difference between a prostitute and a woman who marries to be kept in food, clothing, shelter, and mink coats is that the latter is labeled a wife. Of the two, the prostitute is more honest, since her customers know perfectly well what the tariff will be.

Most women, without being in the prostitutional class, are still forced to be seriously interested in the financial aspects of marriage; since it *does* cost an enormous amount, these days, to keep up a home and family. And no matter how much they love their husbands, the landlord still has to be paid, the children clothed and sent through college, and their own wardrobes kept respectable enough to stave off the pitying stares of their friends. So you have to expect any potential wife to be *somewhat* interested in your earning capacity and your ability to spend money gracefully on some of the good things of life. If she is not so concerned, then you should suspect something about *her* impracticality.

Nonetheless, there are spending wives and spending wives. And not a few women you might marry will always feel financially insecure, and have their eyes on new things to buy, no matter how much money you might make and place at their disposal. These women are not necessarily bitches who are out to rob you. Much more often, they are insecure or disorganized people who must spend money to give themselves a false sense of security or who seem unable to organize themselves well enough to live on a reasonable budget. Whatever the reason for their extravagances, try to discover early in the game that they *are* unable to live in a sensible manner; and either see that they become cured, or love them and copulate with them on a purely nonmarital basis.

Even if you are careful about the kind of woman you marry, and pick one who budgets admirably and pretty well keeps to her budget, you have to face the fact that marriage itself is ordinarily expensive, and that there are pitifully few ways to avoid making considerable financial sacrifices in order to keep a wife and raise a family. Unless you are fairly willing to make these sacrifices, you'd better seriously consider remaining a bachelor—or, perhaps, marrying for economic gain yourself.

Is it wicked of you to think of gaining financially by marriage? Certainly not. If you can somehow manage to marry a rich girl; or one whose parents stake you in a good business arrangement; or one who herself earns a substantial salary every week; don't hesitate to consider marrying her—as long as you realistically face the disadvantages that are usually also attached to such a marital arrangement. For a rich girl may be demanding and hard to please just because she comes from a wealthy family. In-laws who set you up in a good business generally have their own pound of flesh which they expect to get from you in return. Working wives who earn a very good income themselves may easily neglect homemaking activities, be poor mothers, or fail to be the kind of companions you might want them to be. So, although it is hardly a crime to think of marrying a woman who might bring you distinct economic gains, such a marriage is also far from being a complete bed of roses.

The main point we want to emphasize here is that you

fully accept the fact that marriage is largely a socio-economic arrangement, in addition to its being a sexual, affectional, and domestic tie. It might be nice if this were not so, and if people could marry on a purely sexual, loving, and companionable basis. But they rarely can, and practically never do. So if you are contemplating marriage, drop some of the romantic bushwah and face reality. Look for a woman who, among other things, will not be a great economic liability, and who may even be somewhat of an economic asset. You are almost certain to get disadvantages in marrying; but don't go far out of your way to get them.

Summary

Marriage is not love, is not sex, is not companionship. It is all these things—and more. It therefore requires, as a satisfactory mate, one who is not going to be *too* emotionally unstable, sexually unsuitable, uncompanionable, temperamentally inharmonious, physically unattractive, unadmirable, or financially handicapping. Not that you are likely to win for a wife the girl who is ideal in all these respects; for you damned well won't. But at least let her not be totally non-ideal!

The greatest error in marrying, then, is poor selectivity. Although you may be capable of being sexually or amatively happy with hundreds of women, it is probable that you can be truly happy in marriage with relatively few. Look, and look some more, and then look still more for one of those few.

Chapter 18

Overcoming Fears of Marriage

Let us suppose that you have decided that it would be better if you married, and that you have perhaps even met a girl whom you are thinking seriously of marrying. But you find that you are quite fearful, especially after a good many years of bachelorhood, about taking the plunge. How can you overcome such fears? This is the question we shall consider in this chapter.

Rational and Irrational Fears of Marriage

Let us not rashly assume that all fears of getting married are irrational or neurotic; for some aren't. As we have pointed out in the last two chapters, there are many real disadvantages of the marital state, and there is also a good chance that if you do wed you may easily pick the wrong girl. Consequently, there are some very *good* reasons for seriously considering, if not completely avoiding, marriage; and you *do* have some cause for fear in this connection.

You may, for example, truly be unable to afford marriage; and may logically have to put aside any idea of getting hitched for one or more years from now, when you may be in a much better financial condition. Or you may be too emotionally unbalanced, at the moment, to live together with any normal woman; and you may wish to go for therapeutic help, or otherwise to work out some of your emotional problems, before you attempt to do so. Or you may live in a small community where there is very little chance of your obtaining the kind of intelligent, cultured, stable girl whom you would like to marry; and you may decide to put off marrying for a time, until you go to reside in a larger community, where the marital choices might be much better.

Since, in general, marriage *is* a serious affair, and since it *may* be most inconvenient (and expensive!) for you to make a poor choice in the marriage you are contemplating, you should certainly, to say the least, be cautious about marrying, and should not precipitately jump into the first fairly good relationship that presents itself. Live with the girl, if you wish, if you think that there is only a fair chance of your affair with her working out; or court her for a long period of time until you think that the chances of a good mating are improved. But don't marry anyone, normally, until you are reasonably sure that she is for you—unless (and this is rare) you are equally sure that you can easily get out of the marriage, later, without undue costs.

Suppose, however, you have no *good* reason to fear marriage, and you still quake in your boots every time you contemplate taking a specific girl, or for that matter *any* girl, to the license bureau. What then? Then you have a distinctly irrational fear of marriage; and the best thing to do at first is to track it down, to discover specifically what it is. Some of the most common irrational fears of marrying include:

—fear that you will marry the wrong girl, and thereby make a horrible mistake;

—fear that you will marry "below" you and that various friends and relatives will therefore snub you or look down on you;

—fear that you are essentially worthless, and therefore cannot possibly make a good husband or father;

—fear that you will be impotent after marriage, and that your wife will therefore hate you;

—fear that after marriage some other man will come along and seduce your wife and take her away from you;

—fear that your chosen mate could not possibly love you for yourself, and that she is really only marrying you for your money;

—fear that you will not be able to control your terrible temper and that you will mess up your marriage because of it;

—fear that the responsibilities of marriage will totally overwhelm you and prove to everyone, including you and your wife, that you just cannot manage any difficult life situation.

What can you do about such fears as these, if you strongly have any of them? The same thing you can do about any fear: namely, track it down to the irrational, self-defeating *beliefs* that lie behind it; question and challenge these beliefs in a vigorous, constant manner until they fade; replace them with a sensible set of philosophies of living that will prevent the original senseless beliefs from arising again and smiting you.

Let us take a specific example. George K. came for premarital counseling, at the insistence of his fiancée, because he had set and broken wedding dates with her three times; and yet he did not want to give her up and be a bachelor or marry someone else. He was thirty-five years of age; had never been married but had been engaged once previously, and had almost literally left his former fiancée waiting at the church. He had a good income; said he very much wanted to settle down and marry rather than to continue having sex affairs with a number of girls; and also said that he wanted to raise two or three children. He had no specific idea why he could not marry his present fiancée, and insisted that he had no underlying hostility toward her and could find no serious fault with her.

It became clear, during my first two sessions with George, that he had not merely one but several strong fears connected with marrying. First of all, he was afraid of being impotent, since he had had several experiences wherein he had failed sexually; and even though he had not yet failed with his present fiancée, he thought he might do so in the future. Secondly, he thought there was a possibility of his being homosexual, although he had had only minor relations with other males when he was a teenager, and had always been attracted strongly to females. Thirdly, he knew that his mother would oppose almost any marriage that he made, since he was an only child and she was closely attached to him and tried to run his life; and he was guilty about how hurt she would be if he did marry. Finally, he wondered if he could be truly faithful to his wife after marriage, since he had been rather promiscuous in his premarital affairs, and did enjoy making each new sexual conquest.

Quite consciously, then, George K. had several distinct fears of marrying, even though he did not seem to have any specific anxiety in connection with his fiancée. He was most willing to discuss these fears, and for the first few sessions of therapy brought me a great deal of material, which he seemed to tell with relish, about the nightmares he was having every night, the feelings of cold sweat that ran down his spine whenever his fiancée talked about setting another wedding date, and the crazy things he kept doing to break up his present engagement, even though he said he really didn't want to break it up. He would, by way of illustration, get drunk and proposition his fiancée's best girlfriend; have sex relations with his fiancée and make no attempt to satisfy her sexually; and go with her to a formal affair dressed in an informal, rather outlandish manner.

Whenever I tried to get George to see the philosophic reasons for his behavior, or to look at the simple exclamatory sentences he kept telling himself to make himself act in aberrant ways, he seemed to be highly uninterested; and he kept going back to his long, lurid narrations of how fearful he was and how he was doing exactly the wrong thing to keep his fiancée's favor. Finally, seeing that we were getting nowhere, I stopped him in his tracks during the fourth session and said: "Look: what you're telling me is pretty crappy stuff, and you're not going to overcome your problem of fearing marriage, or any other problem for that matter, if we keep going on like this."

"What do you mean?" asked George. "Am I not doing my best to tell you how I feel and how upset I am? You can't say that I'm hiding anything, can you?"

"I damned well can," I replied. "Not that you're hiding any of the details of your feelings from me. Hell, you go on with them ad nauseam, as if you thoroughly enjoyed spilling out your guts before me. But that's not what we're here for."

"It isn't? But I thought that in therapy you had to tell the therapist everything, and that that's what helped him find out what was wrong with you, and released your own pent-up feelings."

"Shit!" I said. "That's psychoanalytic nonsense. Maybe that's what your last therapist encouraged you to do—but look how sick you still are, after four years of going over this kind of stuff with him."

"You mean that in your brand of—uh—rational therapy, you don't go in for this?"

"No, I don't. But unfortunately you still do. And that's why we're not getting anywhere, and probably never will if you go on like this. I'm not that interested in your *feelings*, now that I already know what they are. What I'm interested in is the thoughts, the internalized sentences, that you tell yourself to *create* these goddam feelings. And trying to get you to even look for any of these thoughts is like climbing up the Himalaya Mountains with skis on."

"But I've been trying to find the thoughts that you say lie behind my feelings, and I can't seem to dig them up. It seems to me that I just don't have any."

"The hell you don't! It seems to me that you're just not really trying to get at them. In fact, you're so terribly busy *having* your crummy feelings, and then endlessly *telling* me and others about them, that I don't see how you can possibly have any *time* to look for the ideas that underlie them. Now let's look, right now, for some of these ideas, and show you once again what they are, and what you can do about them."

"All right. I guess I should try things your way, as long as I'm seeing you. And you certainly helped Marcia when she was coming to see you. So where shall we begin?"

"Let's begin with the first of the things you seem to be terribly afraid of in marriage: Being impotent. You think about marrying Marcia, evidently, and then this thought quickly comes to mind—right?"

"Yes. I think 'All right: what's so awful about marrying her. She's pretty. She's bright. She certainly cares a hell of a lot for me, to put up with the kind of crap I've been handing her. And she's even good in bed and *knows* about my fear of being impotent. So what's to fear?' But then I immediately see myself lying next to her, as I've done with several girls before, with my penis absolutely limp, and with it staying limp no matter how much effort she or I take to get it up, and I just shiver and shake at this thought, and say to myself: 'Jesus Christ! Wouldn't *that* be horrible!'"

"O.K.; so the first part of your philosophy seems to be: 'If I marry Marcia, and *if* I start becoming impotent with her, like I have previously become with several other girls at times, that would be highly undesirable. The other girls I could easily leave; but how can I leave her after marriage? So I'll be stuck in this undesirable position.' Is that right?"

"Yes, and then I immediately begin to shake and shiver."

"No, you're jumping the gun. At that point, where you're telling yourself how undesirable it would be if you are impotent with Marcia, you *don't* start to shake and shiver. Not at least if you stop right there. For an *undesirable* thing is far from being a *horror*; and if you were sticking to 'That would be undesirable,' you would feel somewhat uncomfortable, and might even calmly contemplate breaking off the engagement; but you couldn't possibly shake and shiver as you do. To produce *that* effect, we require a second thought: the one you gave before."

"You mean: that it would be horrible if I were impotent after marriage?"

"Right. Or, more specifically: 'If I were impotent, I would be letting Marcia down terribly; she would never forgive me; and I would be a perfect swine for putting her in this position.' Isn't *that* it?"

"No, not exactly, though you're close. More like: 'If I were impotent, I would *once again* be proving what a fuck-up I am; and Marcia *too* would see me as I really am—a first-class fool.'"

"Fool?"

"Yes, a fool for having been so idotic as to think that I could pull the wool over her eyes, and not eventually be found out as the sexual incompetent that I really am."

"All right, let's accept your formulation, since you should know exactly what you're telling yourself. Now, do you see the two basic sentences, one sane and one insane, that you're saying?"

"Let's see: the sane one seems to be: 'If I fail with Marcia, that would be quite undesirable.'"

"Yes: because that's a true sentence. It *would be* undesirable, unpleasant, or frustrating if you failed with Marcia, particularly after you were married to her. Now what's the insane sentence?"

"Evidently: 'If I did fail with her sexually, I would once again prove that I am no damned good, and that I couldn't possibly ever be potent, or be a *man*.'"

"Right again. And can you see how foolish this sentence is?"

"Yes, I think so. It tries to prove, by past performance, that I could not possibly succeed in the future. And that doesn't follow."

"It certainly doesn't. It's an illogical conclusion from an observed fact. Moreover, you say, in this second sentence, not only that you could never be potent again, which is quite unprovable, but also that you would be a *worthless individual* if you never did. Is *that* possible?"

"No, I guess not. For even if I never did succeed in being potent, I would still be worthwhile in many other respects—

I could still have a ball on my job, for example, or could please my wife in nonsexual ways."

"Yes, you certainly could. For that matter, even if you were totally impotent, you could still please her sexually—with your hands or your lips, for example. But success isn't the point. Success does *not* make people worthwhile, though it certainly gives them pleasure. If there can be any realistic definition of self-worth, it must be that the individual is capable of some kind of pleasure, of enjoyment, and not that he is successful. For the most unsuccessful individual is still *alive*; and while he is alive, there must be *some* manner in which he can enjoy himself. When he is dead, and totally incapable of pleasure, he then has zero self-worth. But till that time, it is almost inconceivable that he would be worth absolutely nothing to himself. Unless, of course, he *thinks* he is worthless: in which case he may not in the least *try* to enjoy himself, and may therefore in effect *reduce* his self-worth to near-zero."

"So as long as I am alive and capable of *some* kind of fun, I can be totally impotent and still be very worthwhile. I can see that's a quite different philosophy from the one with which I usually assess my own value."

"It damned well is. Now let's look for a moment at the philosophies behind your other neurotic fears. Take the fear of your being a homosexual. What do you think causes that?"

"I suppose, the idea that if I *were* a homosexual, that would be a terrible thing, and I would be no damned good."

"Precisely! You are probably first telling yourself the sane sentence, 'It would be undesirable for me to be a homosexual,' and then following this with the insane sentence, 'And if I were a homosexual, I would be a no-good rotter, and could never face myself again!' Then, *believing* that it would be awful if you were homosexual, you easily keep dwelling on this problem, and soon come to think, 'Well, maybe I *am* a queer. After all, I *did* have some homosexual experiences in my youth; and I *do* occasionally think of men in a sexual way. Well, that *proves* it—I *must* be queer!'"

"Yes, I see. I'm so afraid of being one that I convince myself that I actually am. But how about the fear I have of hurting my mother by marrying Marcia. What are the things I am telling myself about that?"

"Think, right now, about what you are telling yourself in

that connection, and I am sure that you will start finding it pretty quickly."

"Let's see. I am saying 'My mother would be hurt if I married Marcia, and I certainly wouldn't like her to be hurt.' And, I guess, 'If she is hurt by my marriage, I am a dirty dog for hurting her!'"

"And is that *true*: that you would be a dirty dog if your mother got hurt because you married Marcia?"

"Well, I wouldn't exactly be a nice guy if that occurred, would I?"

"Why not? You're assuming here, and quite falsely, that *you* would be hurting your mother if you married Marcia. But is that true?"

"You mean that she actually would be hurting herself, by refusing to accept the fact that I want to marry someone she doesn't greatly like?"

"Well, *wouldn't* she?"

"Yes, I suppose she would, if you want to look at it that way."

"But isn't that the only sensible way to look at it? You do what you want, in marrying Marcia; and she fascistically refuses to give you the right to do what you want, and insists that you are hurting her by doing it. Then, by a kind of poetic justice, she actually hurts *herself*. Isn't that what's actually happening, if the events we are hypothesizing occur?"

"Yes, I suppose it is; though it might be difficult to get other people—particularly my mother's friends—to think about it that way."

"It probably would be difficult. But isn't that *their* problem, that they think the same fascistic way that she does?"

"Yes. You know, I'm really beginning to see it now. I *do* have a perfect right to marry whom I want. And my mother also has a perfect right not to like whom I marry. But if she insists on upsetting herself about my marrying Marcia, then she is really trying to blackmail me by getting upset; and that, of course, is a kind of fascistic attempt to impose her views on me."

"Right. And if you insist on getting upset by witnessing her upsetting herself, then you are really accepting her authoritarian views, and making them your own."

"Yes, I see. And it's about time I stopped accepting her

fascistic nonsense—and about time that I unfascistically gave her the right to believe this nonsense, and to hurt herself by believing it."

"That's another good point you're making. Every time you get upset—or, rather, upset yourself—over your mother's hurting herself by sticking to her authoritarian views, you are really refusing to let her suffer by having these views, and you are, at least in a mild way, being just as fascistic as she. Your intentions, of course, are very good in that event; but fascists frequently have fine intentions. The main point is that they refuse to let others carry out *their* intentions; and that is what both you and your mother are doing by upsetting yourselves."

"Hm! I'll certainly have to work against *that* kind of nonsense. Now, what about my fear of not being able to remain faithful to Marcia after marriage? No, let me see if I can't answer that one, too, myself. I'm apparently telling myself, first, 'Because I was promiscuous before marriage, I might well be unfaithful to Marcia after I marry her; and I might thereby jeopardize my relationship with her.' That, I guess, is true: since I well *might* be unfaithful, just as any husband might be, and many are. But then I am wrongly concluding: 'And *if* I were unfaithful to Marcia after marriage, I would be a no-good bastard; and since there is a good chance of my being such a bastard, I'd better ward off this chance by staying single.'"

"I think that's a good description of your internalized sentences about your fear of infidelity. Now what's *wrong* with those sentences?"

"The wrong thing is that if I were unfaithful to Marcia, I might not be doing myself and my marriage any good; but that wouldn't mean I was a no-good bastard. It would only mean that I was wrong."

"Yes, that's exactly what it would mean: that you were wrong; and that if you wanted to be wise, you'd better arrange to be less wrong, or less unfaithful, in the future. But you, like everyone else in the world, have a perfect *right to be* wrong, however you may defeat yourself for the present by being wrong."

"In all four of my fears, then, I'm really saying the same foolish thing to myself, aren't I?"

"Yes, in all four cases, you're telling yourself that (a) your behavior would be deplorable or mistaken and that (b) therefore you would be a louse for engaging in that kind of behavior. While (a) may very well be true, (b) never is: since humans can only be human, and cannot be lice, rats, or skunks."

"And if I see this clearly, and stop telling myself that I am a bum for making, or even being in danger of making, serious mistakes, then my fears of marrying Marcia will go. Is that right?"

"Quite right." But don't accept this on my say-so. Try it out in practice, and see for yourself. Get at those irrational, self-defeating sentences that you are telling yourself about your questionable or mistaken behavior, and then see whether the fears that you are creating by convincing yourself of this hogwash do not actually go away, and after a while stay away."

So it happened. George K. did start looking at his internalized sentences which backed up and created his fears of marriage, and then he began to challenge them in a vigorous, concerted manner. Within a few weeks, he not only began to see but to *feel* how idiotic they were, and to believe wholeheartedly in their falsity. Concomitantly, he began to lose his fears of marriage; and seven weeks after treatment began, he firmly announced his wedding date and had no trouble going through with it when the day arrived. Although his marriage has by no means been perfect (since Marcia turned out to have her share of emotional difficulties, too), he has managed to meet the difficulties of day to day domestic living and to maintain a reasonably good marital relationship.

Similarly, virtually anyone can overcome his neurotic fears of marriage if he will really try to track down the simple exclamatory, and usually catastrophizing, internalized sentences with which he creates and sustains these fears. In the final analysis, to be irrationally afraid of marrying is invariably to be afraid of *oneself*: to feel that if one chooses the wrong partner, or fails to satisfy her sexually, or is a poor provider, or does something else badly in connection with marrying, one will be an utter slob, a worthless person. And this kind of a belief in ones' own worthlessness, and a tying up of one's personal value with external achievement or approval, can always be seen, challenged, and forcefully *attacked*. If, with or without psychotherapeutic help, it is thus consistently attacked, it will almost inevitably fade. For, as I keep telling my psychotherapy patients and marriage counseling clients:

"The idea that, if you fail in life, you are utterly worthless is sheer bullshit. And, most fortunately, it is *your* bullshit, *your* self-creation. Consequently, it is always possible for *you* to get rid of it. For whatever you believe, you can also *disbelieve*. And if you keep working and practicing at disbelieving this arrant nonsense, it's simply *got* to go away. O.K.: let's see you get started on this working and practicing!"

Chapter 19

The Art of Proposing

Let us suppose that you have found the girl of your choice and have decided that you really want to marry her. How should you go about popping the question to her? Is there any special kind of technique you should use to ensure success? And if so, what is it?

The main answer to these questions is that there *is* no special method of proposing to the girl you love. Unlike the old days, when the male (so the story books said) used to get down on his knees and formally beg the girl of his dreams to please, please make him the happiest man in the world by accepting his honest proposal of matrimony, the average proposal today is made in a highly informal manner, and sometimes amounts to practically no proposal at all.

"You know," the girl often says to the fellow after they have been going out for a period of time, "we seem to hit it off pretty well, don't we?"

"Yes, we certainly seem to!" he agrees. "I wonder if we'd get along equally well if we were married."

"I've sort of been wondering about that too," she says. "Many people get along beautifully together on a dating basis, but just as soon as they start living together things change, and they're soon at each other's throats."

"Well, I doubt whether we would be," he continues. "We've seen quite a bit of each other recently, and we haven't poisoned each other's tea yet. I think we really might be able to make a go of it, if we decided to take the plunge."

"Come to think of it, we probably would," she concurs. "Do you think maybe we ought to try?"

"Not a bad idea!" he shoots back. "Now that I'm getting along so well on this new job, and making a lot more money than I did last year, I think we might be able to afford it. When do you think would be a good time for the wedding?"

"Well, June's coming up in three months," she says. "I always did want to have a June wedding. Something sentimental in me, I guess."

"Great! Now let's see. What kind of an affair shall we have?"

And, before either of them really knows what is happening, they are on their way to holy wedlock. Not only was there no formal proposal by the bridegroom-to-be; like as not, the girl was one step ahead of him, and did most of the question-popping herself.

Is this kind of proposing cricket?

Why not? The aim of discussing whether or not to marry is just that—to discuss it. Proposing is not, after all, the same thing as signing an international treaty; and the protocol involved can be less than overwhelming. So what if the male is lolling on the grass by the tennis court and his inamorata is lightly swinging her racquet? Or, at the other extreme, what if the discussion of marrying takes place, slowly and methodically, over many sessions, and involves serious discussion of budgets, birth control, and how to live at least two hundred miles away from both sets of in-laws? Proposing should often be exactly what its name implies: one partner's making an initial proposition, the other's goodnaturedly countering with a somewhat different proposition, the first partner's adding more relevant points, the other's asking questions about these points, and so on and so forth, down to the finish line.

Do not many males have great difficulty in asking their girls to marry them? They certainly do. Some of them, as we noted in the last chapter, have serious fears of marriage, and are in deep conflict about proposing. Others know perfectly well that they want to get married, but are afraid that they will be refused. Others are certain that the girl herself will accept them, but are worried about also being accepted by her parents, friends, or relatives. Still others are afraid of the *manner* in which they will propose, even though they think that the chances are that they will be completely accepted.

Many males, in other words, are emotionally insecure about various aspects of their life, particularly their sex-love relations. Because of this insecurity they *make* a huge problem out of the relatively simple task of asking a girl whether or not she will marry them. Such men, similarly, worry about going for job interviews, making a date with a stranger, or engaging in door to door selling. Whatever they try to do, they believe that their entire *self* is involved in the success or failure of their attempt. And since, by their internal definitions, they are putting almost their entire life on the line when they try to gain anyone else's assent, they naturally worry enormously about the outcome of each trial and greatly handicap themselves in the process.

If you happen to be one of these over-anxious males who thinks that he could not possibly *bear* to have his marriage proposal rejected, since that would prove that *he*, in toto, is a worthless lout, a few cautions in this respect may prove of real value:

1. Never overestimate the value of any *given* girl. Certainly your beloved is a fine creature, rare as a perfect rose, and charming as a September morn. But she is not the only girl in the world, nor even the only girl's kid sister. If she somehow benightedly fails to appreciate your unsurpassed ways and means, you *will*, believe me, love again; and you will even, it is very safe to bet, want once again to marry. Moreover, if you keep plodding hopefully onward, it is most unlikely that all the beauteous girls in the universe will reject you, and it is more likely that in a surprisingly short while you will be safely knotted to another equally fine, rare, and charming female, who may even put the present one deeply in the shade.

2. Practically no one ever dies of unrequited love. Some fools kill themselves long before the stabbing pains of amour penetrate their vital parts to polish them off; but many more somehow manage to pull the trigger on an empty gun chamber or swallow a less than lethal dose of sleeping pills, and to live to a ripe old age (with their final demises not infrequently hastened by the alimony demands of their three ex-wives).

3. Your opinion of yourself need not be a bloodied reflection of that of the girl who sends you packing. Maybe she likes only blue-eyed men, while your orbs will never be anything but dark brown. Or maybe she thinks you are too *good* for her, and insists on getting her just marital deserts with a blackguard. Or maybe she really thinks you are a mealy-mouthed *schnook*—as most of the world thought, before they proved themselves, of Socrates, Galileo, Columbus, Wagner, and a few hundred other belatedly recognized geniuses. The

main point is: Why do you have to *agree* with the girl who refuses to keep matrimonial company with you? Is she, just because you care for her, infallible? Is ice cream tasty to *everyone?*

4. Suppose, even, that two or more girls reject you for matehood. Suppose, if you will, that most of the girls you would want are also likely to spurn you for some wealthier, more handsome, or suaver guy. Does this prove that you are a totally no good, utterly worthless, unmistakably putrid nincompoop? Gad, no. It merely proves, at most, that you have serious marital handicaps and that if you are to get the kind of girl you want for a bride you are going to have to shake your rear end and locate more prospects, and work much harder to win the approval of some of these prospects, than the more fortunate and less handicapped members of your sex have to work. Rough going, that is. But hardly hopeless—if you realistically *accept* your liabilities and keep plugging along in spite of them.

5. Don't get the idea that you *have* to marry in order to be a useful citizen or to enjoy life. Marriage is certainly one of life's great experiences; and if it happens to include the raising of children, it is even more a complex and intense part of living. But millions of people, since the beginning of time, have lived very happily without ever marrying; and you may well do the same. As a male residing in this society, the chances are that you can easily marry if you want to do so— since our women are even more anxious to get legally tied and to have children than are most of our men. But there may be various reasons, such as lack of financial backing, why you should never marry. Or you may technically be able to wed, but never meet or win the particular kind of girl you are eager to marry. Tough! But you can still manage to enjoy virtually all the elements of marrying—even including child-rearing— if you really want to do so.

Thus, you can live with a girl for months or years without being formally wed. And you can help bring up your brother's or sister's children, or almost anyone else's children, if you will take the time and effort to cultivate youngsters, find out what they would like to do, and offer them opportunities for companionship. Fatherhood is largely a sociological rather than a biological tie; and many men are better "parents" to relatives' or friends' children than are the biological fathers of these same children.

6. If you are overly eager to have children of your own, and are therefore fretting about not marrying, you'd better look with at least a little suspicion on your fatherhood urges. Most men who are powerfully impelled to have children, and especially to have sons, are trying to boost their own shallow self-confidence thereby. They falsely believe that the begetting of one or more children will make them "stronger" or "better"; and they thereby reveal their own deepseated underlying feelings of inadequacy. It is certainly nice to have children, in many instances (and gruesome to have them, in many other instances); but they can do nothing for your so-called ego unless that "ego" is pitifully small and ragged. Even then, they only illusorily raise your confidence in yourself; since *real* self-esteem does not consist of proving to others how great you are, but of liking yourself *whether or not* others think you are great.

If you feel very proud, then, that your son is a fine ball-player or your daughter the valedictorian of her class, the chances are that what you feel is false and not real pride. If you *need* their successes to bolster your feelings, then you yourself have a crummy philosophy of life and do not sufficiently appreciate yourself. Living vicariously through the exploits of others is not really living at all. You would better make your own attempts at doing something in life, whatever the likelihood of rejection or failure may be, than "safely" enjoying the successes of your offspring.

If, then, you have an inordinate desire to have children, look into your own heart and see how you are failing *yourself*. If you merely take sincere pleasure in being with and helping youngsters, fine; that may be a healthy pursuit. But if you *must* have children of your own to "fulfill" yourself, then the chances are that you are avoiding doing some of the things that would be equally fulfilling in case you never married and never had any progeny. Homosexuals, incidentally, even though they can't get enthusiastic about women, frequently want to marry and have children. By so doing, they figure, they will "prove" to the world how "manly" they really are; will have some helpless creatures around who will completely rely on them; and will easily attain love security, since they realize that it is much easier to get a child to love them than it is to get an adult. Many nonhomosexual males want to marry and have children for similar reasons. If you are in this class, try to recognize your own feelings of inadequacy and worthlessness; and, as noted above, try to determine the philosophic rot you are telling yourself to create these feelings, and then to *do* something about truly ridding yourself of them.

Summing up: the correct frame of mind into which to get yourself before you attempt to propose to any girl is the attitude that you love this girl and would very much want to marry her if she feels equally strongly toward you, but that you do not really *need* her to complete your life or to help make a "man" of you. The most you will get out of her accepting you and living with you in marriage is increased enjoyment and experience—and that is quite a lot, and should be eagerly sought. You will *not*, however, get one additional iota of manhood, or self-worth, or true increased confidence by winning the girl of your dreams. Such qualities come from within, and are dependent on *your* philosophy of life, rather than on any external love or other success. If you fully recognize this, you can be enthusiastically but *unfrantically* desirous of winning a given wife; and with such an attitude you are much more likely to instill confidence in you and raise your chances of getting her to say Yes.

Once you like yourself and are not *desperately* bent on marrying a particular woman, your technique of proposing can be simple and direct, without too many gimmicks or superduper selling techniques. For you are not selling her a one-shot product, you are presumably getting her to accept a long-wearing, lifetime you. And if she will not accept you before you are married pretty much as you are, what are the chances that she will continue to accept you in your own right long after the legal knots are tied?

Some specific pointers that you can keep in mind on proposing are these:

1. Try not to be unusually premature. It is all very well, and often effective, if you can say to a girl on your very first date: "You know, I really like you a lot. In fact, you utterly send me. One of these days, we may well end up getting married." This kind of statement tells the girl that you are very favorably impressed by her and already considering the *possibility* that you may some day wed her; but it does not give her the impression that you are a rash, unthinking individual who really *would* rush into marrying an almost total stranger, who might not be for you in many as yet undisclosed ways. So hint, if you want, quite early in the game of courtship, that

you are seriously *considering* marrying a girl; but do not, too soon, literally ask her to marry you, and thereby lead her to believe (and with some reason!) that there is something most peculiar about you.

2. Don't endlessly dilly-dally. If you have known a girl for a goodly length of time and have decided that you would like to ask her to marry you, don't keep putting your proposal off one time after another, on the excuse that she doesn't feel well that night, or a full moon is not out to light your way, or there is no good opportunity to propose, or some other set of excuses. Certainly it is nice to pick an appropriate time and place and to do your proposing then. But if you are *never*, somehow, able to find exactly the right circumstances to propose, the chances are high that you are making up excuses, and that you are simply scared stiff to pop the question. In which case, you'd better look for your catastrophizing sentences, and do something about contradicting and challenging them. For the longer you shilly-shally about proposing, the more clearly your girlfriend is likely to see that you do have a severe problem in this connection, and the less favorably inclined she may be to accept you. Besides—let's face it—she's not growing any younger, and is probably, if she sees you regularly and monogamously, just as much—or more—interested in marrying as you are, and may go off in disgust to get entangled with someone else if you endlessly cavil with yourself.

3. Watch for significant responses when you have serious discussions with your girlfriend. Put out, from time to time, definite feelers about marriage. Discover, somewhat objectively and impersonally, how she feels about marrying in general, whether she is very interested in having children, how old she thinks she should be before she marries, what her nonmarital and possibly conflicting interests in life are, and other information of this nature. And find out, if you can, how she feels about you—not merely as a steady date and lover, but as a potential mate and breadwinner. As you discover such information, try to show your girlfriend that you are a responsible, serious person—as well, perhaps, as a fun-loving, exciting individual—and that you could well be the kind of man who would make a good husband.

4. It is often good to get some kind of objective checkup on your girl's feelings about you. Speak, if you can, to her girlfriends, and see if you can get some information from them

in this regard. Make friends, if possible, with her parents and relatives. Let her get close to your friends and relatives if you can arrange it. Through her talking to these other people, and then your talking to them, you can usually get a line on her feelings toward you that you may not be able to get merely by speaking with her.

5. If, in the course of talking to your girlfriend or to others in whom she has confided, you do gather significant data about her attitudes to you, be sure to *do* something with this information. If you find, for example, that she objects to your sloppiness or your overmeticulousness, see if you can't do something to modify your behavior in this regard. If she complains about your not being attentive enough or being over-attentive to her, why cannot you change yourself in this area? The more negative feelings she has about you that you can do something to counteract *before* you ask her to marry you, the greater your chances of gaining an acceptance from her should be.

6. Soften her up, if you can, by placing her in marital or semimarital situations with you, and then show her what advantages she has derived from these situations. If you spend an entire weekend with her, for example, and you believe that she has enjoyed it immensely, point up how close you were to being married on this weekend, and how much better off it would be if you actually were mated. If one of you has to get up in the middle of the night to go home, indicate to her how much more convenient it would be if you were married and this sort of thing could stop. If you are practically living together, but still keeping separate apartments, show her how much more economical it would be if you actually married and were able to share the rent on a single dwelling place.

7. In some instances, instead of making one formal, large-scale proposal of marriage, which may well frighten her and which she is likely to reject, make a number of small-scale, informal proposals, which cannot be taken too seriously, and to which a final rejection on her part is not likely to be made. Take it for granted in your conversation with her, for example, that you *will* be married, and every once in a while talk about what you're both going to do after such a marriage has taken place. Or casually remark, now and then, "If you really need money, how about sharing my bank account?" or "Don't even think of taking that out-of-town job,

dear, for then I'll have to propose to you over the phone, and I don't think either of us will like that." In many ways, in some instances, show her that you're available for marriage whenever she wants to take the plunge; and yet don't necessarily formally ask her to set any specific date. This may give her confidence that you are always there; and yet not frighten her off if she has some fear of marrying.

8. Don't necessarily take her initial No for an answer. Even though she is not just being coy and means what she says when she first tells you that she won't marry you, this does not mean that she will feel the same way several days, weeks, or months later. For one thing, you can ask her why she at first refuses you, and can try to do something about changing yourself, so as to remove her initial objections. For another thing, you can keep being as nice to her as possible, so that she becomes more and more attached to you, and surrenders her original negative attitude. This does not mean that you should be a chameleon to please your beloved and induce her to marry you, but merely that if you have nonessential habits to which she objects, these may be worth changing.

Not that I am advocating that you should merely catch her off guard some day, when she is in a relatively good mood. For even though you may get her to marry you in this manner, the chances are that she will still not *really* want to do so, and that therefore she will not cooperate fully after marriage and will not make a good wife. I have seen scores of instances in which the wife married mainly because the husband insisted on keeping after her; and in which she later felt nothing toward him, or began to have definite feelings for some other man. I am sure that there are also cases wherein, despite her initial reluctance, the wife was finally won over *after* marriage, and a good relationship ensued. But it is much more probable that you will get along well in marriage with a girl who willingly and eagerly accompanies you to City Hall than one whom you have to cajole to get her there.

9. Once you have made up your mind to ask a girl to marry you, don't think that you need elegant language or a special mode of putting the question to her. The more you waver *about how* to propose, the more hesitant and indecisive you are likely to be when you do so; and she is hardly likely to consider your indecisiveness flattering to her. It will suffice if you simply say, "You know, dear, I've been thinking things

over about you and me, and I think we would have a good marriage. Will you marry me?" As we noted previously in this chapter, even the most informal kind of proposal may fit the bill. And don't think that you have to go through all kinds of preliminary maneuvering to lead up to the final question. The more you introduce the subject by listing your or her assets, or seventeen reasons why you think the two of you should marry, the more apologetic you may sound to her. If she is the kind of girl who *demands* a big production, then you may have to make one to her order. But a proposal of marriage *is* just that: a *proposal*, not necessarily a formal statement with all kinds of qualifying clauses. You like the girl; you think she also likes you; you would like to suggest that you try the state of matrimony together. That's it. Gilding the lily in this connection may do a lot more harm than good.

10. If you do propose, and you are unqualifiedly refused, and there seems no chance that you will ever be accepted by this particular girl, then that is unfortunate; but it is hardly the end of the world. You may, if you like, honestly ask yourself *why* she refused you; and may even, if you can do so, try to get her to state some reasons in this connection. This kind of information may help you to avoid making the same mistakes again with the next girl in whom you get interested.

Mulling over your loss, however, is not likely to decrease your sorrow about it. Instead, you might well apply at this point the techniques of surviving disappointment in love that we discussed in Chapter 8. In particular, if you are really interested in marrying *someone*, you will tend to find that the more you occupy yourself with the question, "Who is the *next* best possible girl for me?" the less you will have time to give yourself a real pain in the heart over *this* one whom you have just lost. The mere fact that the present girl *has* refused you usually (though, of course, not always) means that she was somehow prejudiced against rather than in favor of you, and that it is most unlikely that she would have made you a good wife. All right: your job is now to find a girl who is not equally prejudiced, and who presumably would be better suited for you. If you forthrightly and intensively go about seeking such a girl, you will very likely be surprised at how well you are able to take the loss of the one who has just turned you down.

Chapter 20

How to Be Happy Though Married

This book is largely designed for the single man and is not a treatise on happy marriage. Dr. Robert A. Harper and I have already written another book, *Creative Marriage*, which does specifically cover marital and family relationships. Let me round off the present volume, however, with at least a few important hints about what you can do to achieve and maintain a fine and enjoyable partnership with your mate if you decide to plunge into matrimony.

Taking a Realistic Attitude Toward Marriage

Persist, if you will, in being ultraromantic about your marriage and you will probably soon be ultramiserable in it. Not that marriage entirely precludes romance; but it is a lot *more* than that. Once you realize and fully accept the fact that Utopia simply does not exist, in marriage or outside of it, and that perfect joy in human affairs is as rare as perfection in any other aspect of the universe, you will have a better possibility of achieving maximum satisfaction in your mating.

You—remember—are hardly an infallible angel; nor is it wise to expect your wife to be one. Once you have taken the giant (but not necessarily fatal) step into marriage, recognize and accept your own and your mate's limitations. By very patient, prolonged therapeutic work with your wife, you may be able to help her change some of her annoying ways; but the chances are that she will not change very much in this respect—and that in some ways she'll even grow worse. Tough! But if you realistically expect her to be human rather than sainted, at least you will not be terribly disillusioned and disheartened.

Increasing Emotional Maturity

The best way to help your wife and your marriage is to help yourself become increasingly mature emotionally. No matter how disturbed your mate may be—and if she is a denizen of Western civilization, you can be reasonably sure that she *is* disturbed at the start—you are not going to help your marital and familial situation by foaming at the mouth yourself. Not only will your own anxiety and hostility prevent you from doing anything effective to help her or your children, but it will also serve as an exceptionally poor model for her own behavior. For if you are continually upsetting yourself about life's little difficulties, you are effectively teaching your family members that it is right and proper to be upset—which, of course, it damned well isn't.

Although anxiety is a bad enough trait for anyone to live with, and almost always tends to make a poor marital situation worse, even greater harm is usually done in marriage by your own feelings of hostility. And such feelings, I strongly insist, are *always* unjustified. Not that your wife (or children) may be behaving well, while you are merely misreading her actions and paranoiacally finding them heinous. On the contrary, the probability is that most of the time you find her wrong or annoying, she really *is*, and that almost any reasonable man would find her so.

All right: so she's wrong or annoying. The real question is: Do *you* have to upset yourself because she is mistaken or irritating? And the obvious answer, if you really *think* about it, is: No, of course you don't.

Not that we expect you to *like* your wife's nasty or stupid behavior. That would be idiotically masochistic, if you did. But why can't you simply dislike it—and then let it go at that?

Why can't you say to yourself—and I mean *convince* yourself—in other words: "I don't like the way she's acting toward me; now let me see if I can't somehow induce her to behave better—especially by acting well toward her *in spite of* her poor behavior toward me." Or: "I don't like what she's doing, and it looks like I won't be able to stop her from doing this, since that's the way she is. All right: why do I have to make myself unhappy just *because* that's the way she is? Why can't I *accept* her bad behavior, even though I'll never like it?"

The art of living happily with an annoying person, as I explain in *How to Live with a Neurotic* (Ellis, 1957), consists not necessarily in getting this person to change, and thereby reducing the annoyance; but primarily in seeing that you yourself are *not annoyed by being annoyed.* For the original annoyance you often cannot control; and in many cases it *is* distinctly irritating to have someone continually criticize you, or keep the house in a mess, or act badly toward your children. But your annoyance at *being* annoyed *is* definitely within your control, since it consists of your own internalized sentences: (a) "I don't like being annoyed in this fashion," and (b) "Because I don't like being annoyed, I *shouldn't* be; and I simply can't *stand* her annoying me in this manner."

Although the first of these sentences is perfectly sane—since who *does* like being annoyed?—the second one is equally insane. There is no reason why you *shouldn't* be annoyed by your wife, even though there are many reasons why *it would be nice* if you weren't. And there is no reason why you can't *stand* her irritating behavior, even though *it might well be better* if you calmly refused to put up with it and unagitatedly kept away from her or divorced her. The *ideas* that she absolutely should not be the way she obviously is and that you can't stand behavior that you simply do not like are the motivating forces behind your getting annoyed at being annoyed; and these ideas are *your* ideas, can be reviewed and challenged by you, and can be surrendered when you face the fact that they are wholly self-defeating.

Irritation, annoyance, and frustration, then, are normal concomitants of virtually all marriages; but downright hatred of your mate or the feeling that you positively can't stand being irritated, annoyed, or frustrated by her is a neurotic consequence of your own dysfunctional philosophy of life and does not stem from the merely annoying marital circumstances. Similarly, although you may have a genuine fear that your wife will refuse to copulate with you, serve you poisonous-tasting meals, or cruelly mishandle your children, your possible anxiety that she will dominate you, or hurt you with her criticism, or stop loving you and thereby break your heart is definitional rather than truly valid, in that *you* create such anxiety by your own self-propagandized nonsense.

Thus, in anxiety you are telling yourself: "I dislike her

continually criticizing me," and "I can't stand her criticism and must feel terribly hurt if she keeps doing it." Although the first of these sentences may well be true and sane, the second is only definitionally true; and since it causes you unnecessary trouble, it is perfectly insane. For your wife's criticism can *not* hurt you, unless you falsely tell yourself that you can't stand it and that it hurts you. Your very *belief* that you can't stand her criticism, and that you are worthless because you live with a termagant like her, is what "hurts" you. For her criticism itself, without this silly belief on your part, is harmless, and merely consists of empty noise.

If, then, you consistently observe and challenge the senseless ideas that invariably lie behind your own hostility and anxiety, you can at least do something about *them*; and, if you do so, you are almost certain to have a better relationship with your wife. *She* may still be irritating or backbiting; but that will then largely be *her* problem and you can—if you wish to do so—live comfortably with it.

Increasing Compatibility of Interests

In some instances, there is comparatively little that can be done to increase your interest compatibility with your mate: since she is naturally one kind of person and you another, and getting either of you actively to keep participating actively in the other's hobbies or interests might take a tremendous amount of compromise and effort; and the game might well not be worth the candle. But in other instances, you definitely can try to learn bridge, enjoy the ballet, or do something else that your wife especially likes to do; and sometimes you may even surprise yourself by coming to like this form of activity in its own right, and to continue to be absorbed in it after she, perhaps, has lost some of her own interest in it. Similarly, although it is true that you may have a ball playing poker with the boys, or gambling on horses, or looking at sporting events on television, it is also possible that you can easily and enjoyably replace some of these activities with other pleasures that are more compatible with those of your mate.

The difficulty mainly arises when your wife tends to abhor and to interfere with one of your vital absorbing interests in life, or you with hers. If you, for example, have always been an avid stamp collector and she thinks this hobby is a complete waste of time and objects most strenuously to every penny spent on your collection; or if she dotes on playing opera most of the day on the phonograph and you simply can't abide opera, your marriage is in for a rough time.

Even in this event, you can at least do your best to *understand* your wife's vital absorptions or her serious objections to your major interests. If you insist on thinking of her as a moron because she doesn't like stamp collecting, or a horrible snob because she does enjoy opera, not only will the two of you clash in regard to your diverging interests, but you will lose respect for each other as *people*. If you can well understand, and even to some considerable degree sympathize with, her hobbies or her objections to yours, then at least you have some kind of basis for open discussion of the problem of clashing absorptions; and both of you may be able gracefully to lump, instead of savagely to keep fuming against, the other's bents. We normally do not greatly enjoy being with others who are extremely different from us (though for a while they may complement us and give us something that we ourselves lack in life). But at least if we can openmindedly *tolerate* their differences, we may be able to get along with them well in other areas where we do easily and mutually agree. If we do not tolerate the differences, then almost *everything* we do with these individuals becomes a focal point of disagreement, and soon we are not enjoying their company at all.

Virtually every married man, therefore, must realize that his wife will be significantly different from him in many respects, because she is a female, because she is a person, and because people can easily love each other when just a few of their tastes and interests overlap, and when they have many aspects of their personalities which are quite diverse. Sometimes these differences can be used to advantage, as when one mate brings to the other things that he would normally never think of even trying himself. But often they are going to create distinct difficulties, which only an attitude of great tolerance will minimize.

Augmenting Sexual Compatibility

The mere fact that you think a girl is physically attractive, like her in many ways, and even get along with her beautifully in most respects does not mean that you are therefore automatically going to get along well with her in bed. Although people who do *not* accept each other nonsexually rarely have good sex lives, the reverse is not necessarily true. Your wife may well be interested in much more or less sex activity than you are; enjoy or not enjoy the same kind of sex relations that you most prefer; and may be either cooperative or noncooperative about having sex relations with you.

If there are sex difficulties between you and your wife, the same kind of approach that you used in courting her may be equally necessary in marriage. For when you were wooing her, you were probably most considerate of her sexual idiosyncrasies; did your best to excite her sufficiently so that she would *want* to copulate with you; and leaned over backward to use those forms of sexuality which were most pleasing to her. After marriage, similar kinds of courting procedures may be most appropriate; since there are many women who have to be wooed sexually all their lives—just as there are many who are always eager for sex play, and are more than willing to do part of the wooing themselves.

The main heart of sex compatibility in marriage is probably adequate communication between mates. It is amazing how many married individuals are failing to achieve sex satisfaction while their mates are blithely assuming they are completely satisfied. Several husbands I have seen for marriage counseling have been shocked to learn that their wives have not been having orgasms for years, when they assumed that they were having them; and many wives I have seen have been surprised to learn that their husbands, who had always easily gained erections and achieved orgasm with them, were still quite unsatisfied sexually and were dreaming of doing sex acts which they had never communicated about to these wives.

Talk to your wife about sex, then. *Ask* her whether she is having orgasms, and whether there is anything that she finds missing about sex with you. *Tell* her what you yourself think is lacking in your sex relations, and what you think can be done to remedy this lack.

Is your wife too puritanical and inhibited for your tastes? Why not, in that case, try to de-puritanize her? Talk to her about the goodness of all kinds of harmless sex acts. Experimentally get her to try certain modes of sexuality until she gets to enjoy them and want them. Bring her suitable books and articles to read on sex. Get her among a group of people who are more liberal than she is, and who are likely to help de-propagandize her. Convince her, by your own attitude and behavior, that *you* wouldn't ever think anything was wrong about various kinds of sex participation, and would never look down on her for engaging in some of the available varieties. If necessary, see that she gets psychological help with her inhibitions. But don't give up too easily and believe, just because your mate is sexually backward, that she always has to remain so. Keep gradually but persistently sniping away at her inhibitions; and show her, in both theory and practice, how self-defeating and ridiculous they are.

If you, on the other hand, are backward about trying various sex activities, try to find out *why* you are so shy, and get at the underlying, anxiety-creating sentences which are holding you back. Force yourself, if you have to do so, to try certain things, and to keep trying them for at least a reasonable period of time, before you become fully convinced that you do *not* like this or that. Would you *really* become disgusted if you had oral-genital or anal-genital relations? How do you know, if you haven't even tried? You might be surprised how certain things grow on you after a while; and, especially, if your wife tends to enjoy some of these acts immensely, giving yourself and her a chance to enjoy them is one of the most cooperative and loving aspects of marriage.

Augmenting Amative Compatibility

Normally, we have relatively little control over our emotions of love; but little, fortunately, doesn't mean no control. Assuming that you want to continue to have reasonably intense love feelings for your wife, and would like her similarly to reciprocate, there are certain things that you can do to encourage such emotions. For one thing, you can make a deliberate effort to see the good points of your mate, and to show yourself how much you can benefit from these points. Her bad traits, on the other hand, you can either learn to ignore; or face clearly while fully accepting and tolerating them.

You can also do your best to induce your wife to modify some of her behavior that interferes with your feeling stronger love for her. This does not mean—of course!—that you should severely criticize her for her bad cooking, or her sexual uncooperativeness, or what you will. It means, rather, that you should calmly and nonpunitively try to show her that some of the things she does are unpleasant to you, and that you would feel more kindly disposed toward her if she did not do these things. Moreover, you can often show her that her behavior is *self*-defeating, as well as obnoxious to you, and that for her *own* sake it would be wise if she changed it.

If there are any particular blocks that are inhibiting your love for your wife, you can try to discover what they are and how to eradicate them. I have seen several husbands, for example, who had lost a great deal of their love for their wives because, they said, the wives were aggressive women who took the initiative in various ways, sometimes including sex, and who thereby castrated them. When I showed these men that no one could possibly castrate them but themselves, and that it was *not* horrible and awful to live with an assertive, initiative-taking woman, they faced the fact that they had severe problems of their own and began to work on these problems. In most (though not all) of these instances, the husbands were able to stop feeling threatened by their wive's behavior; and even when the wives did not significantly change in this respect, the husbands found that a problem no longer existed, and became much more loving again toward their mates. As one of these patients said to me after a few months of therapy: "Not only don't I become disturbed any more when my wife makes passes at me when we go to bed, but I'm beginning to see that it's better and more exciting that way. As long as I don't tell myself that I'm being unmanned by her taking the initiative, I find her a much better sex partner. And my feelings of love for her have grown immensely!"

Similarly, if you find that you are beginning to hate or become indifferent to your wife because *you* feel threatened by some aspect of your marriage, you can often look into your own heart, discover the nonsense you are telling yourself to create the "threat," and solve the problem by changing yourself instead of attempting to change your wife. If you do so, your own love feelings for your wife will often be considerably enhanced or revived.

If it is your wife who seems to have lost some of her love for you, then you may often be able to re-woo her, with the same sort of courtship procedures that originally induced her to care for you. You can make greater efforts to satisfy her in sexual and nonsexual ways; try to understand and sympathize with her more; treat her in an ardently loving manner; and otherwise use the methods we discussed earlier in this book in our chapters on gaining a woman's responsiveness. Women in particular often require continued wooing *after* marriage; and by exerting yourself in this respect you may be able to keep your wife passionately attached to you for an indefinite period of time. As André Tridon (1922) once remarked, "The human fish does not stay caught, and has to be captured over and over again."

The main point we are making here is that loving and being loved by a woman is partially but by no means completely beyond your control. Work and practice in this area, as in so many other areas of life, can sometimes do wonders to keep love alive, or even to revive it when it has fallen miserably on its face. John Cowper Powys, who gave quite a bit of thought to this subject, noted: "It is nonsense to speak of 'love' as something that comes and goes beyond our control. Love comes beyond our control just as our birth into life comes; but, once with us, is a thing we can deal with, strengthen, deepen, intensify—by our imaginative will—and prolong ad infinitum." Powys was probably a little overoptimistic in this regard; but he had a point.

Increasing Domestic Compatibility

We might as well face the fact that most of married life consists of domestic sharing. Husbands and wives do not ordinarily merely love and have sex relations and go out companionably with each other. More importantly, in most instances, they *live* together; and, what is more, they usually live with one or more other persons, such as their in-laws and their children. Consequently, unless a good deal of domestic compatibility exists, all the other forms of agreement that exist between a husband and wife are soon likely negated.

It is, of course, not absolutely *necessary* that a man and woman live together when they are married. Nietzsche (1909) observed that "if married couples did not live together, happy marriages would be more frequent." And people like Havelock Ellis and his wife, Edith, have occasionally deliberately lived apart even though married for a considerable period of time. Mrs. Ellis was firmly devoted to this notion, and in one of her books, *New Horizons in Love and Life* (1921), wrote: "The materialistic idea which supposes that no marital relationship can be truly beautiful unless dependent on constant bodily presence must give way to a new conception. Proximity is not necessarily a part of faithfulness,

nor is a villa residence a necessity for love's development."
R. B. Kerr (World League for Sexual Reform, 1930) later en-
dorsed this view, and stated: "The fact of two people loving
one another is no reason at all why they should live together
in the same house. Indeed it is rather a good reason why they
should not do so, for the intimacy of domestic life is well-
known to be very unfavorable to the continuance of strong
passion."

This is all very well in theory; but the practice is quite
difficult to follow in our society. It is most unlikely that once
you marry you *will* live separately from your wife for any
period of time—though there is no reason, of course, why
you cannot often take separate vacations, or go on business
trips alone, or otherwise on occasion be apart. The chances
are, however, that you will *mostly* live together under the
same roof. Consequently, you must try to find the kind of
roof that you can live comfortably under, and set up the kinds
of schedules and rules which will make this living most gra-
cious.

You need not, for example, necessarily share the same bed,
nor even the same bedroom, with your wife, if one or both
of you have good reason (such as allergy to snoring!) to do
otherwise. You don't have to look at television together because one of you adores a certain show. Although you may
like to stay home and read the newspaper every night in
the week, after a hard day at the office, there is no reason why
your wife similarly has to remain home every evening. And
if you get restless, every once in a while, and feel that you
would very much like to take a walk, or go for a drive, or
visit friends, this does not mean that your wife, merely because you are married to her, *must* accompany you.

Every marriage can seek its own level in regard to domestic arrangements; and since people are enormously different
in these respects, there is no reason why your particular marriage should be just like that of most of the others in your
neighborhood. It is important that both you and your wife,
after trying shared domesticity for a while, determine what
you really like and dislike about it; and then that you frankly
speak up and try to arrange to eliminate as much as you can
those aspects which either or both of you find disagreeable.
You may, as a result of such communication, find that you
want to get a larger apartment, or to live in a different neighborhood, or to make definite schedules of events, or to make

other planned arrangements. But it is usually far better that you definitely plan and execute these arrangements than that you slowly burn underneath or overtly flare up from time to time because either or both of you is chafing at the domestic bit. Just as two roommates discuss and arrange living conditions so that they get along with a minimum of strain, so should most married couples talk freely with each other and plan friendly living.

To sum up: Expect no miracles from your marriage, but work hard at getting all you possibly can get from it. Intelligently regard and approach a marital union—especially before you enter it. Always remember that many people get along beautifully outside marriage, and that modern mating is hardly designed for all individuals.

If you do not happen to have the particular degree of marriageability which is essential for successful union today, or if you cannot find a wife who possesses it and pleases you, your time for marrying has not yet come; and there's no point in trying to force it. When you and your chosen girl are truly suited to marriage, the chances are that it will be truly suited to you. Until that day arrives—there is always sex and there is always love.

If you do marry, you should naturally do your best to adjust to your chosen wife and the family relationship that you would like to have with her. If your best is not quite good enough, and either of you is miserable in the marital state, you fortunately (even in *this* Dark Age!) don't have to stay irrevocably tied. If you can't make the best of marriage, you can still make the best of separation or divorce. The main thing in life is not the particular institutional state—bachelorhood or marriage—you are in but the *you* who is in this state. If you are determined to *be* you, and not to give yourself a hard time about the way others think you *should* be, you can have a real ball whether you are married or single. The choice is yours: make it!

Bibliography

Abramson, H. A. LSD-25 as an adjunct to psychotherapy with elimination of fear of homosexuality. *J. Psychol.*, 1955, 39, 127-155.

Adler, Alfred. The homosexual problem. *Alien. & Neurol.*, 1917, 38, 285.

Allen, Clifford, *The sexual perversions and abnormalities*. London: Oxford, 1949.

Amiel, Henri Frédéric. *Philline*. New York: Knopf, 1930.

Ansbacher, Heinz L. Review of Alfred Adler's "La compensation psychique de l'état d'inferiorité des organes suivi de la problème de l'homosexualité." *J. Individ. Psychol.*, 1958, 14, 191-92.

Arlington, Norman. Sexual starvation in the American male. *Independent*, Oct. 1958, Issue 81, 1, 8.

Beigel, Hugo. *Encyclopedia of sex education*. New York: Daye, 1952.

Beigel, Hugo. The meaning of coital postures. *Int. J. Sexol.*, 1953, 6, 136-41.

Beigel, Hugo. Abstinence. In Ellis, Albert, and Abarbanel, Albert (Eds.), *Encyclopedia of sexual behavior*. New York: Hawthorn Books, 1961.

Benjamin, Harry. An echo of an addendum to "for the sake of morality." *Med. J. & Rec.*, Aug. 5, 1931.

Benjamin, Harry. The treatment of aging. *Senior Citizen*, May 1958.

Benjamin, Harry. *Prostitution*. In Ellis, Albert, and Abarbanel, Albert (Eds.), *Encyclopedia of sexual behavior*. New York: Hawthorn Books, 1961.

Benjamin, Harry, and Ellis, Albert. An objective examination of prostitution. *Int. J. Sexol.*, 1954, 8, 99-105.

Bibby, Cyril. The art of loving. In Ellis, Albert, and Abarbanel, Albert (Eds.), *Encyclopedia of sexual behavior*. New York: Hawthorn Books, 1961.

Blau, Saul. The venereal diseases. In *ibid.*, 1961.

Borden, Mary. *The technique of marriage*. London: Heineman, 1933.

Boy Scouts of America. *Revised handbook for boys.* New York: Boy Scouts of America, 1945.

Branden, Nathaniel. *Who is Ayn Rand?* New York: Random House, 1962a.

Branden, Nathaniel. Benevolence vs. altruism. *Objectivist Newsl.,* July 1962b, 27-28.

Bridges, James W. *The meaning and varieties of love.* Cambridge, Mass.: Sci. Art Publishers, 1935.

Brown, Walter C. *The single girl.* Derby, Conn.: Monarch Books, 1961.

Buckle, Donald. The treatment of sex offenders. *Int. J. Sexol.,* 1949 3, 1-8.

Butler, Samuel. *Hudibras.* Cambridge: Cambridge University Press, 1905.

Calderone, Mary (Ed.). *Abortion.* New York: Hoeber, 1958.

Calderone, Mary. *Release from sexual tension.* New York: Random House, 1960.

Callahan, Roger. Value orientation and psychotherapy. *Amer. Psychologist,* 1960, 15, 269-70.

Caprio, Frank S. *The sexually adequate male.* New York: Citadel, 1952.

Caprio, Frank S. *A psychiatrist talks about sex.* New York: Belmont, 1962.

Carnegie, Dale. *How to win friends and influence people.* New York: Pocket Books, 1954.

Carpenter, Edward. *Love's coming of age.* New York: Kennedy, 1923.

Cauldwell, David. Sex questions answered. *Sexology,* 1958, 24, 738; 1959, 25, 538.

Chesser, Eustace. *The sexual, marital and family relationships of the English woman.* New York: Roy, 1956.

Clark, LeMon. *Sex and you.* Indianapolis: Bobbs-Merrill, 1949.

Clark, LeMon. Overcoming psychological impotence. *Sexology,* 1959, 25, 762-67.

Clark, LeMon. Sexual adjustment in marriage. In Ellis, Albert, and Abarbanel, Albert (Eds.), *Encyclopedia of sexual behavior.* New York: Hawthorn Books, 1961.

Clark, LeMon. Abortions in Budapest. *Sexology,* 1963, 29, 633-35.

Clough, Eric. *The outraged.* Burlingame, Calif.: Author, 1962.

Cory, Donald Webster. Paper delivered at the annual meeting of the Mattachine Society, Sept. 8, 1958.

Cory, Donald Webster. *The homosexual in America.* New York: Paperback Library, 1963.

Craig, Alex. *Sex and revolution.* London: Allen, 1934.

Creadick, R. N. Management of homosexuals. *South. Med. J.,* 1953, 46, 455-60.

Davis, M. Edward. Review of Carl Hartman's "Science and the safe period." *Science*, 1963, 139, 581-82.

Dearborn, Lester. Autoerotism. In Ellis, Albert, and Abarbanel, Albert (Eds.), *Encyclopedia of sexual behavior*. New York: Hawthorn Books, 1961.

Dengrove, Edward. Frigidity: facts and fancies. In *Sexology* Magazine, *The X report*. New York: Belmont Books, 1962a.

Dengrove, Edward. Techniques for heightening sex response. In *ibid.*, 1962b.

Dengrove, Edward. Low sex drive. *Sexology*, 1963, 29, 561-63.

De Ropp, Robert S. *Drugs and the mind*. New York: Grove Press, 1961.

Deutsch, Danica. A case of transvestism. *Amer. J. Psychother.*, 1954, 8, 239-42.

Devereux, George. Institutionalized homosexuality of the Mohave Indians. *Human Biol.*, 1937, 9, 498-527.

Dreiser, Theodore. *A book about myself*. New York: Boni & Liveright, 1922.

Ehrmann, Winston W. *Premarital dating behavior*. New York: Holt, 1960.

Eichenlaub, John E. *The marriage art*. New York: Lyle Stuart, 1961.

Elkan, E. The evolution of female orgastic ability. *Int. J. Sexol.*, 1948, 2, 1-13, 1948, 2, 84-92.

Elkin, Henry. The Northern Arapaho of Wyoming. In Linton, Ralph (Ed.), *Acculturation in seven American tribes*. New York: Appleton Century, 1940.

Ellis, Albert. Some significant correlates of love and family behavior. *J. Soc. Psychol.*, 1949a, 30, 3-16.

Ellis, Albert, A study of human love relationships. *J. Genet. Psychol.*, 1949b, 75, 61-71.

Ellis, Albert. A study of the love emotions of American college girls. *Int. J. Sexol.*, 1949c, 3, 15-21.

Ellis, Albert. Love and family relationships of American college girls. *Amer. J. Sociol.*, 1950, 55, 550-58.

Ellis, Albert. *How to live with a neurotic*. New York: Crown Publishers, 1957.

Ellis, Albert. *Sex without guilt*. New York: Lyle Stuart, 1958.

Ellis, Albert. Why married men visit prostitutes. *Sexology*, 1959, 25, 344-47.

Ellis, Albert. *The art and science of love*. New York: Lyle Stuart, 1960.

Ellis, Albert. *The folklore of sex*. New York: Grove Press, 1961a.

Ellis, Albert. Frigidity. In Ellis, Albert, and Abarbanel, Albert (Eds.), *Encyclopedia of sexual behavior*. New York: Hawthorn Books, 1961b.

Ellis, Albert. Coitus. In *ibid.*, 1961c.

Ellis, Albert. *Reason and emotion in psychotherapy.* New York: Lyle Stuart, 1962a.

Ellis, Albert. *The American sexual tragedy.* New York: Lyle Stuart, 1962b. New York: Grove Press, 1963e.

Ellis Albert. *If this be sexual heresy . . .* New York: Lyle Stuart, 1963a.

Ellis, Albert. *The intelligent woman's guide to man-hunting.* New York: Lyle Stuart, 1963b.

Ellis, Albert. Constitutional factors in homosexuality: a re-examination of the evidence. In Beigel, Hugo (Ed.), *Advances in sex research.* New York: Paul Hoeber, 1963c.

Ellis, Albert. The origin and development of the incest taboo. In Durkheim, Emile, *Incest.* New York: Lyle Stuart, 1963d.

Ellis, Albert. Is the vaginal orgasm a myth? *Liaison,* March 9, 1963f, 2-5.

Ellis, Albert, and Abarbanel, Albert. *Encyclopedia of sexual behavior.* New York: Hawthorn Books, 1961.

Ellis, Albert, and Brancale, Ralph. *The psychology of sex offenders.* Springfield, Ill.: Charles C Thomas, 1956.

Ellis, Albert, and Harper, Robert A. *Creative marriage.* New York: Lyle Stuart, 1961a.

Ellis, Albert, and Harper, Robert A. *A guide to rational living.* Englewood Cliffs, N.J.: Prentice-Hall, 1961b.

Ellis, Albert, and Sagarin, Edward. *Nymphomania: a study of the over-sexed woman.* New York: Julian Messner, 1964.

Ellis, Havelock. *Studies in the psychology of sex.* New York: Random House, 1936.

Ellis, Havelock. *Sex and marriage.* New York: Random House, 1952

Ellis, Havelock. *Psychology of sex.* New York: New American Library, 1960.

English, W. H., and English, Mary. What price adultery? *Sexology,* 1963, 29, 636-38.

Eysenck, H. J. (Ed.). *Handbook of abnormal psychology.* New York: Basic Books, 1961.

Farrow, E. P. *A practical method of self-analysis.* New York: Norton, 1942.

Faust, B. Differentialdiagnostische Betrachtung zu verschiedenen Arten habitueller Ipsation. *Kinderpsychol. Kinderpsychiat.,* 1957, 6, 198-201.

Fielding, William. *Sex and the love life.* New York: Permabooks, 1961.

Finck, Henry T. *Romantic love and personal beauty.* New York: Macmillan, 1887.

Finck, Henry T. *Primitive love and love stories.* New York: Scribner's, 1899.

Finger, F. W. Sex beliefs and practices among male college students. *J. Abnorm. Soc. Psychol.* 1947, 42, 47-57.

Fink, Harold Kenneth. *Long journey.* New York: Julian Press, 1954.

Fitzgerald, F. Scott. *This side of paradise.* New York: Scribner's, 1920.

Fonzi, G. J. The furtive fraternity. *Mattachine Review,* Jan. 1963, 3-28.

Foster, A. W. Treatment of sexual offenders. *Marriage Hyg.,* 1947, 1, 77-80.

French Institute of Public Opinion. *Patterns of sex and love: a study of the French woman and her morals.* New York: Crown Publishers, 1961.

Freud, Anna. Clinical observations on the treatment of manifest male homosexuality. *Psychoanal. Quart.,* 1951, 20, 237-38.

Freud, Sigmund. *Collected papers.* London: Hogarth Press, 1924-50.

Freud, Sigmund. *Basic writings.* New York: Modern Library, 1938.

Freund, K. Laboratory differential diagnosis of homosexuality and heterosexuality—an experiment with faking. *Rev. Czech. Med.,* 1961, 7, 20-31.

Freund, K. Femininity of the homosexual man and his parental relations. *Csl. Psychiat.,* 1961, 57, 170-74. *Excerpta Med.,* 1962, 15, 562.

Freund, K., and Pinkava, V. The question of 'femininity' in homosexual men. *Csl. Psychiat.,* 1960, 56, 386-94. *Excerpta Med.,* 1961, 14, 990.

Freund, Kurt, and Srnec, Jan. Kotazce muske homosexuality. *Sbornik Lekarsky.* 1953, 5-6, 125-53.

Gervis, Stephanie. The homosexual's labyrinth of law and social custom. Mattachine Rev., 1963, 9, 15-18.

Goethe, Johannn Wolfgang von. *Elective affinities.* London: Bell, 1873.

Gottlieb, Sophie B., and Gottlieb, Bernhardt S. *What you should know about marriage.* Indianapolis: Bobbs-Merrill, 1962.

Grant, Vernon. *Psychology of sexual emotion.* New York: Longmans, Green, 1957.

Greenblatt, Bernard R. *A doctor's marital guide for patients.* Chicago: Budlong Press, 1957.

Greenwald, Harold. *The call girl.* New York: Ballantine, 1957.

Groves, Ernest R. *Social problems and education.* New York: Longmans, Green, 1925.

Gurvitz, Milton. Sex offenders in private practice: treatment and outcome. Paper delivered at American Psychological Association annual meeting, Sept. 3, 1957.

Guttmacher, Alan F. Should our abortion laws be changed? *Sexology,* 1963, 29, 436-39.

Guttmacher, Alan F., with Best, W. W., and Jaffe, F. *The complete book of birth control.* New York: Ballantine, 1961.

Guyon. René. *The ethics of sexual acts.* New York: Knopf, 1934.

Guyon. René. *Sexual freedom.* New York: Knopf, 1950.

Guyon, René. *Human rights and the denial of sexual freedom.* Bangkok: Author, 1951.

Hadas, Moses (Ed.). *Essential works of stoicism.* New York: Bantam Books, 1961.

Hadfield, J. A. The cure of homosexuality. *Brit. Med. J.*, June 7, 1958, 1, 1323-26.

Haire, Norman (Ed.). *Encyclopedia of sex practice.* London: Encyclopedia Press, 1951.

Hamilton, Eleanor. *Partners in love.* New York: Ziff-Davis, 1961.

Hamilton, G. V. *A research in marriage.* New York: Lear, 1952.

Harding, T. Swann. The endless war on "vice." *Med. Rec.*, April 20, 1938.

Harper, Robert A. Communication problems in marriage and marriage counseling. *Marr. Fam. Living*, 1958, 20, 107-12.

Harper, Robert A. *Psychoanalysis and psychotherapy: 36 systems.* Englewood Cliffs, N. J.: Prentice-Hall, 1959a.

Harper, Robert A. Psychological aspects of homosexuality. Paper delivered at the meeting of the Society for the Scientific Study of Sex, May 22, 1959b.

Harper, Robert A. Extramarital sex relations. In Ellis, Albert, and Abarbanel, Albert (Eds.), *Encyclopedia of sexual behavior.* New York: Hawthorn Books. 1961a.

Harper, Robert A. Can homosexuals be changed? In Rubin, Isadore (Ed.), *The "third sex."* New York: New Book Co., 1961b.

Harper, Robert A. Jealousy, its prevention and cure. *Sexology*, 1963, 29, 516-18.

Hartman, Carl G. *Science and safe period.* Baltimore: Williams & Wilkins, 1962.

Havemann, Ernest. What the marriage manuals don't say. *Reader's Digest*, Nov. 1962, 129-32.

Heaton, Walter. *Temperament and sex in life and art.* Boston: Badger, 1919.

Hefner, Hugh M. The playboy philosophy. *Playboy*, Dec. 1962, Jan. and Feb. 1963.

Heine, Heinrich. *The poems.* Louis Untermeyer translation. New York: Harcourt, 1937.

Hendrick, Ives. *Facts and theories of psychoanalysis.* New York: Knopf, 1934.

Hirsch, Edwin W. *How to improve your sexual relations.* Chicago: Zeco, 1951.

Hirsch, Edwin W. *Modern sex life.* New York: New American Library, 1957.

Hirsch, Edwin W. *The power to love.* New York: Pyramid, 1962.

Hirschfeld, Magnus. *The sexual history of the world war.* New York: Panurge Press, 1934.

Hirschfeld, Magnus. *Sex in human relationships.* London: Lane, 1935.

Hudson, John. *Values and psychotherapy*. In manuscript, 1961.

Hunt, Morton M. *The natural history of love*. New York: Grove Press, 1963.

Hutton, Laura. *Sex technique in marriage*. New York: Emerson Books, 1938.

Jacobs, Gordon. A new approach to psychotherapy. Talk delivered to the Morristown Unitarian Fellowship, Dec. 9, 1962.

Johnson, Paul. Are virgins obsolete? *New Statesman*, Jan. 4, 1963, 8-9.

Johnson, Virginia E., and Masters, William H. Intravaginal contraceptive study. Phase I. Anatomy. *West. J. Surg. Obstet. & Gynecol.*, 1962, 70, 202-7.

Jung, C. G. *Two essays on analytical psychology*. New York: Meridian, 1960.

Kahol, O. P. Prostitution in India. *Sexology*, 1963, 9, 534-35.

Karpman, Benjamin. *The sexual offender and his offenses*. New York: Julian Press, 1956.

Katz, Barney. *You can have a better marriage*. New York: American Press, 1956.

Katz, Marvin. Love: its definition and analysis. Mimeographed, 1962.

Kelly, G. Lombard. *So you think you're impotent*. Augusta, Ga.: Southern Medical Supply Co., 1957.

Kelly, G. Lombard. *Sexual feeling in married men and women*. New York: Permabooks, 1961.

Kelly, G. Lombard. *Sex manual for those married or about to be*. Augusta, Ga.: Southern Medical Supply Co., 1963.

Kinsey, A. C., Pomeroy, W. B., and Martin, C. E. *Sexual behavior in the human male*. Philadelphia: Saunders, 1948.

Kinsey, A. C., Pomeroy, W. B., Martin, C. E., and Gebhard, P. H. *Sexual behavior in the human female*. Philadelphia: Saunders, 1953.

Kirkendall, Lester A. Toward a clarification of the concept of male sex drive. *Marr. Fam. Living*, 1958, 20, 367-72.

Kirkendall, Lester A. Sex worries of teenage boys. *Sexology*, 1959, 25, 360-65.

Kirkendall, Lester A. *Premarital intercourse and interpersonal relationships*. New York: Julian Press, 1961a.

Kirkendall, Lester A. Sex drive. In Ellis, Albert, and Abarbanel, Albert (Eds.), *Encyclopedia of sexual behavior*. New York: Hawthorn Books, 1961b.

Kirkendall, Lester A. The problem of remaining a virgin. *Sexology*, 1963, 29, 600-2.

Korzybski, Alfred. *Science and sanity*. Lancaster, Pa.: Lancaster Press, 1933.

Kronhausen, E., and Kronhausen, P. *Pornography and the law*. New York: Ballantine, 1959.

Kubie, Lawrence S. *Practical aspects of psychoanalysis.* New York: Norton, 1936.

Kupperman, Herbert S. Sex hormones. In Ellis, Albert, and Abarbanel, Albert (Eds.), *Encyclopedia of sexual behavior.* New York: Hawthorn, 1961.

Lanval, Marc. The curious history of chastity belts. *Sexology,* 1963, 29, 550-52.

Laubscher, B. J. F. *Sex, custom and psychopathology.* New York: McBride, 1938.

Lehfeldt, Hans. Contraception. In Ellis, Albert, and Abarbanel, Albert (Eds.), *Encyclopedia of sexual behavior.* New York: Hawthorn Books, 1961.

Lehfeldt, Hans, and Ellis, Albert (Eds.), Aspects of female sexuality. Monograph of the Society for the Scientific Study of Sex. *Quart. Rev. Surg. & Gynecol.,* 1959, 16, 217-63.

Leonard, William Ellery. *The locomotive god.* New York: Viking, 1927.

Levy, John, and Munroe, Ruth. *The happy family.* New York: Knopf, 1938.

Lewinsky, H. Features from a case of homosexuality. *Psychoanal. Quart.,* 1952, 21, 344-54.

Lichtenberger, J. B. *Divorce.* New York: Whittlesey House, 1931.

Lindsey, Ben, and Evans, W. *Companionate marriage.* New York: Garden City, 1929.

Linton, Ralph. Introduction to Kardiner, Abraham, *The individual and his society.* New York: Columbia University Press, 1939.

Liswood, Rebecca. *A marriage doctor speaks her mind about sex.* New York: Dutton, 1961.

Li Yu. *Jou pu tuan.* New York: Grove Press, 1963.

Loewenstein, J. *Treatment of impotence with special reference to mechanotherapy.* London: Hamilton, 1947.

London, Louis S., and Caprio, Frank S. *Sexual deviations.* Washington: Linacre, 1950.

Ludovici, Anthony. *Woman: a vindication.* New York: Dutton, 1923.

MacDougald, Duncan. Aphrodisiacs. In Ellis, Albert, and Abarbanel, Albert (Eds.), *Encyclopedia of sexual behavior.* New York: Hawthorn Books, 1961.

Mace, David. *Success in marriage.* New York: Abingdon, 1958.

Maddock, L. Perilous pedestal. *Candida,* 1959, 1, No. 3, 21.

Malinowski, Bronislaw. *The sexual life of savages in northwestern Melanesia.* New York: Halcyon House, 1929.

Mallary, N. D., Jr. *On sex and making love.* Atlanta, Ga. Unpublished manuscript, 1961.

Mantegazza, Paolo. *Physiology of love.* New York: Eugenics Publishing, 1936.

Martial. *Epigrams*. London: Bell, 1877.

Masters, William H., and Johnson, Virginia E. The anatomy of female orgasm. In Ellis, Albert, and Abarbanel, Albert (Eds.), *The encyclopedia of sexual behavior*. New York: Hawthorn Books, 1961.

Masters, William H., and Johnson, Virginia E. The sexual response cycle of the human female. III. The clitoris: anatomic and clinical considerations. *West. J. Surg. Obstet. & Gynecol.*, 1962, 270, 248-57.

Mathers, E. Powys. *Eastern love*. New York: Liveright, 1930.

Mauer, D., and Vogel, V. *Narcotics and narcotics addiction*. Springfield, Ill.: Charles C Thomas, 1954.

Maupassant, Guy de. *A woman's heart*. New York, 1926.

Maurois, André. *The art of loving*. New York: Harper, 1940.

McReynolds, David. The gay underground—a reply to Mr. Krim. *Village Voice*, March 25, 1959.

Menaker, Jerome S. Female sex problems. In *Sexology Magazine, The X report*. New York: Belmont Books, 1962.

Mencken, H. L. *Prejudices*. 4th series. New York: Knopf, 1924.

Menninger, Karl. *Love against hate*. New York: Harvest Books, 1959.

Menninger, Karl. *Man against himself*. New York: Harvest Books, 1961.

Mill, John Stuart. *The subjection of women*. New York: Appleton, 1869.

Monchanin, Abbé. In *Body and spirit: essays in sexuality*. New York: Longmans, Green, 1939.

Mozes, Eugene B. Dangers of self-induced abortion. *Sexology*, 1959, 25, 704-9.

Myerson, Abraham. Neuroses and neuropsychoses. *Amer. J. Psychiat.*, 1936, 93, 293.

Nedoma, K. Homosexuality in sexological practice. *Int. J. Sexol.*, 1951, 4, 219-24.

Nelson, Warren G. The physiology of reproduction and its relation to the regulation of fertility. *Marr. Fam. Living*, 1963, 25, 74-80.

Nordau, Max. *The Conventional lies of our civilization*. Chicago: Laird & Lee, 1886.

Nyswander, Marie. *The drug addict as a patient*. New York: International Universities Press, 1958.

O'Rell, Max. *Her royal highness woman*. New York: Abbey Press, 1901.

Ovid. *The love books of Ovid*. New York: Rarity Press, 1930.

Parker, Dorothy. *Not so deep as a well*. New York: Viking Press, 1936.

Peck, M. W., and Wells, F. L. On the sexuality of college graduate men. *Ment. Hyg.*, 1923, 7, 697-714.

Phillips, E. Lakin. *Psychotherapy*. Englewood Cliffs, N.J.: Prentice-Hall, 1956.

Poe, J. S. Successful treatment of a forty-year-old passive homosexual. *Psychoanal. Rev.*, 1952, 29, 23-36.

Powys, John Cowper. *A philosophy of solitude*. New York: Simon and Schuster, 1933.

Rainer, Julia, and Rainer, Jerome. *Sexual pleasure in marriage*. New York: Pocket Books, 1962.

Ramsay, George. *The philosophy and poetry of love*. New York: New York Publishing Co., 1846.

Rand, Ayn. *Atlas shrugged*. New York: New American Library, 1961.

Rand, Ayn. The ethics of emergencies. *Objectivist Newsl.*, 1963, 2, 5-6, 8.

Reich, Wilhelm. *The function of the orgasm*. New York: Orgone Inst. Press, 1948.

Reid, J. *Book of love*. New York: Macmillan, 1911.

Reik, Theodor. *Of love and lust*. New York: Grove Press, 1961.

Reiss, Ira L. *Premarital sexual standards in America*. Glencoe: Free Press, 1960.

Robertiello, C. *Voyage from Lesbos*. New York: Citadel, 1959.

Robie, W. F. *The art of love*. Ithaca, N.Y.: Rational Life Press, 1925.

Robinson, Marie N. *The power of sexual surrender*. New York: New American Library, 1962.

Robinson, Victor (Ed.). *Encyclopedia sexualis*. New York: Dingwall-Rock, 1936.

Robinson, William J. (Ed.). *Sexual Continence*. New York: Eugenics Publishing, 1930.

Rockberger, Harry. Rational-emotive psychotherapy: a few comments. *Bull. Essex County Soc. Clin. Psychologists in Priv. Practice*, March 1963, 6, No. 1, 5-6.

Rubin, Isadore. Illegal abortion. *Sexology*, 1959, 25, 348-53.

Rubin, Isadore. Virgin wives: new findings. *Sexology*, 1962, 29, 313-14.

Rubin, Isadore. The battle to end V.D. *Sexology*, 1963, 29, 520-23.

Rubinstein, J. Psychotherapeutic aspects of male homosexuality. *Brit. J. Med. Psychol.*, 1958, 31, 74-78.

Russell, Bertrand, *Marriage and morals*. New York: Liveright, 1929.

Rutledge, Aaron L. Do premarital visits to prostitutes help marriage? *Sexology*, 1963, 29, 590-92.

Sagarin, Edward. *The anatomy of dirty words*. New York: Lyle Stuart, 1962.

St. Augustine. *Confessions*. New York: Collier, 1962.

Saul, Leon, and Bernstein, C. The emotional settings of some attacks of urticaria. *Psychosom. Med.*, 1941, 3, 350.

Schmalhausen, Samuel. *The new generation.* New York: Liveright, 1930.

Schroeder, Theodore. Guilt and inferiority feelings as the creator of religious experience. *Psychoanal. Rev.,* 1929, 16, 46-54.

Schroeder, Theodore. Mormonism, sexual aspects of. In Robinson, Victor (Ed.), *Encyclopedia sexualis.* New York: Dingwall-Rock, 1936.

Secor, H. W. Sex frustration. *Sexology,* 1959, 25, 480-83.

Semans, James H. Premature ejaculation: a new approach. *South. Med. J.,* 1956, 49, 353-58.

Sentnor, Marvin. Woman's erotic cycle. In *Sexology* Magazine, *The X report.* New York: Belmont Books, 1962.

Seyd, Felicia. *Romantic rebel: the life and times of George Sand.* New York: Viking, 1941.

Shentoub, S. A. De quelques problèmes dans l'homosexualité masculine active. *Rev. Franç. Psychanalyse,* 1957, 21, 485-534. *Excerpta Med.,* VIII, 1959, 12, 958.

Sherry, Madam. *Pleasure was my business.* New York: Lyle Stuart, 1961.

Shuttleworth, Frank. A biosocial and developmental theory of male and female sexuality. *Marr. Fam. Living,* 1959, 21, 163-70.

Sobrero, A. J. Review of C. G. Hartman's "Science and the safe period." *Sexology,* 1963, 29, 573.

Solomon, Richard L., and Wynn, Lyman C. Traumatic avoidance learning. *Psychol. Rev.,* 1954, 61, 353-85.

Spitz, René A. Autoerotism. *Psychoanalytic Study of the Child,* 1949, 3-4, 85-120.

Spitz, René A. Authority and masturbation. *Psychoanal. Quart.,* 1952, 21, 490-527.

Srnec, Jan, and Freund, Kurt. Treatment of male homosexuality through conditioning. *Int. J. Sexol.,* 1953, 7, 92-93.

Stekel, Wilhelm. *Conditions of nervous anxiety and their treatment.* New York: Dodd, Mead, 1923.

Stekel, Wilhelm. *Sexual aberrations.* New York: Liveright, 1930.

Stevenson, Robert L. *Virginibus puerisque.* New York: Scribner's, 1909.

Stokes, Walter R. *Married love in today's world.* New York: Citadel, 1962.

Stokes, Walter R., and Mace, David R. Premarital sex behavior. *Marr. Fam. Living,* 1953, 15, 234-49.

Street, Robert. *Modern sex technique.* New York: Archer House, 1959.

Taylor, W. S. A critique of sublimation in males. *Genet. Psychol. Monogr.,* 1933, 13, 1-115.

Taylor, W. S. Abstinence. In Robinson, Victor (Ed.), *Encyclopedia sexualis.* New York: Dingwall-Rock, 1936.

Terman, Lewis M. Correlates of orgasm adequacy in a group of 556 wives. *J. Psychol.*, 1951, 32, 115-72.

Thornton, Henry, and Thornton, Freda. *How to achieve sex happiness in marriage.* New York: Vanguard, 1939.

Tietze, Christopher. *The clinical effectiveness of contraceptive methods.* New York: National Committee on Maternal Health, 1959.

Tietze, Christopher. The use-effectiveness of contraceptive methods. *Res. Fam. Planning*, 1962, 357-69.

Tietze, Christopher, Intra-uterine contraceptive rings: history and statistical appraisal. *Excerpta Medica Internat. Cong. Series No. 54*, 9-20.

Tietze, Christopher, and Potter, Jr., Robert G. The effectiveness of the rhythm method. *Amer. J. Obstet. & Gynecol.*, Sept. 1, 1962.

Tolstoy, Leo. *The Kreutzer sonata.* New York: Ogilvie, 1890.

Tolstoy, Leo. *Relations of the sexes.* London: Daniel, 1919.

Tridon, André. *Sex happiness in marriage.* Boston: Badger, 1922.

Unwin, J. D. *Sexual relations and human behavior.* London: Williams and Norgate, 1933.

Van de Velde, T. H. *Ideal marriage.* New York: Covici Friede, 1926.

Vatsyayana. *The kama sutra.* New York: Dutton, 1962.

Vega, Lope de. *Four plays.* New York: Scribner's, 1936.

Vollmer, August. *The police and modern society.* Los Angeles: University of California Press, 1936.

Wagner, Edwin E. Techniques of rational counseling. *High Spots*, 1963, 3, No. 6, 2.

Walker, Kenneth. Does chastity affect potency? *Sexology*, 1963, 29, 364-66.

Watts, Alan W. *Nature, man and woman.* New York: New American Library, 1958.

Westermarck, Edward. *The future of marriage.* New York: Macmillan, 1936.

Wettley, Annemarie. Imaginary sex 'disease.' *Sexology*, 1959, 25, 778-84.

Wilde, Oscar. *Novels and fairy tales of Oscar Wilde.* New York: Boni, 1935a.

Wilde, Oscar. *Prose of Oscar Wilde.* New York: Boni, 1935b.

Winch, Robert F. Courtship and mate-selection. In Ellis, Albert and Abarbanel, Albert (Eds.), *Encyclopedia of sexual behavior.* New York: Hawthorn Books, 1961.

World League for Sexual Reform. *Third sexual reform congress.* London: Kegan, Paul, 1930.

Index